D1204001

A RADICAL APPROACH
TO ALGEBRA

MARY GRAY
The American University

ADDISON-WESLEY PUBLISHING COMPANY
Reading, Massachusetts · Menlo Park, California · London · Don Mills, Ontario

This book is in the ADDISON-WESLEY SERIES IN MATHEMATICS

. . . .

Lynn H. Loomis, *Consulting Editor*

Preface

Throughout the last century the study of algebra has featured the search for information about structure. The fundamental theorem of finitely generated abelian groups, the Sylow theorems, and the recent work on finite simple groups are examples of results on the structure of groups. The literature is replete with theorems describing and classifying the structure of rings. The problem is a very broad one and, indeed, by stretching a point one could classify a large percentage of theorems in algebra as structure theorems. However, one technique has proved particularly productive in the study of rings and algebras: the use of the radical. It is around this notion that this book is organized.

Cartan was the first to provide a significant breakthrough in the study of structure by means of radicals. He characterized completely a large class of finite-dimensional nonassociative algebras (Lie algebras); these results are briefly discussed in Chapter 7. Strangely, the associative case proved more stubborn, and for some years a structure theorem for associative algebras was the prize sought by many noted mathematicians. Delay was caused by trying to carry over Cartan's methods to the associative case, but early in the twentieth century Wedderburn obtained a structure theorem for certain associative algebras.

It took nearly forty years for the next spectacular developments in radical theory: the definition of the Jacobson radical of a general ring and the density theorem. Since then a whole series of generalizations and adaptations to systems other than algebras has been developed. The procedure is as follows: consider some class of objects, define an appropriate subobject for each object in the class, call it the radical, and see what can be said about radical-free objects in the class. Hopefully a Wedderburn-type theorem giving the decomposition of the radical-free object into simpler objects will result. If the gods are with the researcher, it may even be possible to classify completely these basic building blocks, as Cartan and Wedderburn did.

We begin with the Wedderburn results (Chapter 2) since they require less background. However, they deal only with rings satisfying some sort of finiteness condition, so we move on to general rings (Chapters 4 and 5). Then we survey radicals and related structure theorems for other systems (Chapters 6 and 7), and finally we unify the results in a general theory (Chapter 9). At

iii

each step we introduce more complex machinery—modules, categories—to deal with the increasingly difficult problems. Chapter 10 is really a recognition that the Wedderburn-type theorems may be inadequate for some purposes; more information is obtained by still another new technique—sheaf theory.

This book is designed to serve in a variety of ways: as a text for a course in algebra or ring theory; as a source for the study of elementary homological algebra, nonassociative algebras, and category theory; and as an introduction to research problems in structure theory.

Complemented by a book on group theory, it can be used for a year's course in algebra at the advanced undergraduate or beginning graduate level. It would be expected that the students in such a course would already have had some abstract algebra and some linear algebra. However, the basic ring material is included (Chapter 1) for ease of access and to establish notation. The material selected for such a course might include Chapters 1, 2, 3, and 8, with Chapters 4 or 7 added if time allowed.

The treatment and the material of these chapters is fairly standard, with the exception of Chapter 7. There the usual approach to the structure theory of Lie algebras is simplified and shortened.

A course in ring theory might cover Chapters 1 through 4 with any or all of the subsequent chapters added as the interests of the instructor and students dictate; the later chapters could also be used in seminars. This would not, of course, present a completely comprehensive picture of present-day ring theory; since there is so much material available, some choice of topics must be made. In this book this selection has been done with the central theme of radical-based structure theory as the unifying notion. Since the approach is somewhat historical—the classical theory, the use of modules, the introduction of categories, and finally the application of sheaves—the reader is led gradually into the more difficult concepts and sees how more and more powerful techniques have been developed and applied to the structure problems.

Individual chapters provide introductions to several topics in modern algebra, either for class use or for independent study. Chapter 3 (modules) depends only on elementary ring theory; Chapter 7 (Lie algebras) is independent of all preceding chapters except 1 and 3; Chapter 8 (categories) requires only a first course in algebra plus some familiarity with modules (except for the examples), and hence it is independent of Chapters 2, 4, 5, 6, and 7. Chapter 10 is independent of Chapters 5, 6, 7, 9, and most of 8. Chapter 3 and the first few sections of Chapter 8 provide the background beyond elementary group theory needed for algebraic topology.

The material in Chapters 5, 6, 9, and 10, for the most part, has been available previously only in journals and some of it is new; thus the beginning researcher will find here a takeoff point for his own work. The extensive bibliography is also an aid to such a reader.

There are no prerequisites for Chapters 1 through 9 beyond some elementary abstract and linear algebra and the small amount of set theory usually acquired in such courses, except that some of the examples require somewhat more advanced group theory and some topology. Chapter 10 definitely presupposes the rudiments of point-set topology.

I would like to thank Professor Alfred Gray for his very helpful advice, Professor Nolan Wallach for his suggestions on Chapter 7, students at California State College at Hayward, American University, and the University of Maryland who used the notes from which parts of this book came, and the staff and consultants of Addison-Wesley.

Washington, D.C.   M. G.
November, 1969

Contents

viii   Contents

CHAPTER 1

Rings and Ideals

In this chapter we provide a brief summary of basic ring and ideal theory, emphasizing the material which will be needed in subsequent chapters.

1. DEFINITION AND EXAMPLES

A *ring R* is a nonempty set of elements together with two binary operations, usually designated by $+$ (addition) and $\cdot$ (multiplication), subject to the following:

1) R is an abelian group under the operation $+$, that is,

   for all $r, s \in R$, $r + s$ is an element of R (closure);

   for all $r, s \in R$, $r + s = s + r$ (commutativity);

   there exists an element $0 \in R$ such that for each $r \in R$, $r + 0 = r$ (identity);

   for each $r \in R$ there exists an element $-r \in R$ such that $r + (-r) = 0$ (inverses);

   for all $r, s, t \in R$, $r + (s + t) = (r + s) + t$ (associativity).

2) R is closed under the operation $\cdot$, that is, for all $s, t \in R$, $s \cdot t \in R$.

3) The operation $\cdot$ is associative, i.e., for all $r, s, t \in R$, $r \cdot (s \cdot t) = (r \cdot s) \cdot t$.

4) The distributive laws hold: for all $r, s, t \in R$, $r \cdot (s + t) = r \cdot s + r \cdot t$ and $(s + t) \cdot r = s \cdot r + t \cdot r$.

   If further:

5) the multiplication is commutative, then the ring is *commutative*.

   If (1) through (4) are satisfied and

6) there exists an element $1 \in R$ such that $1 \cdot r = r \cdot 1 = r$ for all $r \in R$, R is said to be a *ring with identity* (or a ring with unity, or a ring with unit element).

   Henceforth we denote the multiplication of a ring by juxtaposition.

   If the nonzero elements of a ring R form an abelian group under multiplication, that is, R is commutative with identity $1 \neq 0$ and every nonzero element has a multiplicative inverse, R is a *field*. If $a \in R$, a ring with identity, is such that a has a multiplicative inverse, a is a *unit* of R. We note that a ring has at most one unit element, but may have many units. If R is a commutative ring, then $a \neq 0 \in R$ is a *zero divisor* if there exists $b \in R$, $b \neq 0$, such that $ab = 0$. If R is a commutative ring with no zero divisors, then R is an *integral domain*. Clearly a field is an integral domain.

An integral domain D is of *characteristic 0* if the relation $ma = 0$, $0 \neq a \in D$, m an integer, can hold only if $m = 0$. The domain D is of finite characteristic if for some nonzero a in D and some integer $m \neq 0$, $ma = 0$. The *characteristic* of D is then defined to be the smallest positive integer p such that $pa = 0$ for some $a \neq 0$ in D. Note that we define characteristic only for integral domains.

A ring R is a *division ring* (*skew field*) if its nonzero elements form a group under multiplication, i.e., every nonzero element of R is a unit.

Examples

1.   The set of all integers is a commutative ring with identity and is an integral domain. This ring will henceforth be denoted by Z. Its only units are 1 and -1. The positive integers will be denoted by Z^+.

2.   The even integers form an integral domain; we usually write $2Z$ for this ring.

3.   Let P be the set of all symbols $a_0 + a_1 i + a_2 j + a_3 k$, where a_i is a real number, $i = 0, \ldots, 3$. Two such symbols

$$a_0 + a_1 i + a_2 j + a_3 k \qquad \text{and} \qquad b_0 + b_1 i + b_2 j + b_3 k$$

are equal if and only if $a_i = b_i$, $i = 0, \ldots, 3$. We define the addition of two such symbols by means of addition of their coefficients and the multiplication as the formal multiplication with collection of terms according to the following relations:

$$i^2 = j^2 = k^2 = ijk = -1, \qquad ij = -ji = k, \qquad jk = -kj = i, \qquad ki = -ik = j,$$

where the last three may be remembered as the vector cross products of the unit vectors in Euclidean three-space. Thus

$$(a_0 + a_1 i + a_2 j + a_3 k) + (b_0 + b_1 i + b_2 j + b_3 k)$$
$$= (a_0 + b_0) + (a_1 + b_1)i + (a_2 + b_2)j + (a_3 + b_3)k$$

and

$$(a_0 + a_1 i + a_2 j + a_3 k)(b_0 + b_1 i + b_2 j + b_3 k) = (a_0 b_0 - a_1 b_1 - a_2 b_2 - a_3 b_3)$$
$$+ (a_0 b_1 + a_1 b_0 + a_2 b_3 - a_3 b_2)i + (a_0 b_2 + a_2 b_0 + a_3 b_1 - a_1 b_3)j$$
$$+ (a_0 b_3 + a_3 b_0 + a_1 b_2 - a_2 b_1)k.$$

Then P is a division ring, with multiplicative identity $1 + 0i + 0j + 0k$, called the *quaternion ring*.

4.   Let $R[x]$ denote the set of all polynomials in an indeterminate x with coefficients in the ring R:

$$R[x] = \{a_0 + a_1 x + \cdots + a_n x^n \mid a_i \in R, n \text{ a nonnegative integer}\}.$$

We define addition and multiplication in $R[x]$ in terms of the operations in R and the laws of exponents, analogous to the way they are defined for polynomials over the real numbers. This makes $R[x]$ into a ring, called the *polynomial ring* over R. If R is commutative, $R[x]$ is commutative; if R has an identity 1, 1 is also an identity for $R[x]$, since we identify elements of R with the polynomials of degree zero; if R is an integral domain, so is $R[x]$. Later we shall discuss other properties of a ring R which are inherited by a polynomial ring over it. We observe that if F is a field, $F[x]$ is not a field; in fact, the units of $F[x]$ are precisely the nonzero elements of F. By considering the polynomial ring over a polynomial ring, we obtain a polynomial ring in two indeterminates $(R[x_1])[x_2] = R[x_1, x_2]$, and similarly for any finite number of indeterminates.

5. It is also possible to define a *power series ring* over a ring R. Its elements are all formal power series in an indeterminate x with coefficients from R and with the operations defined as for the polynomial ring. The power series ring over R is denoted by $R\langle x\rangle$:

$$R\langle x\rangle = \left\{ \sum_{i=0}^{\infty} a_i x^i \,\middle|\, a_i \in R \right\},$$

$$\sum_{i=0}^{\infty} a_i x^i + \sum_{i=0}^{\infty} b_i x^i = \sum_{i=0}^{\infty} (a_i + b_i) x^i,$$

$$\left(\sum_{i=0}^{\infty} a_i x^i \right)\left(\sum_{i=0}^{\infty} b_i x^i \right) = \sum_{i=0}^{\infty} c_i x^i, \qquad \text{where} \qquad c_i = \sum_{j=0}^{i} a_j b_{i-j}.$$

6. Let R be the set of all real-valued continuous functions defined on the real numbers. We define addition and multiplication pointwise, that is, for $f, g \in R$,

$$(f + g)(x) = f(x) + g(x), \qquad (fg)(x) = f(x)g(x),$$

where the operations on the right are ordinary real number addition and multiplication. Since sums and products of continuous functions are continuous, R is closed under these operations and the other ring axioms are readily verified from the properties of the real numbers. We note that the real numbers (considered as constant functions) constitute a subset of R.

When rings of functions are encountered in other branches of mathematics, sometimes the "multiplication" is defined differently, e.g., as convolution of functions: let V be the set of all continuous functions on the real line of period 2π and for $f, g \in V$ define

$$(f * g)(t) = \int_{-\pi}^{\pi} f(t - u)g(u)\, du.$$

This operation, together with the addition of functions as defined above, makes V into a ring.

7. Let $\mathcal{M}_n(R)$ be the set of all $n \times n$ matrices with entries from a ring R. We define matrix addition and multiplication in the usual way. Then $\mathcal{M}_n(R)$ is called a (*full* or *complete*) *matrix ring over* R. If R has an identity 1, then

$$\begin{pmatrix} 1 & & & \\ & \cdot & & 0 \\ & & \cdot & \\ & & & \cdot \\ 0 & & & 1 \end{pmatrix}$$

is an identity for $\mathcal{M}_n(R)$. We sometimes write R_n for $\mathcal{M}_n(R)$.

8. If V is a vector space over a field K and $\text{Hom}_K(V, V)$ the set of all linear maps $V \to V$, then $\text{Hom}_K(V, V)$ is a ring, called the *endomorphism ring* of V, under the operations of addition and composition of maps. Similarly, for any abelian group A,

$$\text{Hom}(A, A) = \{f : A \to A \mid f \text{ a group homomorphism}\}$$

is a ring. Sometimes $\text{Hom}_K(V, V)$ is denoted by $\text{End}(V)$.

9. The rational numbers, the real numbers, and the complex numbers are fields.

All of the above examples are rings with an infinite number of elements and, in the case of integral domains, with characteristic zero (the latter property is not implied by the former). However, there exist finite rings (whose characteristic, if any, is necessarily finite); in fact, we have a handy source of examples with any desired number of elements. Let Z_n be the integers modulo n, that is, the set $\{0, \ldots, n - 1\}$, with $i + j$ defined to be the remainder of the ordinary sum upon division by n and $i \cdot j$ the remainder of the ordinary product upon division by n. It is easy to verify that under these operations Z_n is a ring.

We consider Z_7. The Cayley table for multiplication of its nonzero elements shows that Z_7 is a field:

	1	2	3	4	5	6
1	1	2	3	4	5	6
2	2	4	6	1	3	5
3	3	6	2	5	1	4
4	4	1	5	2	6	3
5	5	3	1	6	4	2
6	6	5	4	3	2	1

On the other hand, in Z_6, $2 \cdot 3 = 0$ so that Z_6 is not even an integral domain. In fact, Z_n is a field if and only if n is a prime; otherwise it is a commutative ring with identity and zero divisors.

2. IDEALS

As is usual with any mathematical entity we are interested in looking at those subsets of our objects which have certain structures. A *subring S* of a ring R is a subgroup of the additive group of the ring, i.e., a nonempty subset S of R such that $a, b \in S$ implies $a - b \in S$, which is in addition closed under multiplication. Thus a subring S is itself a ring whose operations are those of R restricted to S.

Examples. The integers are a subring of the ring of rational numbers and the even integers are a subring of the integers.

A *left ideal I* of a ring R is a subring closed under left multiplication by an arbitrary element of R, that is, if $r \in R, j \in I$, then $rj \in I$. Similarly we define *right ideal*. A (two-sided) *ideal* is a left ideal which is also a right ideal. If R is commutative, it is clear that all one-sided ideals are ideals. In this and subsequent chapters, definitions involving one-sided ideals will usually be made in terms of left ideals, but analogous definitions can be made for right ideals.

Examples. The first example above of a subring is not an ideal, but the second is. In fact $nZ = \{nz \mid z \in Z\}$ is an ideal of Z for any integer n. It is important to observe that nZ is not, however, an ideal of the rational numbers Q, although it is a subring. Thus, provided the operations are the same, the property of being a subring is independent of the containing ring, whereas that of being an ideal is not.

Consider the ring of $n \times n$ matrices with entries from the rational numbers. For each $i = 1, \ldots, n$, the set of all matrices with zeros everywhere except possibly in row i forms a right ideal and that of all matrices with zeros except possibly in column i a left ideal. Neither is an ideal and in fact we shall show later that any matrix ring over a division ring has only the ideal consisting of zero alone, denoted by (0), and itself as ideals.

Let S be a nonempty subset of a ring R. Then

$$A_r(S) = \{x \in R \mid ax = 0 \text{ for all } a \in S\}$$

is a right ideal in R, called the *right annihilator* of S. If $S = \{a\}$ is a single element, we usually write $A_r(S) = \{a\}_r$. Similarly, the left annihilator of a set is a left ideal.

If A is a subset of a ring R, we denote the smallest ideal containing the elements of A, called the *ideal generated by A*, by (A). If A is finite, the ideal (A) is *finitely generated*. (A) contains all inverses of elements of A, all sums of elements and sums of inverses, all products of elements of A and elements of R, and all sums of these products. We can express (A) as

$$\{r_1 a_1 + \cdots + r_n a_n + a_1' r_1' + \cdots + a_m' r_m' + m_1 a_1'' + \cdots$$
$$+ m_k a_k'' \mid r_i, r_i' \in R,\ a_i, a_i', a_i'' \in A,\ m_i \in Z,\ n, m, k \text{ nonnegative integers}\}.$$

If A consists of a single element, (A) is a *principal ideal*. If R is a ring with identity, then the notation for the integer multiples of the elements of A can be omitted since they will be included as sums of products of an element of R, namely the identity, with elements of A.

Examples. If A is the subset of Z consisting of 5 and 10, then $(A) = 5Z$; indeed, $nZ = (n)$. Considering Z as a subset of the rational numbers Q we have that $(Z) = Q$. In fact, the only ideals of Q are (0) and Q itself.

The set

$$Ra = \{ra \mid r \in R\}$$

is, for any $a \in R$, a left ideal of R, said to be the *principal left ideal determined by a*. The principal right ideal determined by an element $a \in R$ is defined analogously. If R is a commutative ring with identity, then $Ra = aR = (a)$. The zero ideal is of course determined by the additive identity and if R has a multiplicative identity, $R = (1)$. If every ideal of a commutative ring R with identity is a principal ideal, R is said to be a *principal ideal ring* (PIR). For example, the integers are a PIR.

If the product of any two elements of a ring R is zero, we write $R^2 = (0)$ and call R a *zero ring*. If R is not a zero ring and the only ideals of R are (0) and R, R is a *simple ring*. An ideal I of R which is not all of R is called a *proper ideal* of R.

Examples. Let R be the integers under the usual addition and define $rs = 0$ for all $r, s \in R$. Then R is a zero ring; (0) is itself a zero ring. No ring with a multiplicative identity $1 \neq 0$ can be a zero ring. Any field is a simple ring, and in fact it can be shown that any simple commutative ring with identity is a field.

We now define some operations on the set of ideals of a ring.
If I_1, I_2 are left ideals in a ring R, then

$$I_1 + I_2 = \{a_1 + a_2 \mid a_i \in I_i\},$$
$$I_1 I_2 = \{a_1 b_1 + \cdots + a_n b_n \mid a_i \in I_1,\ b_i \in I_2,\ n \text{ a positive integer}\},$$

and

$$I_1 \cap I_2 = \{a \mid a \in I_1 \text{ and } a \in I_2\}, \quad \text{that is, the set-theoretic intersection,}$$

are left ideals in R—analogously for right and two-sided ideals. These ideals are called the *sum*, *product*, and *intersection*, respectively. Note that for ideals

$$I_1 I_2 \subset I_1 \cap I_2 \quad {\overset{\displaystyle I_1}{\underset{\displaystyle I_2}{\subset \ \ \supset \atop \supset \ \ \subset}}} \quad I_1 \cup I_2 \subset I_1 + I_2.$$

Moreover, $I_1 + I_2 = (I_1 \cup I_2)$, that is, $I_1 + I_2$ is the smallest ideal containing both I_1 and I_2. We can also define the sum of a not necessarily finite collection of ideals $\{I_\alpha\}_{\alpha \in A}$ to be all finite sums of elements of the I_α:

$$\sum_{\alpha \in A} I_\alpha = \{a_{\alpha_1} + \cdots + a_{\alpha_n} \mid a_{\alpha_i} \in I_{\alpha_i},\ n \text{ a positive integer}\}.$$

$\sum_{\alpha \in A} I$ is again an ideal. The procedure is the same in the one-sided cases.

In the ring of integers the intersection of nZ and mZ is rZ, where r is the least common multiple of n and m; this is also their product if and only if $(n, m) = 1$. Their sum, being the smallest ideal containing them both, is dZ, where d is the greatest common divisor of m and n.

If I and J are ideals of a ring R, we also define their *quotient*

$$I:J = \{a \in R \mid ab \in I \text{ for all } b \in J\}.$$

$I:J$ is an ideal of R.

We list some properties of quotient ideals. The proof is in each case a straightforward verification:

1. $I \subset I:J$,
2. $(I:J)J \subset I$,
3. $(I \cap J):K = (I:K) \cap (J:K)$,
4. $I:(J + K) = (I:J) \cap (I:K)$,
5. $I:J = I:(I + J)$,
6. $(I:J):K = I:(KJ)$.

If I is a proper left ideal of a ring R such that for any two left ideals A, B of R, $AB \subset I$ implies that $A \subset I$ or $B \subset I$, then I is a *prime left ideal*. If M is a left ideal of a ring R such that $M \neq R$, and for any left ideal I such that $M \subset I \subset R$, $I = M$ or $I = R$, then M is a *maximal left ideal* of R. If N is a left ideal of a ring R such that $N \neq (0)$, and for any left ideal I such that $(0) \subset I \subset N$, $I = N$ or $(0) = I$, then N is a *minimal left ideal* of R. Prime, maximal, and minimal right ideals and two-sided ideals are defined similarly. R is a *prime ring* if the zero ideal is a prime ideal of R.

Examples

1. Since Z is a principal ideal ring, when looking for its maximal ideals we ask what properties an integer n must have in order that $(n) = nZ$ be maximal. Suppose p is prime and $I = (n)$ is an ideal of Z such that $(p) \subset I \subset Z$. Then $p \in I$ so there exists an integer m such that $mn = p$. Since p is prime $m = \pm 1$ or $n = \pm 1$. If $m = \pm 1$, $n = \pm p$ and $(p) = I$; if $n = \pm 1$, $I = Z$. Hence (p) is maximal. On the other hand, if $M = (m)$ is maximal, we let $m = nq$. But then $M \subset (n)$, so $(n) = M$ or $(n) = Z$. If $(n) = M$, $m = \pm n$, and if $(n) = Z$, $n = \pm 1$. Hence m is prime. Also, (n) is a prime ideal of Z if and only if n is prime. Thus the maximal ideals of Z are precisely the prime ideals of Z. However, the concepts are not in general synonymous. Z has no minimal ideals.

2. Let R be the ring of all real-valued continuous functions on $[0, 1]$ and

$$M = \{f \in R \mid f(0) = 0\}.$$

It is clear that M is an ideal of R. Suppose that M is contained in an ideal I. If $M \neq I$, there is a $g \in I$ such that $g(0) = c \neq 0$. Let $h(x) = g(x) - c$. Then $h(0) = 0$ and $h \in M \subset I$. Thus $g - h = c \in I$. But c, being a real number, has an inverse in R, so that $cc^{-1} = 1 \in I$ and $I = R$. In fact, it can be shown that the maximal ideals of R are in one-one correspondence with the points of $[0, 1]$, with each maximal ideal consisting of functions which are zero at some particular point in $[0, 1]$.

In the proof of the following theorem we use Zorn's lemma, an equivalent form of the axiom of choice. We state it for convenience:

Zorn's Lemma. If S is a nonempty partially ordered set such that any totally ordered subset of S has an upper bound in S, then S has a maximal element.

Theorem 1. *If R is a ring with identity, every proper ideal of R is contained in a maximal ideal of R.*

Proof. Given a proper ideal I of R we consider the set $\mathfrak{A}$ of all proper ideals of R containing I. $\mathfrak{A}$ is partially ordered by set inclusion. We let $\{A_\alpha\}$ be any totally ordered subset of $\mathfrak{A}$. Then $\bigcup A_\alpha$ is an ideal of R. Suppose $\bigcup A_\alpha = R$. Then $1 \in \bigcup A_\alpha$ and so 1 is contained in some element of $\{A_\alpha\}$, say A_β. But then $A_\beta = R$, a contradiction. Hence $\bigcup A_\alpha \in \mathfrak{A}$. Thus any totally ordered subset of $\mathfrak{A}$ has an upper bound in $\mathfrak{A}$; hence by Zorn's lemma $\mathfrak{A}$ has a maximal element, which is clearly a maximal ideal of R containing I.

3. QUOTIENT RINGS AND HOMOMORPHISMS

The procedure sketched here is analogous to that for the construction of quotient groups. Let I be an ideal of a ring R. For $a, b \in R$ we say

$$a \equiv b \qquad \text{if and only if} \qquad a - b \in I.$$

Then this defines an equivalence relation on R. We denote the equivalence class of a by $a + I = \{a + i \mid i \in I\}$ and the set of disjoint equivalence classes by R/I. We define ring operations on this set of equivalence classes in the obvious way in terms of the operations of the ring R:

$$(a + I) + (b + I) = (a + b) + I,$$

$$(a + I)(b + I) = ab + I.$$

Noting that it is necessary that I be a two-sided ideal in order for the multiplication to be well defined, we can easily verify that these operations turn R/I into a ring. We call the ring so constructed the *quotient ring of R modulo I.*

Example. The ring Z_n which we have discussed previously is the quotient ring of Z modulo the ideal nZ. We note that if R is commutative, any quotient ring formed from it is commutative and if 1 is the identity of R, then $1 + I$ is the identity of R/I (if $I \neq R$). However, as we have seen in the case of Z, not all properties are inherited by the quotient ring; an integral domain may yield a field or a ring with zero divisors as a quotient ring.

Once we have introduced and provided examples of an algebraic system the next problem is that of relations among various examples, i.e., we are interested in functions with rings as domain and range. A function f from a ring R into a ring R', denoted by $f: R \rightarrow R'$, is a *(ring) homomorphism* if for all $a, b \in R$,

$$f(a + b) = f(a) + f(b) \qquad \text{and} \qquad f(ab) = f(a)f(b),$$

where the operations on the left of each equation are those of the ring R and those on the right are those of the ring R'. Thus just as a group homomorphism preserves the single operation of a group or a linear transformation preserves the operations on a vector space, a ring homomorphism preserves both of the operations of a ring.

If a homomorphism is one-one, i.e., if $f(a) = f(b)$ implies that $a = b$, it is said to be *injective.* If $f: R \rightarrow R'$ is a homomorphism such that its image, $f(R) = \{r' \in R' \mid \text{there is an } r \in R \text{ with } f(r) = r'\}$, is all of R', that is, f is onto, then f is *surjective.* We note the distinction between the range and the image of a homomorphism. If a ring homomorphism f is both injective and surjective (bijective), it is an *isomorphism.* In this case it has an inverse which is also an isomorphism. If there exists an isomorphism with domain R and range R', we say that R and R' are *isomorphic* and write $R \simeq R'$. This defines an equivalence relation on rings. If there is an injective homomorphism

$f: R \rightarrow R'$, we say that R can be *embedded* in R'; if R and R' have identities 1 and $1'$ we require also that $f(1) = 1'$ in order for f to be an embedding. If $f: R \rightarrow R$ is a homomorphism, we say it is an *endomorphism*, and an endomorphism which is an isomorphism is an *automorphism*.

It is clear that the image of a homomorphism $f: R \rightarrow R'$ is a subring of R'. Moreover, $\{x \in R \,|\, f(x) = 0\}$ is an ideal of R, called the *kernel* of the homomorphism f. If the kernel of $f: R \rightarrow R'$ is all of R we call f a *zero homomorphism*.

On the other hand, given an ideal I of a ring R we can always define a homomorphism with I as its kernel. We define $f: R \rightarrow R/I$ by $f(a) = a + I$. Then I is the kernel of the homomorphism f, called the *canonical projection* onto the quotient ring R/I.

Theorem 2 (Homomorphism Theorem). *If $f: R \rightarrow R'$ is a surjective ring homomorphism with K as its kernel, then $R/K \simeq R'$.*

Proof. Define $g: R/K \rightarrow R'$ by $g(a + K) = f(a)$. It is clear that g is a well-defined homomorphism and that it is surjective since f is. Moreover, g is injective since $g(a + K) = g(b + K)$ implies that $f(a - b) = 0$, that is, $a - b \in K$, and thus $a + K = b + K$. Hence g is the desired isomorphism.

Corollary. A ring homomorphism is injective if and only if its kernel is the zero ideal.

Since we now have the notion of isomorphism available, we are able to discuss one more method for generating new examples of rings. Let R_1 and R_2 be rings and $R_1 \times R_2$ the set of all ordered pairs $\{(r_1, r_2) \,|\, r_i \in R_i, i = 1, 2\}$, that is, the Cartesian product of R_1 and R_2 as sets. We define componentwise operations:

$$(r_1, r_2) + (r_1', r_2') = (r_1 + r_1', r_2 + r_2'),$$

$$(r_1, r_2)(r_1', r_2') = (r_1 r_1', r_2 r_2'),$$

to turn the product into a ring, denoted by $R_1 \oplus R_2$ and called the (external) *direct sum* of R_1 and R_2. Any ring which is isomorphic to the direct sum of R_1 and R_2 is also said to be their direct sum.

Examples. $Z_6 \simeq Z_2 \oplus Z_3$ is the direct sum of Z_2 and Z_3; indeed, $Z_{mn} \simeq Z_m \oplus Z_n$ if and only if m and n are relatively prime. We remark that not only the set but also the operation must be considered since if $C =$ complex numbers and $R =$ real numbers, $C \not\simeq R \oplus R$ (as rings), since multiplication of complex numbers is not defined componentwise.

Theorem 3 (Lattice Theorem for Ideals). *If R is a ring and I an ideal of R, there is a one-one correspondence between the ideals of R/I and the ideals of R containing I.*

Proof. If J is an ideal of R containing I, let $\bar{J} = \{a + I \,|\, a \in J\}$. It is simple to verify that $\bar{J}$ is an ideal in the quotient ring.

Conversely, suppose that $\bar{J}$ is an ideal of R/I and let $p: R \to R/I$ be the projection. Let $J = \{a \in R \mid p(a) \in \bar{J}\}$. Again, since p is a homomorphism, it is easy to see that J is an ideal. We usually indicate the correspondence by $J \leftrightarrow J/I$.

The question naturally arises of why this theorem should be called *lattice theorem*. We recall that a lattice is a partially ordered set in which any two elements have both a least upper bound and a greatest lower bound in the set. Hence the set of ideals of a given ring forms a lattice with inclusion as the partial ordering, intersection as the greatest lower bound, and sum as the least upper bound. Thus the preceding theorem could be formulated as "there is a lattice isomorphism between the ideals of R containing I and the ideals of R/I," since the correspondence given is one which preserves the lattice operations of lub and glb.

Theorem 4. *If R is a commutative ring with identity, M is a maximal ideal of R if and only if R/M is a field.*

Proof. By Theorem 3, M is a maximal ideal if and only if R/M is simple. As we have remarked, a field is simple. If R is a simple commutative ring with identity, let Ra be the ideal generated by $a \neq 0$. Since $1 \in R$, $a \in Ra$, so $Ra \neq (0)$. Hence $Ra = R$ and there is an element $a^{-1} \in R$ such that $a^{-1}a = 1 \in Ra$. Thus R is a field.

4. THE FIELD OF QUOTIENTS

We observe that the ring of integers can be extended to the rational numbers by considering equivalence classes of quotients of integers and that the ring of polynomials in one indeterminate over the real numbers can be extended to the field of rational expressions in one indeterminate by a similar process. We shall generalize the method to any integral domain by proving:

Theorem 5. *Any integral domain D can be embedded in a field.*

Proof. Let $\mathfrak{A} = \{(a, b) \mid a, b \in D, b \neq 0\}$. Intuitively, $\mathfrak{A}$ is the set of all quotients a/b, $b \neq 0$, of elements of D. We define a relation on $\mathfrak{A}$ as follows:

$$(a, b) \equiv (c, d) \qquad \text{if and only if} \qquad ad = bc.$$

It is easy to see that this is reflexive and symmetric. Moreover, if $(a, b) \equiv (c, d)$ and $(c, d) \equiv (e, f)$, then $ad = bc$ and $cf = de$. Thus $bcf = bde$ and $adf = bde$. D is commutative, so $afd = bed$; but since D is an integral domain and $d \neq 0$, $af = be$ (see Problem 1). Hence $(a, b) \equiv (e, f)$ and the relation is transitive and thus an equivalence relation.

Let $[a, b]$ denote the equivalence class of (a, b) and let F be the set of equivalence classes of $\mathfrak{A}$. Again following the procedure used for rational numbers we define addition and multiplication:

$$[a, b] + [c, d] = [ad + bc, bd],$$
$$[a, b][c, d] = [ac, bd].$$

F is closed under these operations since D has no zero divisors. We check that the addition is well defined and leave the case of the multiplication to the reader.

Suppose $[a, b] = [a', b']$, $[c, d] = [c', d']$. We want to show that

$$[a, b] + [c, d] = [a', b'] + [c', d'],$$

that is, that

$$[ad + bc, bd] = [a'd' + b'c', b'd'].$$

But this requires only that

$$(ad + bc)b'd' = bd(a'd' + b'c').$$

However, $ab' = ba'$ and $cd' = dc'$, so

$$(ad + bc)b'd' = adb'd' + bcb'd' = ab'dd' + bb'cd'$$
$$= ba'dd' + bb'dc' = bd(a'd' + b'c')$$

as desired.

It is clear that $[0, b]$ is the additive identity and $[a, a]$ the multiplicative identity. $[-a, b]$ is the additive inverse of $[a, b]$ and if $a \neq 0$, $[a, b]^{-1} = [b, a]$. The other axioms for a field are easily verified.

It remains to show that D can be embedded in F. We observe that $[ax, x] = [ay, y]$ for all nonzero x and y in D. Hence we shall denote this equivalence class by $[a, 1]$, even though there may be no identity in D. Now we define $f: D \rightarrow F$ by $f(a) = [a, 1]$. It is clear that f is a homomorphism. If $f(a) = [0, 1]$, then $a = 0$, so f is injective and if 1 is an identity for D, $f(1)$ is the identity of F.

The field constructed in this manner is called the *field of quotients* of D. If R is a commutative ring with zero divisors but with at least one nonzero element which is not a zero divisor, we can construct a generalization of a field of quotients as follows: Let S be the set of all zero divisors in R together with zero. Then we form the set of all ordered pairs (a, b), $a \in R$, $b \in R \setminus S$, where $R \setminus S = \{r \in R \mid r \notin S\}$. We define an equivalence relation on the set as above, and proceeding in an analogous manner we can show that the set of equivalence classes with appropriately defined operations forms a ring, called the *full ring of quotients* of R.

5. MINIMAL AND MAXIMAL CONDITIONS

The theory of rings with minimal and maximal conditions arose from studying the properties of matrix and polynomial rings, respectively, in an abstract setting, just as integral domains were defined as an abstraction and generalization of the integers.

A ring R is said to be *left Artinian* (or to have the *left minimal condition*) if every nonempty set $\mathfrak{S}$ of left ideals of R, partially ordered by set inclusion, has a minimal element, i.e., there is an $I \in \mathfrak{S}$ such that if $J \in \mathfrak{S}$ and $J \subset I$, then $I = J$. Right Artinian and Artinian rings are defined in an analogous manner. Similarly, we define maximal conditions for rings. The type of finiteness condition found in Artinian rings will be studied in Chapter 2; the theory of the structure of rings with maximal condition is primarily interesting because of applications to algebraic geometry.

If whenever

$$I_1 \supset I_2 \supset I_3 \supset \cdots \supset I_i \supset \cdots$$

is a sequence of left ideals of a ring R there is an integer N such that $I_n = I_N$ for $n \geq N$, then R is said to have the *descending chain condition* (dcc) on left ideals. If any increasing sequence of left ideals of a ring R becomes constant after a finite number of terms, then R is said to have the *ascending chain condition* (acc) on left ideals. We can also define descending and ascending chain conditions for right ideals or for ideals.

It is apparent that the descending chain condition and the minimal condition are equivalent. In the acc case we have a further result.

If every ideal of a ring R is finitely generated, R is said to be *Noetherian*. *Right* and *left Noetherian* rings are defined analogously and theorems corresponding to the one below hold in these cases.

>**Theorem 6.** *For a ring R, the following are equivalent:*
>1) *R is Noetherian.*
>2) *The acc for ideals holds in R.*
>3) *The maximal condition for ideals holds in R.*

Proof. (1) implies (2). Let R be Noetherian and consider the increasing sequence

$$A_1 \subset A_2 \subset A_3 \subset \cdots$$

of ideals of R. Let $A = \bigcup_{i=1}^{\infty} A_i$. A is clearly an ideal in R and so A is generated by some finite set of elements $a_1, \ldots, a_n \in R$. But $a_1, \ldots, a_n \in A$ and hence $a_i \in A_{m_i}$ for some m_i. Let $m = \max\{m_1, \ldots, m_n\}$. Then $a_i \in A_m$ for $i = 1, \ldots, n$. Hence $A \subset A_m$ and

$$A \subset A_m \subset \cdots \subset A.$$

Therefore $A_n = A_m$ for $n \geq m$.

(2) implies (3). Suppose the acc holds in R. Let $\mathfrak{S}$ be a nonempty set of ideals in R. Let $A_1 \in \mathfrak{S}$. Either A_1 is maximal in $\mathfrak{S}$ or there exists $A_2 \in \mathfrak{S}$ such that $A_1 \subsetneqq A_2$. If by repeating this argument a finite number of times we do not arrive at a maximal element of $\mathfrak{S}$, then we obtain an infinite increasing sequence of distinct ideals, a contradiction.

(3) implies (1). Suppose the maximal condition holds in R and let A be an ideal in R. Let $\mathfrak{S}$ be the set of all ideals of R which are contained in A and which are finitely generated. $\mathfrak{S}$ is not empty since $(0) \in \mathfrak{S}$. By the maximal condition, $\mathfrak{S}$ has a maximal element, say $(a_1, \ldots, a_n)$. If $(a_1, \ldots, a_n) \neq A$,

we can find $b \in A$, $b \notin (a_1, \ldots, a_n)$. But then

$$(a_1, \ldots, a_n) \subsetneqq (a_1, \ldots, a_n, b) \subset A,$$

so that $(a_1, \ldots, a_n, b) \in \mathfrak{S}$, contradicting the maximality of $(a_1, \ldots, a_n)$. Hence $(a_1, \ldots, a_n) = A$.

Examples. Any principal ideal ring is Noetherian; in particular every field is a PIR and hence Noetherian since its only ideals are those generated by 0 and by 1. Also, the integers, being a PIR, are Noetherian.

It is clear that left or right Artinian implies Artinian, and similarly for Noetherian. However, let

$$T = \left\{ \begin{pmatrix} x & 0 \\ y & z \end{pmatrix} \middle| x \text{ rational}, y, z \text{ real numbers} \right\}.$$

Then T is left Artinian but not right Artinian.

It seems that we are abundantly supplied with Noetherian rings. In fact, a quick survey of our examples of rings will show that we are very short of examples of non-Noetherian rings.

Thus let us consider the set $\mathscr{S}$ of finite subsets of an infinite set X. For $S, T \in \mathscr{S}$, define

$$S + T = S \cup T \setminus S \cap T \quad \text{(symmetric difference)},$$

$$S \cdot T = S \cap T.$$

This makes $\mathscr{S}$ into a commutative ring. Now if T is an infinite subset of X,

$$2^{\mathscr{T}} = \{S \mid S \subset T, S \text{ finite}\}$$

is an ideal of $\mathscr{S}$ which is not finitely generated.

6. PRIMARY DECOMPOSITION

Throughout this section we shall assume that our rings are commutative with identity. For these rings we have the following characterization of prime ideals.

Theorem 7. *P is a prime ideal of a commutative ring R with identity if and only if $ab \in P$ implies that $a \in P$ or $b \in P$.*

Proof. Suppose P is a prime ideal and $ab \in P$. Then $(a)(b) = (ab) \subset P$ so that $(a) \subset P$ or $(b) \subset P$. Thus $a \in P$ or $b \in P$.

Conversely, suppose A and B are ideals of R with $AB \subset P$. If $A \subset P$ or $B \subset P$, we are through; so suppose $a \in A \setminus P$, $b \in B \setminus P$. But $ab \in P$, so $a \in P$ or $b \in P$, a contradiction.

Directly from this theorem and the definition of prime ideal we obtain:

Corollary. If P is a prime ideal in a commutative ring R with identity and $a_1 \cdots a_n \in P$, then $a_i \in P$ for at least one i. If $A_1 \cdots A_n \subset P$, A_i an ideal of R, $i = 1, \ldots, n$, then $A_i \subset P$ for at least one i.

An ideal Q in a commutative ring R with identity is a *primary ideal* if whenever $ab \in Q$ and $a \notin Q$, then $b^n \in Q$ for some $n \in Z^+$. If A is an ideal of a commutative ring R, we set

$$\sqrt{A} = \{a \mid a \in R, a^n \in A \text{ for some } n \in Z^+\}.$$

$\sqrt{A}$ is called the *radical* of A.

Theorem 8. $\sqrt{A}$ is an ideal of R and $A \subset \sqrt{A}$. If A is primary, then $\sqrt{A}$ is the smallest prime ideal containing A.

Proof. Let $a, b \in \sqrt{A}$. Then there are positive integers n, m such that $a^n \in A$, $b^m \in A$. It suffices to show that $\sqrt{A}$ is closed under subtraction (i.e., addition and additive inverses) and arbitrary multiplication. We have

$$(a - b)^{n+m} = \sum_{k=0}^{n+m} \binom{n + m}{k} a^k b^{n+m-k} (-1)^{n+m-k}.$$

Either $k \geq n$ or $n + m - k > m$. In the first case, $a^k \in A$ and in the second, $b^{n+m-k} \in A$. Thus for each k, $a^k b^{n+m-k} \in A$ and so $(a - b)^{n+m} \in A$ and $a - b \in \sqrt{A}$.

If $a \in \sqrt{A}$, $r \in R$, then for some $n \in Z^+$, $a^n \in A$ so $(ra)^n = r^n a^n \in A$, that is, $ra \in \sqrt{A}$. It is clear that $A \subset \sqrt{A}$.

Now suppose Q is a primary ideal. If $ab \in \sqrt{Q}$ and $a \notin \sqrt{Q}$, then there is an $n \in Z^+$ such that $(ab)^n = a^n b^n \in Q$, but $a^n \notin Q$. Then since Q is primary, there is a $t \in Z^+$ such that $b^{nt} \in Q$. Thus $b \in \sqrt{Q}$ and $\sqrt{Q}$ is prime.

Finally let P be a prime ideal such that $Q \subset P$. Let $a \in \sqrt{Q}$. Then there is a positive integer n such that $a^n \in Q \subset P$. Thus by the corollary to Theorem 7, $a \in P$ and $\sqrt{Q} \subset P$.

If Q is a primary ideal and P is the prime ideal such that $P = \sqrt{Q}$, Q is said to be *P-primary*.

The following corollaries are easy to verify.

Corollary 1. If Q is P-primary, $ab \in Q$ and $a \notin P$, then $b \in Q$.

Corollary 2. If Q is P-primary and A and B are ideals such that $AB \subset Q$, $A \not\subset P$, then $B \subset Q$.

Corollary 3. If Q is P-primary and $A \not\subset P$, then $Q:A = Q$.

If an ideal A of a commutative ring R with identity can be written as

$$A = Q_1 \cap \cdots \cap Q_n,$$

with Q_i a primary ideal of R, $i = 1, \ldots, n$, A is said to have a *primary decomposition*.

If $A \subset P$ and P is a prime ideal of R, then P is a *minimal prime ideal of A* (or *belonging to A*) if there is no prime ideal P' of R such that $A \subset P' \subset P$.

> **Theorem 9.** *If $A = Q_1 \cap \cdots \cap Q_n$ is a primary decomposition of an ideal A of a commutative ring R with identity, and Q_i is P_i primary, $i = 1, \ldots, n$, then the minimal prime ideals of A are those P_i not properly containing P_j, $j \neq i$ (we may have $P_i = P_j$). Furthermore $\sqrt{A}$ is the intersection of the minimal prime ideals of A.*

Proof. Let P be a prime ideal containing A. We have

$$Q_1 \cdots Q_n \subset Q_1 \cap \cdots \cap Q_n = A \subset P.$$

Hence $Q_i \subset P$ for some i. Thus by Theorem 8, $P_i \subset P$. Now suppose P is one of the minimal prime ideals of A. We cannot have $P_i \subsetneq P$, so we must have $P_i = P$. If $j \neq i$, we cannot have $P_j \subsetneq P$.

On the other hand, if P_i does not properly contain any P_j, then P_i is minimal, for suppose P_i is not a minimal prime ideal of A. Then there is a prime ideal P' such that $A \subset P' \subsetneq P_i$. By the first part of the proof there is a P_j such that $P_j \subset P' \subsetneq P_i$, a contradiction.

Finally, by Problem 22 we have

$$\sqrt{A} = \sqrt{(Q_1 \cap \cdots \cap Q_n)} = \sqrt{Q_1} \cap \cdots \cap \sqrt{Q_n} = P_1 \cap \cdots \cap P_n.$$

(We may discard from the intersection any of the terms which contain one of the other terms.)

> **Corollary.** If an ideal A has a primary decomposition, then A has only a finite number of minimal prime ideals, and each of these minimal prime ideals occurs as the radical of some primary component in any primary decomposition of A.

An ideal A in a ring R is *irreducible* if whenever $A = I \cap J$, I and J ideals of R, then either $A = I$ or $A = J$.

> **Theorem 10.** *In a commutative Noetherian ring with identity every ideal has a primary decomposition.*

Proof. The theorem is a direct consequence of the following two lemmas:

> **Lemma 1.** In a Noetherian ring every ideal can be written as the intersection of a finite number of irreducible ideals.

Proof. Let $\mathfrak{S}$ be the set of all ideals of R which cannot be written as the intersection of a finite number of irreducible ideals. If the lemma is not true, $\mathfrak{S}$ is not empty and so has a maximal element, say A. Since A cannot be written as the intersection of a finite number of irreducible ideals, A itself is not irreducible.

Thus we have $A = B \cap C$, where B, C are ideals in R, $A \subsetneq B$, and $A \subsetneq C$. But then B and C are not in $\mathfrak{S}$. Hence B and C can both be written as finite intersections of irreducible ideals. Thus the same is true of A, a contradiction. Therefore $\mathfrak{S}$ is empty and the lemma is true.

Lemma 2. In a commutative Noetherian ring R with identity every irreducible ideal is primary.

Proof. Let A be an ideal in R which is not primary. We show that A is not irreducible. Since A is not primary, there are elements b, $c \in R$ such that $bc \in A$, $c \notin A$ and no power of b belongs to A. We have $A \subset A:(b)$, but $c \in A:(b)$ and $c \notin A$; hence $A \subsetneq A:(b)$. We have

$$A:(b^r) \subset (A:(b^r)):(b) = A:(b^{r+1}).$$

Thus there is a chain

$$A \subset A:(b) \subset A:(b^2) \subset A:(b^3) \subset \cdots.$$

Since R is Noetherian, there is an integer N such that

$$A:(b^N) = A:(b^n) \qquad \text{for} \quad n \geq N.$$

We now want to show

(∗) $$A = (A:(b^N)) \cap (A + (b^N)).$$

This will show that A is not irreducible since $A \subsetneq A:(b^N)$ from above and $A \subsetneq A + (b^N)$ since $b^N \notin A$.

Clearly A is contained in the right-hand side of (∗), so let

$$x \in (A:(b^N)) \cap (A + (b^N)).$$

We have $x = a + rb^N$, $a \in A$, $r \in R$. But since $x \in A:(b^N)$,

$$xb^N = ab^N + rb^{2N} \in A.$$

Thus $rb^{2N} \in A$, that is, $r \in A:(b^{2N})$. But from the way N was selected, $A:(b^{2N}) = A:(b^N)$ so $rb^N \in A$. Hence $x \in A$.

Theorem 11. *In a commutative Noetherian ring R with identity, every ideal contains a power of its radical.*

Proof. Let A be an ideal in R with $\sqrt{A} = (a_1, \ldots, a_n)$. Let m_i be a positive integer such that $a_i^{m_i} \in A$ and $m = m_1 + \cdots + m_n$. Every element of $(\sqrt{A})^m$ is a finite sum of terms of the form

$$b_1^{u_1} \cdots b_t^{u_t}, \qquad \text{where} \qquad b_j \in \sqrt{A}, \quad j = 1, \ldots, t \quad \text{and} \quad u_1 + \cdots + u_t = m.$$

For each $j = 1, \ldots, t$, we have

$$b_j = r_{j_1} a_1 + \cdots + r_{j_n} a_n, \qquad r_{j_k} \in R, \quad k = 1, \ldots, n.$$

Hence $b_1^{u_1} \cdots b_t^{u_t}$ is the sum of a finite number of terms of the form

(*) $ra_1^{v_1} \cdots a_n^{v_n},$ where $r \in R,\quad v_i \geq 0,\quad i = 1, \ldots, n,$

and

$$v_1 + \cdots + v_n = m = m_1 + \cdots + m_n.$$

But then for some l, $1 \leq l \leq n$, we must have $v_l \geq m_l$. Hence $a_l^{v_l} \in A$ and so the product (*) belongs to A.

Corollary. If R is Noetherian and Q is P-primary, then $P^r \subset Q$ for some $r \in Z^+$.

7. UNIQUE FACTORIZATION DOMAINS

We discuss in this section two other special types of rings which have been the subject of extensive investigation. Both arise from abstracting properties of integers: unique factorization of an integer as the product of powers of primes and the division algorithm.

If a and b are elements of a ring R, then b *divides* a if there is a $c \in R$ such that $a = bc$; we write $b \mid a$. Thus the units of a ring are precisely the elements which divide the identity. If $a = bu$, where u is a unit, a and b are called *associates*. In fact, if a and b are associates, $a \mid b$ and $b \mid a$. If R is an integral domain, the converse also holds. An element $a \neq 0$ of a ring R is *prime* if it is not a unit and if its only divisors are associates of a and units of R. An integral domain R is a *unique factorization domain* (UFD) if R has an identity and if every nonzero nonunit of R can be written as a finite product of prime factors and the factorization is unique to within order and unit factors.

Examples. The integers, any field and the polynomial ring $F[x]$, where F is a field, are unique factorization domains.

If a, b, c are elements of a ring R such that $c \mid a$ and $c \mid b$ and if whenever $d \in R$ is such that $d \mid a$ and $d \mid b$, then $d \mid c$, then c is said to be a *greatest common divisor* of a and b, and we write $(a, b) = c$. Any pair of elements in a UFD has a greatest common divisor, unique to within units. Since in an integral domain all greatest common divisors of a pair of elements are associates, we call any such *the* greatest common divisor. If $(a, b) = 1$, a and b are said to be *relatively prime*.

A UFD R has the following properties, all of which are straightforward consequences of the definition:

U1) If p is a prime element of R and $p \mid ab$, then $p \mid a$ or $p \mid b$.

U2) If $(a, b) = 1$ and $b \mid ac$, then $b \mid c$.

U3) If $(a, b) = 1$ and if $a \mid c$ and $b \mid c$, then $ab \mid c$.

A principal ideal ring which is also an integral domain is a *principal ideal domain* (PID).

Theorem 12. *In a principal ideal domain D, any pair of nonzero elements (a, b) has a greatest common divisor which can be written as a linear combination*

$$d = sa + tb$$

of a and b for some s, t ∈ D.

Proof. Let $I = \{xa + yb \mid x, y \in D\}$. I is an ideal of D. Hence there is a $d \in D$ such that $I = (d)$, where $d = sa + tb$. Then d is certainly a divisor of a and b, since $a, b \in I$. On the other hand, if $d' \mid a$ and $d' \mid b$ so that $a = a'd'$, $b = b'd'$, $a', b' \in D$, then $d = sa'd' + tb'd'$ for some $s', t' \in D$. Thus d is a multiple of d'. Hence d is a greatest common divisor of a and b.

Corollary. If p is a prime in a PID and $p \mid ab$, then $p \mid a$ or $p \mid b$.

Proof. Suppose $p \nmid a$. Then $(a, p) = 1 = sa + tp$, for some s, t in the PID and $b = sab + tpb$. Then p divides the right-hand side, so $p \mid b$.

The corollary attributes a property of UFD's to PID's and thus might lead us to conjecture that a PID is a UFD; in fact the result holds.

Theorem 13. *A principal ideal domain is a unique factorization domain.*

Proof. Suppose $a \neq 0$ is a nonunit of a principal ideal domain D and has no prime factorization. Then a is not a prime and hence it has a proper factorization, say $a = a_1a_2$. Either a_1 or a_2 has no prime factorization, say a_2. Then $a_2 = a_3a_4$. We repeat the argument to get an ascending sequence of ideals of D,

$$(a) \subsetneq (a_2) \subsetneq (a_4) \subsetneq \cdots,$$

which contradicts the Noetherian property of D.

We show the uniqueness of the factorization by induction on the number n of prime factors in a factorization. If $n = 1$, a is a prime, so the trivial factorization is unique. Thus we assume that uniqueness holds for any element which is the product of m prime factors. Suppose

$$p_1p_2 \cdots p_m p_{m+1} = q_1q_2 \cdots q_r.$$

Since p_{m+1} is a prime and divides the left-, and hence the right-hand side, p_{m+1} divides one of the q_i, by the corollary to Theorem 12. Thus $up_{m+1} = q_i$ for some unit u and some q_i. This leaves a factorization of m primes, which by the induction assumption is unique.

The converse does not hold; for example, if D is a UFD, then $D[x_1, \ldots, x_n]$ is also, but if D is a PID, $D[x_1, \ldots, x_n]$ is a UFD, but not a PID (if $n > 1$). For example, the ideal (x, y) in the ring $R[x, y]$, R the real numbers, is not principal.

An integral domain R is a *Euclidean ring* if R has an identity and if for every $a \neq 0$ in R there is defined a nonnegative integer $d(a)$ such that:

1) For all $a, b \in R$, $a \neq 0 \neq b$, $d(a) \leq d(ab)$.

2) For any $a, b \in R$, $a \neq 0 \neq b$, there exist $t, r \in R$ such that

$$a = tb + r,$$

where $r = 0$ or $d(r) < d(b)$ (Euclidean algorithm).

Examples. The integers, with $d(a) = |a|$, are a Euclidean ring. Any field, with $d(a) = 1$ for all nonzero a, is a Euclidean ring. That the polynomial ring over any field, with $d(p) = $ degree of the polynomial p, is Euclidean will be shown in Section 8.

If we let $Z[i] = \{a + bi \mid a, b \in Z\}$, then $Z[i]$, under the usual addition and multiplication of complex numbers, is an integral domain, called the *Gaussian integers*. If we define $d(a + bi) = a^2 + b^2$, then this function makes $Z[i]$ into a Euclidean ring. The verification of (1) is straightforward. To obtain (2) we consider first the case of an ordinary positive integer y and a Gaussian integer $a + bi$. Using the Euclidean algorithm for integers, we can write

$$a = uy + r_1,$$
$$b = vy + r_2, \qquad |r_i| \leq \tfrac{1}{2}y, \quad i = 1, 2.$$

We let $t = u + vi$, $r = r_1 + r_2 i$. Then

$$a + bi = uy + r_1 + (vy + r_2)i = (u + vi)y + r_1 + r_2 i = ty + r.$$

Moreover, if $r \neq 0$,

$$d(r) = d(r_1 + r_2 i) = r_1^2 + r_2^2 \leq y^2/4 + y^2/4 \leq y^2 = d(y).$$

Now suppose $a + bi \neq 0$ and $c + di$ are arbitrary elements of $Z[i]$; then

$$(a + bi)(a - bi) = a^2 + b^2$$

is a positive integer; so applying the above to $(c + di)(a - bi)$ and $a^2 + b^2$, we get

$$(c + di)(a - bi) = t(a^2 + b^2) + r,$$

with $r = 0$ or $d(r) < d(a^2 + b^2)$. Thus

$$d((c + di)(a - bi) - t(a^2 + b^2)) < d(a^2 + b^2) = d((a + bi)(a - bi)).$$

Also since $d((a + bi)(a - bi)) = d(a + bi)d(a - bi)$,

$$d((c + di)(a - bi) - t(a^2 + b^2)) = d((c + di) - t(a + bi))d(a - bi),$$

so that

$$d((c + di) - t(a + bi))d(a - bi) < d(a + bi)d(a - bi).$$

But $d(a - bi)$ is a positive integer, so

$$d((c + di) - t(a + bi)) < d(a + bi).$$

Thus we write

$$c + di = t(a + bi) + r,$$

where $r = c + di - t(a + bi)$, to get the desired result.

We close this section by showing the relations among these various generalizations of properties of the integers.

Theorem 14. *A Euclidean ring is a PID (and hence a UFD).*

Proof. Let I be an ideal of a Euclidean ring R. If $I = (0)$, then it is principal; so suppose there is an $a \neq 0$ in I. We select an $a_0 \in I$ such that $d(a_0)$ is minimal. Then $(a_0) \subset I$. Let a be any element of I. We can write $a = ta_0 + r$, where $r = 0$ or $d(r) < d(a_0)$. Since $r = a - ta_0$, $r \in I$. Hence $d(r) \not< d(a_0)$ by minimality. Thus $r = 0$ and $a \in (a_0)$. Thus $(a_0) = I$.

The converse is not true.

8. POLYNOMIAL RINGS

The concept of a polynomial was introduced in Section 1 by considering expressions involving coefficients from a ring and powers of an indeterminate. It is clear that the role of the indeterminate is a passive one; the essential notion is that of the coefficients and their order. Hence we may think of a polynomial as a map f from the nonnegative integers to a ring R such that there exists a nonnegative integer N with $f(n) = 0$ for $n > N$. We identify the map with its set of values $(a_0, \ldots, a_i, \ldots)$, $a_i \in R$, $f(i) = a_i$, and obtain a ring by defining addition and multiplication of the maps in the obvious way:

$$(a_0, \ldots, a_i, \ldots) + (b_0, \ldots, b_i, \ldots) = (a_0 + b_0, \ldots, a_i + b_i, \ldots)$$

and

$$(a_0, \ldots, a_i, \ldots)(b_0, \ldots, b_i, \ldots) = (c_0, \ldots, c_i, \ldots),$$

where

$$c_i = \sum_{j=0}^{i} a_j b_{i-j}.$$

We call this the *polynomial ring in one indeterminate over R* and denote it by $R[x]$. Then if some $a_i \neq 0$, we define the *degree* of f to be $\max\{i \mid a_i \neq 0\}$. If degree $f = 0$, f is a *constant polynomial*. If degree $f = n$, a_n is the *leading coefficient* of f and f is *monic* if $a_n = 1$.

It is clear that we can iterate the process to obtain a polynomial ring in any finite number of indeterminates.

Once we have made the point that it is the map which is important, we identify the image $(a_0, \ldots, a_i, \ldots)$ with the expression $\sum a_i x^i$ and proceed to deal with polynomials in the usual way.

We have previously discussed some properties inherited by polynomial rings. We also have:

Theorem 15 (Hilbert's Basis Theorem). *If R is a commutative Noetherian ring with identity, then the polynomial ring $R[x]$ is a Noetherian ring.*

Proof. Given an ideal A of $R[x]$ it is clear that we must somehow connect to it ideals of R, since they are finitely generated. An obvious approach would be to consider ideals of leading coefficients of polynomials of various degrees in A. However, the degree of the polynomials in A is not bounded, so we adopt a refinement to this approach.

Let A be an ideal in $R[x]$ and let A' be the subset of R consisting of 0 and of all the leading coefficients of all polynomials in A. A' is an ideal in R and so $A' = (a_1, \ldots, a_n)$, $a_1, \ldots, a_n \in A'$. If f is a polynomial in A with some a_i as its leading coefficient, then there are polynomials in A of any degree larger than the degree of f which are obtained by multiplying f by an appropriate power of $x \in R[x]$. Thus let $f_{N,i}$ be a polynomial in A of degree N with a_i as its leading coefficient.

Now we consider all polynomials in A of degree $\leq N - 1$. The coefficients of x^{N-1} in these polynomials form an ideal, say A_{N-1}, in R and

$$A_{N-1} = (a_{N-1,1}, \ldots, a_{N-1,k}), \qquad a_{N-1,1}, \ldots, a_{N-1,k} \in A_{N-1}.$$

Choose polynomials $f_{N-1,1}, \ldots, f_{N-1,k} \in A$ such that $a_{N-1,i}$ is the leading coefficient of $f_{N-1,i}$.

Continuing in this way, we obtain a finite set of polynomials $\{f_{j,i}\}$, where $j = N - 1, \ldots, 0$, and the i in each case ranges over the indices of the generators of the ideal of the coefficients of x^j in polynomials of degree $\leq j$ in A. We shall show that A is generated by this set together with the $f_{N,i}$, $i = 1, \ldots, n$.

Let g be an arbitrary polynomial in A, say of degree p,

$$g = ax^p + \text{terms of lower degree.}$$

First suppose that $p \geq N$. Since $a \in A'$, we have

$$a = r_1 a_1 + \cdots + r_n a_n, \qquad r_i \in R.$$

Then

$$g - r_1 x^{p-N} f_{N,1} - r_2 x^{p-N} f_{N,2} - \cdots - r_n x^{p-N} f_{N,n}$$

has degree $\leq p - 1$. If the degree of this polynomial is also greater than or equal to N, then we repeat the process, finally obtaining a polynomial in A

$$h = g - A_1 f_{N,1} - \cdots - A_n f_{N,n}$$

with degree $\leq N - 1$. We now show that h can be expressed as a linear combination of the $f_{j,i}, j = N - 1, \ldots, 0$, with i as before. Then since

$$g = A_1 f_{N,1} + \cdots + A_n f_{N,n} + h,$$

we shall have the desired result. (If degree $g < N$, $g = h$.)

Since h is of degree $\leq N - 1$, its coefficient of x^{N-1}, say h_{N-1}, is in A_{N-1} and we can find $s_1, \ldots, s_k \in R$ such that

$$h_{N-1} = s_1 a_{N-1,1} + \cdots + s_k a_{N-1,k}.$$

Since $a_{N-1,i}$ is the coefficient of x^{N-1} in $f_{N-1,i}$,

$$h - s_1 f_{N-1,1} - \cdots - s_k f_{N-1,k}$$

has degree $< N - 2$. Continuing in this manner, we obtain a polynomial in A of degree 0, which can be written as a linear combination the $f_{0,i}$ selected above; then h can be expressed as the sum of it and a linear combination of the $f_{j,i}, j > 0$ as desired.

Corollary. If R is a commutative Noetherian ring with identity, then $R[x_1, \ldots, x_n]$ is Noetherian.

In particular, if F is a field, then $F[x_1, \ldots, x_n]$ is a Noetherian ring.

Before proceeding with results on polynomial rings we discuss an allied notion. One considers substituting a ring element for the indeterminate x in a polynomial expression and obtaining as the value of the polynomial some element of the ring. Thus if R' is a ring containing R (it could be R itself) and if $p = p(x) \in R[x]$, $p(x) = \sum a_i x^i$, we define a polynomial function $p : R' \to R'$ by $p(r) = \sum a_i r^i$. Observe that we distinguish between polynomials, which are elements of $R[x]$ and which may be considered as functions from a subset of the nonnegative integers to R, and polynomial functions which have R' as their range and domain.

If $R' \supset R$ is a ring and $r \in R'$ is such that $p(r) = 0$, r is said to be a *root* of the polynomial p. Not all polynomials with coefficients in a given ring have roots in that ring, for example $x^2 - 2 \in Z[x]$, $x^2 + 1 \in R[x]$ (R the real numbers). If, in fact, every polynomial with coefficients in a ring R has a root in R, R is said to be *algebraically closed*. The complex numbers are constructed to obtain a root for $x^2 + 1 \in R[x]$; we want to develop a general process for extending the domain of a polynomial function in order to obtain roots. To do this we must look more closely at the structure of polynomial rings.

Theorem 16. *If R is an integral domain, $R[x]$ is an integral domain.*

Proof. Everything is clear except the nonexistence of zero divisors. To prove that $f(x)g(x) = 0$ implies that $f(x)$ or $g(x)$ is the zero polynomial, it suffices to show that if $f(x)$ and $g(x)$ are nonzero elements of $R[x]$, then

$$\text{degree}(f(x)g(x)) = \text{degree} f(x) + \text{degree} g(x).$$

Let

$$f(x) = \sum_0^m a_i x^i, \quad g(x) = \sum_0^n b_i x^i, \quad a_m \neq 0, \quad b_n \neq 0.$$

$$f(x)g(x) = \sum_0^k c_i x^i, \quad \text{where} \quad c_i = \sum_{j=0}^i a_j b_{i-j}.$$

It is clear that $c_{m+n} = a_m b_n$. If $i > m + n$, then c_i is the sum of terms $a_j b_{i-j}$ with either $j > m$ or $(i - j) > n$. Then $a_j = 0$ or $b_{i-j} = 0$ and so $c_i = 0$. Thus $\text{degree}(f(x)g(x)) = m + n$.

Thus it is possible to construct the field of quotients of $R[x]$, R an integral domain. This field is called the *field of rational functions* over R, and is denoted by $R(x)$. (Although in fact its elements are not functions but rational expressions.)

When R is a field we have the further result:

Theorem 17. *If R is a field, $R[x]$ is a Euclidean ring.*

Proof. The degree of a polynomial defines the required function and property (1) in the definition of Euclidean ring is clear. We show that the Euclidean algorithm holds.

Let

$$f(x) = \sum_0^m a_i x^i, \qquad g(x) = \sum_0^n b_i x^i, \qquad a_m \neq 0, \quad b_n \neq 0.$$

If degree $f(x) <$ degree $g(x)$, we let $f(x) = t(x)g(x) + r(x)$ with $t(x)$ the zero polynomial and $r(x) = f(x)$, so we may as well assume $m \geq n$. We proceed by induction. If $m = 0$, we use the fact that R is Euclidean.

Let $f_1(x) = f(x) - (a_m/b_n)x^{m-n}g(x)$. Then degree $f_1 \leq m - 1$, so we can write

$$f_1(x) = t_1(x)g(x) + r(x), \qquad r(x) = 0 \qquad \text{or} \qquad \text{degree } r(x) < \text{degree } g(x).$$

Then

$$f(x) = ((a_m/b_n)x^{m-n} + t_1(x))g(x) + r(x).$$

This is the required factorization with $t(x) = (a_m/b_n)x^{m-n} + t_1(x)$.

We now know, from Theorem 14, that every ideal of a polynomial ring over a field is principal. If $p = p(x) \in R[x]$ cannot be written as

$$p = qr, \qquad q, r \in R[x], \qquad \text{degree } q < \text{degree } p, \qquad \text{degree } r < \text{degree } p,$$

p is said to be *irreducible*. Thus the irreducible polynomials are the prime elements of $R[x]$, and hence (see Problem 27) M is a maximal ideal of $R[x]$ if and only if $M = (p)$, p an irreducible polynomial. Now we see by Theorem 4 that if R is a field and p an irreducible polynomial over R, $R[x]/(p)$ is a field. We embed R in $R[x]/(p)$ by identifying $r \to r + (p)$ and in fact consider R to be a subring of $R[x]/(p)$. If p is an irreducible polynomial of degree > 1, p can have no roots in R, for if a is a root of p, $x - a$ is easily seen to be a factor of $p(x)$.

Let us now consider an irreducible polynomial p as a polynomial over $R[x]/(p)$; that is, p is a map $p: Z^+ \cup \{0\} \to R[x]/(p)$, or

$$p = (a_0 + (p), \ldots, a_i + (p), \ldots).$$

Let us consider the value of the polynomial function at the element $x + (p)$:

$$p(x + (p)) = \sum a_i(x + (p))^i = \sum a_i x^i + (p) = p(x) + (p) = (p).$$

But (p) is the zero of $R[x]/(p)$, so $x + (p)$ is a root of p, considered as an element of $(R[x]/(p))[x]$. Thus we have embedded R in a field in which p has a root.

For example, we embed the real numbers R in $R[x]/(x^2 + 1)$ to obtain a root: clearly $R[x]/(x^2 + 1)$ is isomorphic to the complex numbers under the mapping

$$x + (x^2 + 1) \to i,$$

so that we can think of every element of $R[x]/(x^2 + 1)$ being written in the form

$$a + bi, \qquad a, b \text{ real numbers}, \quad i \text{ a root of } x^2 + 1.$$

Does this notion generalize?

We recall that every element q of $R[x]$ can be written as

$$q = tp + r, \qquad \text{degree } r < \text{degree } p \quad \text{or} \quad r = 0.$$

Thus every element $q + (p)$ of $R[x]/(p)$ can be written as $r + (p)$, degree $r <$ degree p or $r \in (p)$.

We can now replace x in the polynomial expressions by a, where a is a root of p contained in some field containing R (for example, $a = x + (p)$) and consider $R[a]$, that is, all expressions of the form $\sum r_i a^i$, $r_i \in R$, and from that construct $R[a]/(p(a))$. Every element of $R[a]/(p(a))$ can then be written as

$$\sum_{0}^{n-1} r_i a^i + (p(a)), \qquad n = \text{degree } p, \qquad r_i \in R.$$

But $(p(a))$ is the zero ideal since a is a root. Thus all expressions of the form $\sum s_i a^i$, $s_i \in R$, that is, all elements of $R[a]$, can be written as

$$\sum_{0}^{n-1} r_i a^i,$$

where n is the degree of an irreducible polynomial over R of which a is a root. Thus $R[a]$ is isomorphic to the field $R[x]/(p(x))$ under the correspondence

$$\sum r_i a^i \to \sum r_i x^i + (p).$$

We now have that $R[a]$ is a field containing R and a; in fact, it is the smallest field containing R and a and is called the *field of rational expressions* in a, usually denoted by $R(a)$.

This section is only a brief introduction to the theory of polynomial rings over fields. For extensive treatment see, e.g., Artin, *Galois Theory*, 2nd ed. Notre Dame Mathematical Lectures, no. 2, 1959.

PROBLEMS

1. Prove that a commutative ring R is an integral domain if and only if R obeys the cancellation law: $ab = cb$, $b \neq 0$, implies that $a = c$.

2. Prove or provide a counterexample: Any finite integral domain is a field.

3. Prove that if D is an integral domain of characteristic p, then $px = 0$ for all $x \in D$.

4. Prove that the characteristic of an integral domain is either 0 or a prime number.

5. Prove that if R has a right inverse and a two-sided identity for an associative product, then the right inverse is also a left inverse and hence a unique two-sided inverse.

6. If I is an ideal of a ring R such that the identity of R is in I, prove that $I = R$.

7. If a ring R has an identity 1 and $f: R \to R'$ is a nonzero homomorphism, prove that $f(1)$ is an identity for $f(R)$. Prove that if R' is an integral domain with an identity $1'$, then $f(1) = 1'$.

8. If R has an identity and for every $x \in R$, $x^2 = x$, R is a *Boolean ring*. Prove that any Boolean ring is commutative.

9. If R is a commutative ring with identity, prove that the units of R form an abelian group under multiplication.

10. If I is an ideal of a ring R and J is an ideal of R contained in I, prove that

$$R/I \simeq (R/J)/(I/J).$$

11. If A and B are ideals of a ring R, prove that

$$(A + B)/B \simeq A/(A \cap B).$$

12. Prove or provide a counterexample: If R is a commutative ring, End(R), the set of endomorphisms of R, is a commutative ring under operations defined pointwise.

13. Prove that if I and J are ideals of a ring R such that $R = I + J$ and $I \cap J = (0)$, then $R \simeq I \oplus J$. In this case, R is said to be the *internal direct* sum of I and J.

14. What can be said about the intersection of a left ideal and a right ideal of a ring R?

15. Let $b \in Q$, the field of rational numbers, and define

$$Q(\sqrt{b}) = \{a + d\sqrt{b} \mid a, d \in Q\}.$$

Prove that $Q(\sqrt{b})$ is a field, the smallest containing Q and $\sqrt{b}$. Find a quotient ring of $Q[x]$ isomorphic to $Q(\sqrt{b})$.

16. Prove that any ring R can be embedded in a ring with identity $R \oplus (1)$, where $(1) \simeq Z$.

17. Prove that the field of quotients of an integral domain D is the smallest (up to isomorphism) field containing D.

18. Prove that an automorphism of an integral domain can be extended in a unique way to an automorphism of its field of quotients.

19. Let R be a commutative ring with identity and S a multiplicative subset ($a, b \in S$ implies that $ab \in S$) not containing 0. Prove that if P is a maximal element in the set of ideals of R whose intersection with S is empty, then P is a prime ideal of R.

20. Give an example of an infinite field with finite characteristic. Show that any two finite fields with the same number of elements are isomorphic.

21. Give an example of a ring which is left Noetherian but not right Noetherian.

22. Show that if I and J are ideals of a commutative ring R with identity, then
$$\sqrt{IJ} = \sqrt{I \cap J} = \sqrt{I} \cap \sqrt{J}.$$

23. If I is an ideal of a commutative ring R with identity and I is not prime, show that there exist ideals J and K of R such that $I \subsetneqq J$, $I \subsetneqq K$ and $JK \subset I$.

24. Show that a primary ideal need not be a power of a prime ideal and that a non-primary ideal may have a prime radical. [*Hint:* Show that in $R[x, y]$, (x, y^2) is (x, y)-primary and $\sqrt{(x^2, xy)} = (x)$.]

25. If R is a Euclidean ring, prove that a is a unit of R if and only if $d(a) = d(1)$, where 1 is the identity of R.

26. Prove that if R is a unique factorization domain, then $R[x]$ is a UFD.

27. Give an example of a prime ideal which is not a maximal ideal. Prove that in a Euclidean ring all prime ideals are maximal and that an ideal is prime if and only if it is generated by a prime element. In what kind of rings are maximal ideals prime?

28. Find the roots of $x^2 - 1 \in Z_{15}[x]$.

29. If $f(x) \in Z_p[x]$, p a prime, and $f(x)$ is irreducible of degree n, prove that $Z_p[x]/(f(x))$ has p^n elements.

30. Show that $R[x]/(x^2 + x + 1)$ (R the real numbers) is isomorphic to the complex numbers.

CHAPTER 2

The Classical Radical

In this chapter we discuss nil and nilpotent ideals, showing the existence in certain types of rings of a maximum nilpotent ideal called the *Wedderburn-Artin* or *classical radical of the ring*. After examining various properties of this radical, we prove a structure theorem which makes use of the radical to describe precisely a large class of rings. Briefly, the idea is as follows: if we eliminate the "bad" or radical part of a ring by factoring it out, what can be said about what is left? It turns out that a radical-free ring is, under a minimality condition, the direct sum of simple rings and moreover that simple rings are, up to isomorphism, merely matrix rings.

It should be noted that the term "radical" derives not from any obstreperous behavior on the part of the entity described, but rather from its connection with powers and roots.

1. NILPOTENT IDEALS AND THE RADICAL

Let R be an arbitrary ring. An element $x \in R$ is *nilpotent* if $x^n = 0$ for some positive integer n. An ideal (left ideal, right ideal) I in R is *nil* if every element of I is nilpotent, while I is *nilpotent* if there is a positive integer n such that $I^n = (0)$, where I^n is the product of I with itself n times.

Theorem 1. *The sum of a finite number of nilpotent left (right) ideals in a ring R is a nilpotent left (right) ideal of R.*

Proof. It suffices to show that if I, J are nilpotent, then $I + J$ is nilpotent. If $I^m = J^n = (0)$, then consider $(I + J)^{m+n}$. Each element of this ideal is a finite sum of terms of the form

$$(a_1 + b_1) \cdots (a_{m+n} + b_{m+n}), \qquad a_i \in I, \quad b_j \in J.$$

Hence each element of $(I + J)^{m+n}$ is the sum of a finite number of terms which are the products of $m + n$ factors, at least m of which are from I or at least n of which are from J. Hence $(I + J)^{m+n} = (0)$.

Corollary. Let $\{I_\alpha\}_{\alpha \in A}$ be a family of nilpotent left (right) ideals of a ring R. Then $\sum_{\alpha \in A} I_\alpha$ is a nil left (right) ideal (where the sum is in the sense of Chapter 1, i.e., every element of $\sum_{\alpha \in A} I$ can be represented as the sum of a finite number of elements, each in some I_α).

This leads to an important construction.

Theorem 2. *Let $\{I_\alpha\}_{\alpha\in A}$ be the family of all nilpotent right ideals in a ring R, $\{J_\beta\}_{\beta\in B}$ the family of all nilpotent left ideals in R, and $\{K_\gamma\}_{\gamma\in C}$ the family of all nilpotent ideals in R. Let*

$$W_r = \sum_{\alpha\in A} I_\alpha, \qquad W_l = \sum_{\beta\in B} J_\beta, \qquad \text{and} \qquad W = \sum_{\gamma\in C} K_\gamma.$$

Then $W = W_r = W_l$.

Proof. Let I be a nilpotent left ideal, $I^n = (0)$. Then $I + IR$ is an ideal and $(I + IR)^n \subset I^n + I^nR = (0)$. Hence $I + IR \subset W$ and since $I \subset I + IR$, $I \subset W$. Thus $W_l \subset W$. But each ideal is a left ideal, so $W \subset W_l$, and hence they are equal. Similarly, $W_r = W$.

We denote this ideal, which by the corollary to Theorem 1 is nil, by W and call it the *nil radical of R*. We want to know when it is actually nilpotent.

Theorem 3. *If a ring R is left (right) Noetherian, then W is nilpotent.*

Proof. Let $\mathfrak{S}$ be the family of all nilpotent left ideals of R which are contained in W. $\mathfrak{S}$ is not empty because $(0) \in \mathfrak{S}$. Since R is left Noetherian, $\mathfrak{S}$ has a maximal element, say I. If $I = W$ we are finished, so suppose $I \neq W$.

Let $a \in W \setminus I$. Then there are nilpotent left ideals $I_1, \ldots, I_n$ such that $a \in I_1 + \cdots + I_n$. Let $I' = I + I_1 + \cdots + I_n$. $I' \subset W$ and by Theorem 1, I' is nilpotent, contradicting the maximality of I.

It turns out that minimality conditions also give us the desired result; in fact we have:

Theorem 4 (Hopkins' Theorem). *If R is left (right) Artinian, then every nil left (right) ideal is nilpotent.*

Proof. Let I be a nonnilpotent left ideal in R. Since R is left Artinian, the family of all nonnilpotent left ideals of R contained in I has a minimal element, say I_1. We have $I_1^2 \subset I_1$, but since I_1 is nonnilpotent, I_1^2 is nonnilpotent. Thus by the minimality of I_1, $I_1^2 = I_1$.

Now we let $\mathfrak{S}$ be the family of all left ideals J in R such that $I_1J \neq (0)$ and $J \subset I_1$. $\mathfrak{S}$ is not empty since $I_1 \in \mathfrak{S}$. Hence $\mathfrak{S}$ has a minimal element, say J_1. Let $x \in J_1$ be such that $I_1x \neq (0)$. I_1x is a left ideal in R, $I_1(I_1x) = I_1^2x = I_1x \neq (0)$ and $I_1x \subset I_1$. Hence $I_1x \in \mathfrak{S}$ and since $I_1x \subset J_1$, $I_1x = J_1$.

Let $a \in I_1$ be such that $ax = x$. Then for any positive integer n,

$$a^nx = a^{n-1}x = \cdots = ax = x.$$

Hence $a^n \neq 0$ for all positive integers n, that is, a is not nilpotent. But $a \in I_1 \subset I$. Hence I is not nil.

By an analogous process we can show the result for R right Artinian.

Corollary. If a ring R is left or right Artinian, then $W = W_l = W_r$ is nilpotent.

Whenever the sum W of all nilpotent ideals is itself nilpotent, we call W the (*Wedderburn-Artin, classical,* or *nilpotent*) *radical* of R, writing $W(R)$ when the distinction is necessary.

We shall investigate the properties of this radical in rings where it exists, i.e., where the sum of all the nilpotent ideals is again a nilpotent ideal.

Theorem 5. *Let R be a ring which has W as its radical. Then R/W has no nonzero nilpotent ideals.*

Proof. Let $W^m = (0)$ and let $\bar{N}$ be a nilpotent ideal in R/W, say $\bar{N}^r = (0)$. Then if we let N be the corresponding ideal in R, $N = \{x \in R \mid x + W \in \bar{N}\}$, $N^r \subset W$ and $N^{rm} \subset W^m = (0)$. Thus N is a nilpotent ideal in R, so $N \subset W$ and $\bar{N} = (0)$.

A ring R which has no nonzero nilpotent ideals is called *semiprime*. If, in addition, R is left Artinian, R is *semisimple*. Thus the (classical) radical of a semisimple ring is zero and in fact this is sometimes taken as the definition of semisimplicity. A word of caution, however: semisimplicity is defined also for more general rings in terms of other radicals, as we shall see in later chapters. Moreover, it is also possible to define semisimplicity by requiring that the ring be right Artinian. It will be shown that the definitions in terms of left and right minimality conditions are equivalent.

Corollary. If R is left Artinian, then R/W is semisimple.

Proof. The quotient ring inherits the minimality condition because of the lattice theorem for ideals.

2. THE RADICAL OF RELATED RINGS

We recall that assuming I is an ideal of a commutative ring R with identity, in Chapter 1 we defined the radical of I as follows:

$$\sqrt{I} = \{x \in R \mid x^n \in I, n \text{ some positive integer}\}.$$

Then the radical of the ring is defined to be the radical of the zero ideal; our nil radical gives the same ideal when R is commutative. It is also possible to define the radical of an ideal by considering the ideal itself as a ring; this is the procedure we follow.

Theorem 6. *If A is an ideal of a left (right) Artinian ring R, $W(A)$ the radical of A, and $W(R)$ the radical of R, then*

$$W(A) = W(R) \cap A.$$

Proof. Let I be a nilpotent ideal of R, say $I^n = (0)$. Then $I \cap A$ is an ideal of A and $(I \cap A)^n \subset I^n \cap A = (0)$ so that $I \cap A \subset W(A)$. But $W(R)$ is nilpotent so that $W(R) \cap A \subset W(A)$.

For the converse, suppose first that $W(R) = (0)$ and let $A_l(A)$ be the set of left annihilators of A. $A_l(A)$ is a left ideal of R. $W(A)A$ is a right ideal of R. Since $W(A)A \subset W(A)$, $W(A)A$ is nilpotent. Thus $W(A)A \subset W(R) = (0)$, and $W(A) \subset A_l(A) \cap A$. But $A_l(A) \cap A$ is nil and hence nilpotent and $A_l(A) \cap A \subset A$. Therefore $A_l(A) \cap A \subset W(A)$. Thus $W(A) = A_l(A) \cap A$ and is a left ideal of R. Hence $W(A) \subset W(R)$.

In the general case $(A + W(R))/W(R)$ is an ideal in the ring $R/W(R)$, which by Theorem 5 has zero radical. Therefore, $W((A + W(R))/W(R)) = (0)$ and so

$$W(A)/(A \cap W(R)) \subset W(A \mid A \cap W(R)) = (0)$$

since $(A + W(R))/W(R) \simeq A/(A \cap W(R))$ (Problem 11 of Chapter 1). Hence $W(A) \subset W(R) \cap A$.

Theorem 7. *If W is the radical of a left (right) Artinian ring R, then W_n is the radical of the complete matrix ring R_n.*

Proof. Since if M is a nilpotent ideal of R, M_n is a nilpotent ideal of R_n, clearly $W_n \subset W(R_n)$. On the other hand, the elements of the matrices contained in $W(R_n)$ constitute a nilpotent ideal of R. But W contains all nilpotent ideals of R. Hence $W(R_n) \subset W_n$.

3. ARTINIAN RINGS

Having examined some of the properties of the radical, we shall now confine our attention to the study of rings with minimal condition for the remainder of the chapter, with the goal of determining their precise structure.

An element a of a ring R is *idempotent* if $a^2 = a$.

Theorem 8 (Brauer's Theorem). *If R is left (right) Artinian, then any non-nilpotent left (right) ideal in R has a nonzero idempotent element.*

Proof. As in Hopkins' theorem, we let I_1 be a minimal element of the family of all nonnilpotent (and hence nonnil) left ideals of R which are contained in a given nonnilpotent left ideal I and let a be a nonnilpotent element of I_1. Then $Ra \subset I_1$ and is nonnilpotent since $a^2 \in Ra$; thus $Ra = I_1$ by minimality. Similarly $Ra^2 = I_1$. Thus there is an $a_1 \in Ra$ such that $a = a_1 a$. Then $a_1^2 a = a_1 a = a$ so $(a_1 - a_1^2)a = 0$ and $a_1 - a_1^2 \in \{a\}_l \cap Ra$, where $\{a\}_l$ is the set of left annihilators of a. Now we let $a_2 = a + a_1 - aa_1$ so that

$$a_2 a = a^2 + a_1 a - aa_1 a = a^2 + a - a^2 = a.$$

Also

$$\begin{aligned}
(a_1 - a_1^2)a_2 &= a_1 a + a_1^2 - a_1 aa_1 - a_1^2 a - a_1^3 + a_1^2 aa_1 \\
&= a + a_1^2 - aa_1 - a - a_1^3 + aa_1 \\
&= a_1^2 - a_1^3.
\end{aligned}$$

Since $a_2a = a$, a_2 is not nilpotent. Hence $Ra_2 = Ra = I_1$ and

$$\{a_2\}_l \cap Ra \subset \{a\}_l \cap Ra.$$

Either $a_1^2 = a_1^3$ or $a_1^2 \neq a_1^3$. If $a_1^2 = a_1^3$, then

$$(a_1^2)^2 = a_1^3a_1 = a_1^2a_1 = a_1^3 = a_1^2,$$

so a_1^2 is idempotent and we are finished.

On the other hand, if $a_1^2 \neq a_1^3$, then $(a_1 - a_1^2)a_2 \neq 0$ and

$$a_1 - a_1^2 \notin \{a_2\}_l \cap Ra.$$

Therefore,

$$\{a_2\}_l \cap Ra \subsetneqq \{a\}_l \cap Ra.$$

We can now repeat the process with a_2 playing the role of a. We obtain elements a_3, $a_4 \in I_1$ such that either $a_3^2 = a_3^3$ or $a_3^2 \neq a_3^3$ and $\{a_4\}_l \cap Ra \subset \{a_2\}_l \cap Ra$. If $a_3^2 = a_3^3$, a_3^2 is our desired idempotent. If $a_3^2 \neq a_3^3$, then the containment is strict. Thus if an idempotent is not obtained after a finite number of steps, we have an infinite descending chain of left ideals, contradicting the fact that R is left Artinian. The proof for R right Artinian is analogous.

If all the nonzero ideals of an Artinian ring are nonnilpotent, we can strengthen the above result as follows:

Theorem 9. *Any nonzero left ideal in a semisimple ring R has an idempotent generator.*

Proof. Let I be a nonzero left ideal of R. Since R is semisimple, I is non-nilpotent and, by Brauer's theorem, I has a nonzero idempotent element. Using the minimality condition, we choose a nonzero idempotent $e \in I$ such that $\{e\}_l \cap I$ is as small as possible.

Suppose $\{e\}_l \cap I \neq (0)$. Then $\{e\}_l \cap I$ is nonnilpotent and thus contains a nonzero idempotent e_1. Let $e_2 = e + e_1 - ee_1$. We note that $e_2 \neq 0$. Then $e_2 \in I$ and since $e_1e = 0$, we have

$$e_2^2 = e^2 + e_1e - ee_1e + ee_1 + e_1^2 - ee_1^2 - e^2e_1 - e_1ee_1 + ee_1ee_1$$
$$= e + e_1 - ee_1$$
$$= e_2.$$

Moreover, $\{e_2\}_l \cap I \subset \{e\}_l \cap I$, since $e_2e = e + e_1e - ee_1e = e$, and so if $xe_2 = 0$, we have $xe = xe_2e = 0$. But $e_1e = 0$, so that $e_1 \in \{e\}_l \cap I$, and $e_1e_2 = e_1e + e_1 - e_1ee_1 = e_1 \neq 0$ and hence $e_1 \notin \{e_2\}_l \cap I$. Thus

$$\{e_2\}_l \cap I \subsetneqq \{e\}_l \cap I,$$

which is a contradiction.

Hence we must have $\{e\}_l \cap I = (0)$.

Now we let $x \in I$. Then $(x - xe)e = xe - xe^2 = xe - xe = 0$, so $x - xe \in \{e\}_l \cap I = (0)$ and therefore $xe = x$. Thus $I = Re$ and $e^2 = e$.

Corollary. Any semisimple ring R is left Noetherian.

Of course, if a semisimple ring is defined to be a semiprime right Artinian ring, then a semisimple ring is right Noetherian, and in fact we shall see later that either definition of semisimplicity gives both left and right maximality conditions. However, the converse is not true. The integers are Noetherian and semiprime but not Artinian.

In general the generator of Theorem 9 is not unique, but we do have:

Theorem 10. *Any nonzero ideal I in a semisimple ring R has a unique idempotent generator.*

Proof. Let $I = Re$, e a nonzero idempotent. Clearly $I_r = \{e\}_r$ and

$$(I \cap I_r)^2 \subset I_r I = (0).$$

$I \cap I_r$ is a right ideal in R and since R is semisimple, it has no nonzero nilpotent right ideals. Hence $I \cap I_r = (0)$.

For each $x \in I$, $e(x - ex) = 0$ so $x - ex \in \{e\}_r \cap I = I_r \cap I = (0)$. Thus $x = ex$ for all $x \in I$. Also, for any $x \in I$, $x \in Re$, that is, $x = re$ for some $r \in R$, so that $xe = re^2 = re = x$. Hence e is a two-sided identity in the ring I and as such is unique.

Corollary 1. A semisimple ring R has an identity.

Corollary 2. A commutative semisimple ring R is a principal ideal ring.

4. DIRECT SUM DECOMPOSITIONS

We extend the definition of the direct sum of two rings given in Chapter 1 to any finite number of rings in the obvious way: A ring R is the (*external*) *direct sum* of rings $R_1, \ldots, R_n$ if it is isomorphic to the set of ordered n-tuples of elements of $R_1, \ldots, R_n$, with operations defined pointwise.

Let R be a ring and let $R_1, \ldots, R_n$ be subrings of R. R is the (*internal*) *direct sum* of $R_1, \ldots, R_n$, written

$$R = R_1 \oplus \cdots \oplus R_n,$$

if $R = R_1 + \cdots + R_n$ and for each $i = 1, \ldots, n$,

$$R_i \cap (R_1 + \cdots + \hat{R}_i + \cdots + R_n) = (0),$$

where the caret indicates omission. This is equivalent to saying that each $r \in R$ can be written *uniquely* in the form $r_1 + \cdots + r_n$, $r_i \in R_i$.

It is clear that an internal direct sum is also an external direct sum and conversely (up to isomorphism). Hence we use simply "direct sum" without regard to whether the summands are in fact subrings of the given ring.

We now establish a series of theorems giving us the structure of a semisimple ring in terms of its minimal ideals.

Theorem 11. *Let* I *be an ideal in a semisimple ring* R. *Then* $I \oplus I_l = R$ *and this decomposition is unique in the sense that if* $R = I \oplus K$ *for an ideal* K *in* R, *then* $K = I_l$.

Proof. We first show that $I_l = I_r$. We have $I_l I = (0)$, so $(II_l)^2 = I(I_l I)I_l = (0)$ and $II_l = (0)$, by semisimplicity. Hence $I_l \subset I_r$. But similarly $I_r \subset I_l$.

Let $I = Re$, e an idempotent. Then $I_r = \{e\}_r$. Let $x \in \{e\}_r$ so that $ex = 0$ and $x = x - ex = (1 - e)x \in (1 - e)R$. Furthermore, if $x \in (1 - e)R$, that is, $x = r - er$ for some $r \in R$, then $ex = er - e^2 r = 0$. Hence $x \in \{e\}_r$. Therefore $I_l = I_r = \{e\}_r = (1 - e)R = R(1 - e)$.

Now we let $x \in R$. Then $x = xe + x(1 - e)$ so $x \in I + I_l$, and $R = I + I_l$.

Suppose $y \in I \cap I_l = Re \cap R(1 - e)$. Then $y = se = t - te$, for some $s, t \in R$. Hence $ye = see = se = y$ and $ye = (t - te)e = te - te^2 = 0$. Therefore $y = 0$ and $I \cap I_l = (0)$. Thus $R = I \oplus I_l$.

Now let $R = I \oplus K$, where K is an ideal of R. Then $KI \subset I \cap K = (0)$. Thus $K \subset I_l$. On the other hand, let $x \in I$. Then $x = t + k$, where $t \in I$ and $k \in K$ are unique. Then $x - k = t \in I \cap I_l = (0)$. Hence $x = k \in K$. Thus $I_l \subset K$.

Theorem 12. *A semisimple ring* R *has only a finite number of minimal ideals and is their direct sum. Moreover, each minimal ideal is a simple ring.*

Proof. We first show that R is the direct sum of minimal ideals. Let $\mathfrak{S}$ be the family of all ideals of R of the form $R_1 \oplus \cdots \oplus R_s$, where the R_i are minimal ideals of R. $\mathfrak{S}$ is not empty since R has minimal ideals. Since R has the maximal condition for right ideals, $\mathfrak{S}$ has a maximal element, say $S = R_1 \oplus \cdots \oplus R_n$. Suppose $S \neq R$.

By Theorem 11, $R = S \oplus S_l$ and $S_l \neq (0)$. S_l must contain a minimal ideal, say R_{n+1}, of R. Then $S \oplus R_{n+1} \in \mathfrak{S}$ and S is not maximal. Hence $S = R$.

Now let R_0 be any minimal ideal of R. Then

$$R_0 = R_0 R = R_0(R_1 \oplus \cdots \oplus R_n) \subset R_0 R_1 \oplus \cdots \oplus R_0 R_n.$$

Since $R_0 \neq (0)$, we have $R_0 R_i \neq (0)$ for some i. However, $R_0 R_i \subset R_0$ and $R_0 R_i \subset R_i$. Therefore $R_0 = R_0 R_i = R_i$. Thus any minimal ideal of R is one of the ideals in the direct sum representation.

We note that minimal ideals in semisimple rings must always be idempotent since they cannot be nilpotent.

Now let I be an ideal in R_1, R_1 a minimal ideal of R. Since the algebraic structure of R is determined by those of its direct summands, I is an ideal of R. Thus $I = (0)$ or $I = R_1$, and R_1 is a simple ring.

We restate the above result:

Fundamental Theorem of Semisimple Rings. *Every semisimple ring is the direct sum of a finite number of simple rings.*

5. IDEALS IN SEMISIMPLE RINGS

Next we shall consider the structure of left ideals in semisimple rings. As usual, analogous results can be obtained if the definitions are made in terms of conditions on right ideals.

Lemma 1. Let I be a left ideal in a semisimple ring R and J_1 a left ideal of R such that $J_1 \subset I$. Then there exists a left ideal J_2 of R such that $J_2 \subset I$ and $I = J_1 \oplus J_2$.

Proof. If $J_1 = (0)$, $J_2 = I$, so we assume that $J_1 \neq (0)$. We let $I = Re$, $J_1 = Re_1$, e and e_1 idempotents, and let

$$J_2 = \{x - xe_1 \mid x \in I\}.$$

J_2 is clearly a left ideal of I.

If $x \in I$, we may write $x = xe_1 + (x - xe_1)$; thus $I = J_1 + J_2$. We now let $z \in J_1 \cap J_2$. Then, as in the proof of Theorem 11, $z = xe_1 = y - ye_1$ for some $x, y \in I$ and so $z = xe_1 = xe_1e_1 = ze_1 = (y - ye_1)e_1 = 0$. Therefore $J_1 \cap J_2 = (0)$ and $I = J_1 \oplus J_2$.

We still need that J_2 is a left ideal of R. We let $x - xe_1 \in J_2$ and $r \in R$. Then $rx \in I$ and so $r(x - xe_1) = rx - (rx)e_1 \in J_2$, giving the desired result.

We now seek to express the decomposition in terms of idempotents; to do this we make the following definitions:

Let $e_1, \ldots, e_n$ be nonzero idempotents in a ring R. They are *mutually orthogonal* if $e_i e_j = 0$ whenever $i \neq j$. In this case $e = e_1 + \cdots + e_n$ is also idempotent. We shall show that

$$Re = Re_1 \oplus \cdots \oplus Re_n$$

when the e_i are mutually orthogonal. An idempotent is *primitive* if it cannot be written as the sum of two orthogonal idempotents.

Lemma 2. In a semisimple ring R, an idempotent e is primitive if and only if Re is a minimal left ideal of R.

Proof. We know that if $I = Re$ is not minimal, it has a nontrivial direct sum decomposition as in Lemma 1. We show that J_1 and J_2, where $I = J_1 \oplus J_2$, have orthogonal idempotent generators. We let $J_1 = Re_1, J_2 = \{x - xe_1 \mid x \in I\}$ as above and let $e_1' = ee_1$ and $e_2' = e - ee_1$. Then e_1' and e_2' are idempotents and $e_1'e_2' = e_2'e_1' = 0$.

Since $e_1 \in Re$, $e_1 e = e_1$ and so $e_1 = e_1^2 = e_1 e e_1 = e_1 e_1'$. Since $e_1' \in J_1$, $Re_1' \subset J_1$ and for $x \in J_1$, $x = re_1$, $r \in R$, and thus $x = re_1 e_1'$, which is in Re_1'. If $x \in I$, then $x = re$, $r \in R$. Hence

$$J_2 = \{x - xe_1 \mid x \in I\} = \{re - ree_1 \mid r \in R\}$$

$$= \{r(e - ee_1) \mid r \in R\} = \{re_2' \mid r \in R\} = Re_2'.$$

Therefore, $e = e_1' + e_2'$, where e_1' and e_2' are orthogonal idempotents and $Re = Re_1' \oplus Re_2'$.

On the other hand, if $I = Re$ and $e = e_1 + e_2$, where e_1 and e_2 are nonzero idempotents and $e_1e_2 = e_2e_1 = 0$, then $(0) \quad Re_1 \quad I$. For if $e_2 \in Re_1$, then $0 = e_2e_1 = xe_1e_1 = xe_1 = e_2$, $x \in R$, a contradiction. Hence I is not minimal.

Lemma 3. Any idempotent e in a semisimple ring R can be written as the sum of mutually orthogonal primitive idempotents.

Proof. Let $I = Re$, where e is a nonzero idempotent. If I is minimal, e is primitive and we are finished. If I is not minimal, there exists a minimal left ideal J_1 of R such that $J_1 \subset I$. Then by Lemma 1 there exists an ideal J_1' such that $J_1' \neq (0)$ and $I = J_1 \oplus J_1'$ and by Lemma 2 there exist orthogonal idempotents e_1, e_1' such that $J_1 = Re_1$, $J_1' = Re_1'$, and $e = e_1 + e_1'$. Since J_1 is minimal, e_1 is primitive. If J_1' is minimal, then e_1' is primitive and we are finished.

If J_1' is not minimal, we decompose it as $J_1' = J_2 \oplus J_2'$ as above, where e_2 and e_2' are orthogonal idempotent generators of J_2 and J_2', respectively. Since J_2 is minimal, e_2 is primitive and $e = e_1 + e_2 + e_2'$. Now e_1 and e_2 are orthogonal since $e_1e_1' = 0$ and thus $e_1e_2 + e_1e_2' = 0$ while $e_2'e_2 = 0$, giving us

$$0 = (e_1e_2 + e_1e_2')e_2 = e_1e_2 + e_1e_2'e_2 = e_1e_2,$$

and similarly $e_2e_1 = 0$.

After n steps we obtain

$$I = J_1 \oplus J_2 \oplus \cdots \oplus J_n \oplus J_n',$$

$J_i = Re_i$, $i = 1, \ldots, n$, $J_n' = Re_n'$, $e_1, \ldots, e_n$ mutually orthogonal and primitive and $e = e_1 + \cdots + e_n + e_n'$. But this process must terminate in a finite number of steps, since

$$Re_1' \supsetneqq Re_2' \supsetneqq Re_3' \supsetneqq \cdots,$$

and R is left Artinian.

Corollary. Any nonzero left ideal in a semisimple ring can be written as the direct sum of a finite number of minimal left ideals.

Theorem 13. *If R is a semiprime ring and e an idempotent, then Re is a minimal left ideal if and only if eRe is a division ring.*

Proof. We first observe that eRe is a subring of R with e as its identity.

Suppose Re is minimal and $a \in eRe$, $a \neq 0$. Then $a \in Re$ and so $Ra \subset Re$. Hence $Ra = Re$ or $Ra = (0)$. But $a = ea \in Ra$, so that $Ra \neq (0)$. Therefore $Ra = Re$. Hence $e \in Ra$, that is, there is an $x \in R$ such that $e = xa$. Then exe is a left inverse in eRe for a. This, together with associativity and the identity, gives the existence of a left inverse and the necessary uniqueness (see Problem 5, Chapter 1).

Conversely, suppose eRe is a division ring and that I is a left ideal of R with $I \subset Re$. Then eI is a left ideal in the division ring eRe. Hence either

$eI = (0)$ or $eI = eRe$. If $eI = (0)$, then $I^2 \subset ReI = (0)$ and $I = (0)$ since R is semiprime. Now suppose that $eI = eRe$. Then there is an $x \in I$ such that $ex \in eRe$ and $ex \neq 0$. Also, $exe = ex$ since e is the identity for eRe. Moreover, ex has an inverse in eRe, say eye. Then $(eye)(exe) = e$ and $e \in Rexe = Rex \subset I$. Then $Re \subset I$ and $I = Re$, so that Re is a minimal left ideal of R.

Corollary. If e is an idempotent in a semiprime ring R, then Re is a minimal left ideal if and only if eR is a minimal right ideal.

Theorem 14. *Let R be an arbitrary ring. If*

$$R = I_1 \oplus \cdots \oplus I_m = J_1 \oplus \cdots \oplus J_n,$$

where the I_i and J_j are distinct minimal left ideals of R, then $m = n$.

Proof. Let $S = J_2 \oplus \cdots \oplus J_n$. If $S \cap I_i \neq (0)$ for all i, then $S \supset I_i$ and so $S = R$, a contradiction. Hence $S \cap I_i = (0)$ for some i, say $S \cap I_1 = (0)$.

Suppose $m > n$ and consider $I_1 \oplus S$. If $(I_1 \oplus S) \cap J_1 = (0)$, then $(J_1 \oplus S) \cap I_1 = R \cap J_1 = (0)$, a contradiction. Hence $(I_1 \oplus S) \cap J_1 \neq (0)$, so $J_1 \subset I_1 \oplus S$. Moreover, since $J_j \subset I_1 \oplus S$ for $j = 2, \ldots, n$, $J_j \subset I_1 \oplus S$ for all j and so

$$R = I_1 \oplus S = I_1 \oplus J_2 \oplus \cdots \oplus J_n = I_1 \oplus \cdots \oplus I_m.$$

We repeat this procedure $m - 1$ times, obtaining

$$R = I_1 \oplus \cdots \oplus I_m = I_1 \oplus \cdots \oplus I_m \oplus J_{m+1} \oplus \cdots \oplus J_n.$$

But this implies that $J_{m+1} \oplus \cdots \oplus J_n = (0)$, a contradiction. We obtain an analogous result if we assume $m > n$. Hence $m = n$.

Theorem 14 permits us to make the following definition. If

$$R = I_1 \oplus \cdots \oplus I_n,$$

where the I_i are minimal left ideals of R, n is called the *left dimension* of R. If such a (finite) decomposition is not possible, R is said to have *infinite left dimension*. We have shown that semisimple rings have finite left dimension.

6. MATRIX RINGS

We now study the simple rings which are the components of the decompositions of semisimple rings.

Theorem 15. *Let R be a simple left Artinian ring. Then there exist a division ring D and a positive integer n such that R is isomorphic to D_n, the ring of $n \times n$ matrices over D.*

Proof. Let Re, e idempotent, be a minimal left ideal of R. Then $D = eRe$ is a division ring and eR is a minimal right ideal of R. Also $(eRe)(eR) = DeR$ is a right ideal of R contained in eR, nonzero since it contains e. Hence $DeR = eR$. Thus eR is a (left) vector space over D.

We now prove:

(*) $a_1, \ldots, a_k \in eR$ are linearly independent over D if and only if

$$Ra_1 + \cdots + Ra_k$$

is a direct sum.

First suppose $Ra_1 + \cdots + Ra_k$ is not a direct sum. Then there exist $x_1, \ldots, x_k \in R$ such that not all $x_i a_i$ are zero and

$$x_1 a_1 + \cdots + x_k a_k = 0.$$

Let $X_i = \{x \in Re \mid xa_i \in Ra_1 + \cdots + \widehat{Ra_i} + \cdots + Ra_k\}$. X_i is a left ideal in R and $X_i \subset Re$ for all i. For some i, say $i = j$, $x_j a_j = x_j e a_j \neq 0$ so that $x_j e \neq 0$. But $x_j e \in X_j$, so $(0) \subsetneqq X_j \subset Re$. Then since Re is a minimal left ideal, we have $X_j = Re$. Thus $e \in X_j$. Hence

$$a_j = ea_j \in Ra_1 + \cdots + \widehat{Ra_j} + \cdots + Ra_k,$$

so that $a_j = y_1 a_1 + \cdots + \widehat{y_j a_j} + \cdots + y_k a_k$. But for each i, $y_i a_i = y_i e a_i$ and so

$$a_j = ea_j = (ey_1 e')a_1 + \cdots + \widehat{(ey_j e)a_j} + \cdots + (ey_k e)a_k.$$

Therefore $a_1, \ldots, a_k$ are linearly dependent over D.

Conversely, if $Ra_1 + \cdots + Ra_k$ is a direct sum, then

$$eRea_1 + \cdots + eRea_k = Da_1 + \cdots + Da_k$$

is a direct sum. Hence $a_1, \ldots, a_k$ are linearly independent, completing the proof of (*).

Now we let $a_1, a_2, \ldots$ be elements of eR such that for any $k \geq 1$, $a_1, \ldots, a_k$ are linearly independent over D. Then by (*), Ra_1, $Ra_1 + Ra_2$, $Ra_1 + Ra_2 + Ra_3, \ldots$ are all direct sums. Hence

$$Ra_1 \subsetneqq Ra_1 + Ra_2 \subsetneqq Ra_1 + Ra_2 + Ra_3 \subsetneqq \cdots.$$

But under the hypothesis of the theorem, R is semisimple and hence has the acc for left ideals. Thus there are only a finite number of such a_i so that eR is a finite-dimensional vector space over D, say of dimension n.

For $a \in R$ we define a mapping f_a of eR into eR by

$$f_a(x) = xa, \qquad x \in eR.$$

Then f_a is a linear transformation of eR into itself. Moreover, the mapping $a \to f_a$ is a homomorphism from R into the ring of linear transformations of the vector space eR. The kernel of this homomorphism, being a (two-sided) ideal of R must be (0) or R. But $f_e(e) = ee = e \neq 0$, so f_e is not the zero linear transformation. Hence the kernel must be (0) and the homomorphism is injective.

We now show that the homomorphism is surjective, i.e., that if g is any linear transformation of eR, then there exists $a \in R$ such that $g(x) = f_a(x) = xa$ for all $x \in eR$. In order to do this we first establish the following:

(**)   If $u_1, \ldots, u_n$ is a basis of eR over D and if $y_1, \ldots, y_n \in eR$, then there
exists $a \in R$ such that $u_i a = y_i$, $i = 1, \ldots, n$.

We need only consider the case when $y_1, \ldots, y_{n-1} = 0$, for the a in the general case is the sum of the a's obtained in each case where all but one y_i are zero.

Let $I' = Reu_1 + \cdots + Reu_{n-1}$. I' is a left ideal in R so $I' = Re'_n$, where e'_n is an idempotent. For each i, $u_i \in eR$ and so $eu_i = u_i$. Hence $u_i \in I'$, $i = 1, \ldots, n - 1$. Therefore $u_i = re'_n$ and so

$$u_i(1 - e'_n) = re'_n(1 - e'_n) = r(e'_n - e'^2_n) = 0, \qquad i = 1, \ldots, n - 1.$$

Suppose that $u_n(1 - e'_n) = 0$. Then $u_n = u_n e'_n \in I'$ so that

$$u_n = x_1 eu_1 + \cdots + x_{n-1} eu_{n-1}, \qquad x_i \in R, \quad i = 1, \ldots, n - 1.$$

Hence

$$(ex_1 e)u_1 + \cdots + (ex_{n-1} e)u_{n-1} - eu_n = 0,$$

which contradicts the linear independence of $u_1, \ldots, u_n$. Thus $u_n(1 - e'_n) \neq 0$. Now we have $u_n(1 - e'_n)R \subset eR$ and $u_n(1 - e'_n)R \neq (0)$. Since eR is minimal, $u_n(1 - e'_n)R = eR$. Thus there exists $r_n \in R$ such that $u_n(1 - e'_n)r_n = y_n$. Let $a = (1 - e'_n)r_n$; then

$$u_1 a = \cdots = u_{n-1} a = 0, \qquad u_n a = y_n,$$

which proves (**). Since a linear transformation is completely determined by what it does on a basis, this gives us the surjectivity; if g is an endomorphism of eR such that $g(u_i) = y_i$ for a basis $u_1, \ldots, u_n$ and a is the element whose existence is guaranteed by (**), then

$$g(u_i) = f_a(u_i) = u_i a = y_i, \qquad i = 1, \ldots, n$$

and $g = f_a$.

Thus R is isomorphic to the ring of linear transformations of the n-dimensional vector space eR over D. But this is isomorphic to D_n. Hence R is isomorphic to D_n.

We now know that any semisimple ring can be written as the direct sum of a finite number of simple rings and that any simple left Artinian ring is isomorphic to the ring of $n \times n$ matrices over a subring which is a division ring. Before establishing the converses of these results, we remark that it is now evident that right Artinian could have been used in the definition of semisimplicity and would have led to the same results since matrix rings, and consequently direct sums of matrix rings, are in fact both left and right Artinian (see the proof of the following theorem).

Theorem 16. *Let D be a division ring and n a positive integer. Then D_n is a simple left Artinian ring. Furthermore, the left dimension of D_n is n.*

Proof. Let I be a nonzero ideal in D_n. Let $0 \neq A = (a_{ij})$ be in I. We can write

$$A = \sum_{i,j} a_{ij} E_{ij}, \qquad \text{where} \qquad E_{ij} \text{ is the matrix } (\varepsilon_{i'j'}),$$

$\varepsilon_{i'j'} = 1$ when $i' = i$ and $j' = j$ and $\varepsilon_{i'j'} = 0$ otherwise. Since $A \neq 0$, there are i, j such that $a_{ij} \neq 0$. For all k, l

$$E_{ki} A E_{jl} = \sum_{i,j} a_{i'j'} E_{ki} E_{i'j'} E_{jl}$$

$$= a_{ij} E_{kl} \in I.$$

Let

$$E = \begin{pmatrix} 1 & & 0 \\ & \ddots & \\ 0 & & 1 \end{pmatrix}.$$

Then we have

$$(a_{ij} E) E_{kl} = a_{ij} E_{kl} \in I.$$

Now since $a_{ij} \neq 0$, $a_{ij} E$ is a unit in D_n, and its inverse is $a_{ij}^{-1} E$. Hence

$$E_{kl} = (a_{ij}^{-1} E) \underbrace{(a_{ij} E) E_{kl}}_{\in I} \in I.$$

Hence $E = E_{11} + \cdots + E_{nn} \in I$. Since E is the identity matrix, $I = D_n$ and D_n is a simple ring.

To show that D_n is left Artinian we simply note that D_n is a left vector space over D of dimension n^2, and that every left ideal of D_n is certainly a vector subspace of D_n. Any nonempty family of vector subspaces of a finite-dimensional vector space has a minimal element.

As before we let E be the $n \times n$ identity matrix. Then

$$E = E_{11} + \cdots + E_{nn},$$

and each E_{ii} is an idempotent. Then

$$D_n = D_n E_{11} + \cdots + D_n E_{nn}.$$

Since $E_{ii} E_{jj} = 0$ for $i \neq j$, the idempotents $E_{11}, \ldots, E_{nn}$ are mutually orthogonal. Thus

$$D_n = D_n E_{11} \oplus \cdots \oplus D_n E_{nn}.$$

We now show that for each i, $D_n E_{ii}$ is a minimal left ideal. To do this it suffices to show that E_{ii} is a primitive idempotent. We do so for E_{11}; the proof in the other cases is similar.

Suppose

$$E_{11} = A + B, \qquad A^2 = A, \qquad B^2 = B, \qquad AB = BA = 0, \qquad A \neq 0.$$

We shall show that $A = E_{11}$, $B = 0$.

Partition A and B as follows:

$$A = \begin{pmatrix} \overbrace{a}^{1} & \overbrace{A_1}^{n-1} \\ A_2 & A_3 \end{pmatrix} \begin{matrix} \}1 \\ \}n-1 \end{matrix}, \qquad B = \begin{pmatrix} b & B_1 \\ B_2 & B_3 \end{pmatrix}.$$

Then we actually have

$$B = \begin{pmatrix} b & -A_1 \\ -A_2 & -A_3 \end{pmatrix}, \qquad A^2 = \begin{pmatrix} - & aA_1 + A_1A_3 \\ - & - \end{pmatrix} = \begin{pmatrix} - & A_1 \\ - & - \end{pmatrix},$$

so $aA_1 + A_1A_3 = A_1$. Also

$$AB = \begin{pmatrix} - & -aA_1 - A_1A_3 \\ - & - \end{pmatrix} = 0,$$

so $-aA_1 - A_1A_3 = 0 = aA_1 + A_1A_3 = A_1$. Hence $A_1 = 0 = B_1$.

From $B^2 = B$ and $BA = 0$ we obtain $A_2 = 0$. Then

$$AB = \begin{pmatrix} - & - \\ - & -A_3^2 \end{pmatrix} = 0,$$

so $-A_3^2 = 0$. But

$$A^2 = \begin{pmatrix} - & - \\ - & A_3^2 \end{pmatrix} = \begin{pmatrix} - & - \\ - & A_3 \end{pmatrix} = A,$$

so $A_3 = A_3^2 = 0$. Hence

$$E_{11} = \begin{pmatrix} 1 & 0 \\ 0 & 0 \end{pmatrix} = \begin{pmatrix} a & 0 \\ 0 & 0 \end{pmatrix} + \begin{pmatrix} b & 0 \\ 0 & 0 \end{pmatrix},$$

and we have $1 = a + b$, $a^2 = a$, $b^2 = b$, $ab = 0$, $ba = 0$, $a \neq 0$. Then $a = 1$ and so $b = 0$. Thus E_{11} is a primitive idempotent.

7. THE WEDDERBURN THEOREM

To complete our structure theory we need the converse of the fundamental theorem of semisimple rings.

Theorem 17. *Let $R_1, \ldots, R_k$ be simple left Artinian rings. Then*

$$R = R_1 \oplus \cdots \oplus R_k$$

is semisimple.

Proof. Let I be a left ideal in R. To each element $a \in I$ there correspond unique elements $a_i \in R_i$, $i = 1, \ldots, k$, such that $a = a_1 + \cdots + a_k$.

Then the mapping $a \to a_i$ is a homomorphism of I onto a left ideal I_i of R_i. Clearly, $I = (0)$ if and only if $I_1 = \cdots = I_k = (0)$. Also it is evident that

$I = I_1 \oplus \cdots \oplus I_k$ and $I^n = I_1^n \oplus \cdots \oplus I_k^n$. If $I^n = (0)$, then $I_i^n = (0)$ for $i = 1, \ldots, k$. Hence since each R_i is semisimple, $I_i = (0)$. Therefore, $I = (0)$. Thus R is semiprime.

To show that R is left Artinian, it is sufficient to show that R satisfies the dcc for left ideals. Let

$$I^{(1)} \supset I^{(2)} \supset I^{(3)} \supset \cdots$$

be a descending chain of left ideals in R. Then for each $i = 1, \ldots, k$,

$$I_i^{(1)} \supset I_i^{(2)} \supset I_i^{(3)} \supset \cdots$$

is a descending chain of left ideals in R_i, I_i defined from I as above.

Since R_i is left Artinian, there is an n_i such that for all $n \geq n_i$

$$I_i^{(n)} = I_i^{(n+1)}.$$

Now choose $m = \max_{1 \leq i \leq k} n_i$. Then for $n \geq m$ and for all $i = 1, \ldots, k$,

$$I_i^{(n)} = I_i^{(n+1)}.$$

But then

$$I^{(n)} = I^{(n+1)} \qquad \text{for} \quad n \geq m.$$

Hence R is left Artinian.

Combining the above results we obtain:

Theorem 18. *A ring R is semisimple if and only if R is isomorphic to*

$$D_{n_1}^{(1)} \oplus \cdots \oplus D_{n_k}^{(k)},$$

where for $i = 1, \ldots, k$, $D^{(i)}$ is a division ring, and $D_{n_i}^{(i)}$ is the ring of all $n_i \times n_i$ matrices over $D^{(i)}$.

PROBLEMS

1. Show that every maximal left ideal of a left Artinian ring R contains the Wedderburn radical of R.

2. Give an example of a nonzero nilpotent element in the ring of 2×2 matrices over the real numbers, if such exists. Give an example of an idempotent element in this ring not of the form of those used in Theorem 16.

3. Give an example of a left Artinian ring which is not semisimple.

4. What is the Wedderburn radical of the integers? Are the integers semisimple?

5. Consider the ring of all continuous functions on $[0, 1]$. Is it Artinian? What is its Wedderburn radical, if it exists?

6. Show that if R is a ring such that R_n, the ring of $n \times n$ matrices over R, has an identity, then R has an identity.

7. Show that between the ideals of a ring R and a subset of the ideals of R_n there is a one-one correspondence given by $I \leftrightarrow I_n$. Show that

$$R_n/I_n \simeq (R/I)_n.$$

8. Describe the minimal left and right ideals of the ring of $n \times n$ matrices over the real numbers.

9. Find the Wedderburn radical of
   a) Z_{24} b) Z_{10}.

10. Let R be the ring of lower triangular matrices over the real numbers, i.e.,
$$R = \{(a_{ij}) \mid a_{ij} \in R, a_{ij} = 0 \text{ for } j > i\}.$$
Find the radical of R.

11. Let K be a field, $f(x) \in K[x]$ a nonconstant polynomial, $R = K[x]/(f(x))$. If
$$f(x) = \prod_{m=1}^{m} f_i(x)^{r_i}$$
is a factorization of $f(x)$ into powers of distinct irreducible polynomials, prove that
$$R \simeq \sum_{i=1}^{m} K[x]/(f_i(x)^{r_i}),$$
where the sum is direct. Show that
$$W(R) \simeq \sum_{i=1}^{m} (f_i(x))/(f_i(x)^{r_i}) \quad \text{and} \quad R/W(R) \simeq \sum_{i=1}^{m} K[x]/(f_i(x)).$$

CHAPTER 3

Modules

Modules were considered in the 1890's by Hilbert and in the early part of this century by E. Noether, but it was not until the 1940's that the scope of their application to the study of the internal structure of rings was realized. As will become apparent in a later chapter, it is a case of stepping outside an algebraic structure in order to characterize the structure effectively and was one of a series of notable efforts to treat the problem of investigating one entity by looking at related objects; a similar procedure is the basis of algebraic topology, although there one studies nonalgebraic systems by investigating associated algebraic structures. In this chapter we shall develop many of the results about modules which are necessary in order to use modules in the study of other systems. Thus we shall provide an introduction to homological algebra.

1. PRELIMINARIES

Let R be a ring; a nonempty set M is said to be a (left) *R-module* if M is an abelian group under an operation $+$ such that for every r in R and m in M there exists an element rm in M subject to:

1) $r(a + b) = ra + rb$,

2) $r(sa) = (rs)a$,

3) $(r + s)a = ra + sa$,

for all $a, b \in M$, $r, s \in R$.

    If R has a unit element 1, and if $1m = m$ for every $m \in R$, then M is called a *unital R-module*. We note that if R is a field, a unital R-module is just a vector space over R. If a ring R has an identity, then we assume that our R-modules are unital.

Examples

1. Every abelian group is a module over Z, the ring of integers.

2. Let R be a ring, M a left ideal of R. For $r \in R$, $m \in M$, we let rm be the product of these elements as elements in R. By the definition of left ideal, $rm \in M$ and by the definition of ring the other conditions for M to be an R-module are satisfied.

43

3.   Any ring R is an R-module over itself.

4.   Let R be any ring and I a left ideal of R. Let M consist of all the cosets of I in R. In M we define

$$(a + I) + (b + I) = (a + b) + I \quad \text{and} \quad r(a + I) = ra + I.$$

Then M is an R-module, sometimes called the *difference* or *quotient module* of R by I and written $R - I$ or R/I. Of course, if I is an ideal, then M is also a ring.

We can define right R-module in an analogous manner. If M is both a left R-module and a right S-module, where S is a ring, possibly but not necessarily R, then if

$$r(ms) = (rm)s \quad \text{for} \quad r \in R, \quad s \in S, \quad m \in M,$$

M is called an R, S-*bimodule*. We shall use "module" to mean left module. A word of caution: the commutativity of a ring R does not assure that all one-sided R-modules are bimodules.

An additive subgroup A of an R-module M is called a *submodule* of M if whenever r is in R and a is in A, then $ra \in A$. Given an R-module M and a submodule A, one constructs the quotient module M/A analogously to the construction of quotient rings.

If M is an R-module, we define the *annihilator* of M:

$$A(M) = \{r \in R \mid rm = 0 \text{ for all } m \in M\}.$$

It is easy to verify that $A(M)$ is an ideal of the ring R.

Given two R-modules M and N, a function $f: M \to N$ is called a *homomorphism* (or *R-homomorphism* or *module homomorphism*) if

1) $f(m + m') = f(m) + f(m')$,

2) $f(rm) = rf(m)$,

for all $m, m' \in M$ and all $r \in R$. That is, the function is linear. We shall frequently omit parentheses in the notation for the image of an element if no confusion is possible, writing $f(m) = fm$. As usual, if f is a homomorphism of M into N, we define the *kernel* of f to be $\{x \in M \mid fx = 0\}$. Clearly this is a submodule of M and the *image* of $f = \{fx \mid x \in M\}$ is a submodule of N. f is *injective* if it is one-one and *surjective* if its image is all of N. If f is both injective and surjective, it is an *isomorphism*.

Analogously to the cases of groups and rings we have: f is injective if and only if its kernel is the zero submodule. Module homomorphisms compose in the usual way.

The analog of the homomorphism theorem also holds: if $f: M \to N$ is a surjective homomorphism with kernel $f = A$, then N is isomorphic (as a module) to M/A. Also, given a submodule N of a module M, we can define a homomorphism with N as its kernel, namely $p: M \to M/N$ given by $p(m) = m + N$. As in the ring case, we call p the *canonical projection* of M onto M/N.

To obtain these results and those listed below, we observe that a module is an abelian group under addition and that the theorems hold for groups; then the proofs consist of checking that everything goes well with the multiplication.

The set-theoretic intersection of two submodules of a given module is clearly a submodule, but, as we should expect, their union need not be a submodule. If A and B are submodules of a module M,

$$A + B = \{a + b \mid a \in A, b \in B\}$$

is called the *sum* of A and B.

We have the module versions of the isomorphism theorems:

1) If A is a submodule of B and B a submodule of M, then

$$M/B \simeq (M/A)/(B/A).$$

2) If A and B are submodules of M, then

$$(A + B)/A \simeq B/(A \cap B).$$

An R-module M is *simple* if its only submodules are (0) and M. If

$$RM = \{rm \mid m \in M, r \in R\} = (0),$$

then M is said to be a *trivial* module. If M is simple and $RM \neq (0)$, then M is *irreducible*. An R-module M is *cyclic* if there is an element $m_0 \in M$ such that every $m \in M$ is of the form $m = rm_0$ for some $r \in R$.

Theorem 1. *If an R-module M is irreducible, then it is cyclic.*

Proof. Let $0 \neq m \in M$ and consider $Rm = \{rm \mid r \in R\}$. This is clearly a submodule of M. Since M is irreducible, for some $m \in M$, Rm must be all of M.

We mention one more result for groups which can be easily extended to modules, namely the Jordan-Hölder theorem.

A (normal) *series* for a module M is a collection of submodules of M

$$(*) \qquad\qquad (0) = M_0 \subset M_1 \subset \cdots \subset M_n = M.$$

We assume that a series is without repetition, that is, each M_i is distinct. Another series

$$(**) \qquad\qquad (0) = M_0' \subset \cdots \subset M_m' = M$$

is a *refinement* of $(*)$ if every M_i is some M_j'. A series is said to be a *composition series* if it has no proper refinements. Equivalently, $(*)$ is a composition series if M_i/M_{i-1}, $i = 1, \ldots, n$, is a simple module. The quotient modules M_i/M_{i-1} are called *composition factors* of M.

The two series $(*)$ and $(**)$ are *equivalent* if $n = m$, for each $i = 1, \ldots, n$,

$$M_i/M_{i-1} \simeq M_j'/M_{j-1}' \qquad \text{for some} \quad j \in \{1, \ldots, m\},$$

and for each $j = 1, \ldots, m$, $M'_j/M'_{j-1} \simeq M_i/M_{i-1}$ for some $i \in \{1, \ldots, n\}$. In other words, the factor groups are, after possible rearrangement, isomorphic as modules.

> **Lemma (Schreier's Theorem).** Any two series for a module M have equivalent refinements.

Proof. Let (∗) and (∗∗) be series for the R-module M. We define

$$M_{ij} = M_{i-1} + (M_i \cap M'_j), \qquad i = 1, \ldots, n; \quad j = 0, \ldots, m.$$

We have $M_{i0} = M_{i-1}$, and $M_{im} = M_i$ and a refinement of (∗),

$$(0) = M_0 = M_{10} \subset M_{11} \subset M_{12} \subset \cdots \subset M_{im} = M_1 \subset \cdots \subset M_{n-1}$$
$$= M_{n0} \subset \cdots \subset M_{nm} = M_n = M.$$

Similarly we refine (∗∗) by letting

$$M'_{ji} = M'_{j-1} + (M'_j \cap M_i), \qquad i = 0, \ldots, n; \quad j = 1, \ldots, m.$$

But then by Zassenhaus' lemma (Problem 2),

$$M_{ij}/M_{i,j-1} \simeq M'_{ji}/M'_{j,i-1}.$$

Each of the refinements has $(n - 1)(m - 1) + 1$ elements so that this isomorphism gives the desired equivalence.

> **Theorem 2 (Jordan-Hölder).** *Any two composition series of a module are equivalent.*

Proof. In this case the factor modules of the refinements given by the lemma are those of the original series; hence the composition series are equivalent.

We note that a module may fail to have a composition series. As in the case of groups, however, a composition series for a finite module can always be constructed.

2. DIRECT SUMS AND FREE MODULES

If M is an R-module and if $M_1, \ldots, M_n$ are submodules of M, then M is said to be the (internal) *direct sum* of $M_1, \ldots, M_n$ if every element $m \in M$ can be written in a unique manner as $m = m_1 + \cdots + m_n$, where $m_i \in M_i$. Equivalently, $M = M_1 + \cdots + M_n$ and $M_i \cap (M_1 + \cdots + \hat{M}_i + \cdots + M_n) = (0)$, $i = 1, \ldots, n$, where the caret indicates omission of that term.

It is clear that if M is the internal direct sum of $M_1, \ldots, M_n$, M is isomorphic to the set of n-tuples $(m_1, \ldots, m_n)$, $m_i \in M_i$, with componentwise addition and module multiplication $r(m_1, \ldots, m_n) = (rm_1, \ldots, rm_n)$, $r \in R$, $m_i \in M_i$. Since we construct a new module (with submodules isomorphic to the M_i) from the set of n-tuples, we call it the *external direct sum* of the M_i, in contrast to the internal case where the M_i are actually submodules of the direct sum. The internal and external direct sums and any other modules which are isomorphic to them are called *the* direct sum of the M_i. The module homomorphisms $u_i : M_i \to M$ given by $u_i(m) = (0, \ldots, m, \ldots, 0)$ and $p_i : M \to M_i$ given by $p_i(m_1, \ldots, m_n) = m_i$ are called *injections* and *projections*, respectively. Note that $p_i : M \to M_i$ is essentially the canonical projection

$$M \to \frac{M}{M_1 \oplus \cdots \oplus \hat{M}_i \oplus \cdots M_n} \simeq M_i,$$

so the terminology is unambiguous. We also use "injection" for any injective homomorphism which carries a submodule into a module which contains it.

The notion of direct sum can be extended in two ways to the infinite case. If $\{M_\alpha\}_{\alpha \in A}$ is a collection of modules, we can consider the set of all A-tuples with all but a finite number of entries 0 and define module operations in the obvious componentwise way. The resulting module is called a (weak) *direct sum*, denoted by $\sum_{\alpha \in A} M_\alpha$. A *strong direct sum* (or *direct product*) $\prod_{\alpha \in A} M_\alpha$ can be defined by considering *all* A-tuples. To be more precise, we can define the direct sum of modules $\{M_\alpha\}_{\alpha \in A}$ to be the set of all functions $m : A \to \bigcup_{\alpha \in A} M_\alpha$ with $m(\alpha) \in M_\alpha$ for all $\alpha \in A$, specifying in the weak case that $m(\alpha)$ be 0 for all but a finite number of α. We then identify the functions with their values.

A module M is *completely reducible* if every submodule of M is a direct summand of M.

Lemma. If an R-module M is the sum (not necessarily direct) of irreducible submodules, then M is completely reducible.

Proof. Let N be a submodule of M and N' a submodule of M maximal with respect to the property that $N' \cap N = (0)$. We want to show that

$$M = N' + N.$$

Suppose not. Then there exists m in M such that $m \notin N' + N$. We have

$$m = m_1 + \cdots + m_s,$$

$m_i \in M_i$, an irreducible submodule, $i = 1, \ldots, s$. Some $m_j \notin N' + N$ and there exists an irreducible submodule M_j such that $M_j \not\subset N' + N$. Because M_j is irreducible,

$$M_j \cap (N' + N) = (0).$$

But then $N' \subset N' + M_j$ and $(N' + M_j) \cap N = (0)$, contradicting the maximality of N'. Thus $N' + N = M$.

Theorem 3. *A left Artinian ring R with identity is semisimple if and only if every left R-module is completely reducible.*

Proof. If R is semisimple, we have from Theorem 12, Chapter 2,

$$R = Re_1 \oplus \cdots \oplus Re_n,$$

where the Re_i are minimal left ideals of R. If M is an R-module, we can write

$$M = \sum_{m \in M} \sum_{i=1}^{n} Re_i m.$$

Each $Re_i m$ is clearly a submodule, but the sum is not necessarily direct.

Each Re_i is an irreducible R-module, so that each $Re_i m$ is either irreducible or else $Re_i m = (0)$. Thus by the lemma, M, being the sum of irreducible submodules, is completely reducible.

If every R-module is completely reducible then R is completely reducible. Let $W(R)$ be its radical. Then

$$R = W(R) \oplus N',$$

N' some left ideal of R. Then

$$1 = x + x', \quad x \in W(R), \quad x' \in N'.$$

Then

$$x - x^2 = xx' \in W(R) \cap N'.$$

Hence $x - x^2 = 0$ and $x = x^2 = \cdots = 0$ since $x \in W(R)$ and hence is nilpotent. Thus $x' = 1$ and $N' = R$. Therefore $W(R) = (0)$.

An R-module M is said to be *finitely generated* if there exist elements $a_1, \ldots, a_n \in M$ such that every m in M is of the form

$$m = r_1 a_1 + \cdots + r_n a_n, \quad r_i \in R.$$

If M is finitely generated, among all generating sets there are those with a minimum number of elements. The number of elements in a minimal generating set is called the *rank* of M.

The notion of generation can be used even when the generating set is not finite. We let M be a unital R-module and let $\{m_\alpha\}_{\alpha \in A}$ be a subset of M such that each element $m \in M$ can be written in at least one way in the form

$$m = r_1 m_{\alpha_1} + \cdots + r_n m_{\alpha_n}, \quad r_i \in R, \quad \alpha_i \in A;$$

$\{m_\alpha\}_{\alpha \in A}$ is called a set of *generators* for M. Such a set always exists since the set of all elements of M has this property. If each $m \in M$ can be written in *only* one way in this form, $\{m_\alpha\}_{\alpha \in A}$ is a *basis* for M. A unital R-module M is said to be a *free* R-module if it has a basis (finite or infinite), i.e., if each element of M can be written in precisely one way as

$$m = r_1 m_{\alpha_1} + \cdots + r_n m_{\alpha_n}, \quad r_i \in R, \quad m_{\alpha_i} \in \{m_\alpha\}_{\alpha \in A},$$

then M is free on the basis $\{m_\alpha\}_{\alpha \in A}$. Thus a free R-module is isomorphic to the direct sum of copies of R, considered as a module over itself. We can think of (0) as free with empty basis. We note that vector spaces are free modules over their base field. A free Z-module is just a free abelian group.

Since we know how to construct direct sums, it is clear that we can produce free modules, at least up to isomorphism. However, we now turn to the general problem of constructing a free module with a given set as basis.

Given a set of symbols $\{x_\alpha\}_{\alpha \in A}$, A an arbitrary set and R a ring with identity, we let F be the set of all formal sums $\sum_{\alpha \in A} r_\alpha x_\alpha$, where, for each $\alpha \in A$, $r_\alpha \in R$, and all but a finite number of the r_α are zero. We identify the element x_α with the element $1x_\alpha$ in F. We write

$$\sum_{\alpha \in A} r_\alpha x_\alpha = \sum_{\alpha \in A} r'_\alpha x_\alpha$$

if and only if $r_\alpha = r'_\alpha$ for all $\alpha \in A$. In F we define

$$\left(\sum_{\alpha \in A} r_\alpha x_\alpha\right) + \left(\sum_{\alpha \in A} s_\alpha x_\alpha\right) = \sum_{\alpha \in A} (r_\alpha + s_\alpha) x_\alpha,$$

and for $r \in R$,

$$r \sum_{\alpha \in A} r_\alpha x_\alpha = \sum_{\alpha \in A} r r_\alpha x_\alpha.$$

It is then clear that F is a free R-module with $\{x_\alpha\}_{\alpha \in A}$ as a basis.

Theorem 4. *Every R-module is isomorphic to a quotient module of a free module.*

Proof. Given the module M, we take a subset U of M which generates M, for example, take M itself, and form a free module F on U as above. We define a map $p : F \to M$ by letting $p(u) = u \in M$ and requiring that it be a module homomorphism. Since U generates M, p is surjective and so M is isomorphic to $F/\text{kernel } p$.

We shall make frequent use of free modules and homomorphisms obtained in this way from a given module.

This theorem illustrates a property of free modules which is sometimes taken as the definition. Namely, if U is a basis for the free module F and for a module M there is a set function $U \to M$, then there exists a unique homomorphism $F \to M$ such that

where i is the injection map, is commutative, that is, $fi = s$.

We now use the notion of free modules to prove an important structure theorem for modules over a principal ideal domain. First we prove a lemma about the construction of bases for free modules which generalizes the following property of vector spaces: any linearly independent set of elements of a finite-dimensional vector space V can be extended to a basis for V.

Lemma. If $\{x_1, \ldots, x_n\}$ is a basis for a free module M over a principal ideal domain R and $y_1 = \sum_{i=1}^{n} a_i x_i$, then $\{y_1\}$ can be completed to a basis $\{y_1, \ldots, y_n\}$ for M if and only if the greatest common divisor of the a_i is 1.

Proof. Suppose $M = Ry_1 \oplus \cdots \oplus Ry_n$ and suppose $a_i = db_i$, $i = 1, \ldots, n$. Since $y_1 \neq 0$, $d \neq 0$. But $d(\sum b_i x_i + Ry_1) = y_1 + Ry_1 = Ry_1$. However,

M/Ry_1 is free with basis $\{y_2 + Ry_1, \ldots, y_n + Ry_1\}$, so that $\sum b_i x_i + Ry_1 = Ry_1$. Thus $\sum b_i x_i = r \sum a_i x_i$, but M is free so $b_i = ra_i = rdb_i$, $i = 1, \ldots, n$, with at least one $b_i \neq 0$. Consequently, $rd = 1$ and $d \,|\, 1$, so that 1 is the gcd of the a_i.

For the converse we induct on the rank of M. If the gcd of a_1 is 1, $Ra_1 = R$, a must be a unit, and $a_1 x$ is a basis. So we assume that $n > 1$ and that the result holds for any module of rank $< n$. We let

$$y_1 = \sum_{i=1}^{n} a_i x_i.$$

$Ra_2 + \cdots + Ra_n$ is an ideal of R; hence it is principal, say $Ra_2 + \cdots + Ra_n = Rd$, $db_i = a_i$, $i = 2, \ldots, n$. Then $R = Rb_2 + \cdots + Rb_n$ and if we let

$$z_2 = \sum_{i=2}^{n} b_i x_i,$$

then there is a basis $\{z_2, \ldots, z_n\}$ for $Rx_2 + \cdots + Rx_n$ and $\{x_1, z_2, \ldots, z_n\}$ is a basis for M with $y_1 = a_1 x_1 + dz_2$. Thus we need to show that if the gcd of a and d is 1, then there is a y_2 such that $M = Ry_1 \oplus Ry_2$.

Now since R is a PID we can write $1 = ra_1 + sd$, $r, s \in R$, and we let $y_2 = -sx_1 + rz_2$. We have that

$$x_1 = ra_1 x_1 + sdx_1 + rdz_2 - rdz_2 = ry_1 - dy_2$$

and

$$z_2 = ra_1 z_2 + sdz_2 + sa_1 x_1 - sa_1 x_1 = sy_1 + a_1 y_2.$$

Thus $Ry_1 + Ry_2 = Rx_1 + Rz_2 = M$. Finally suppose that $y \in Ry_1 \cap Ry_2$. Then $y = u(a_1 x_1 + dz_2) = v(-sx_1 + rz_2)$, but since $\{x_1, z_2\}$ is a basis for a free module, the expression is unique, so $ua_1 = -vs$ and $ud = vr$. Thus $u = u(ra_1 + sd) = -vsr + vsr = 0$.

Corollary. If M is a free module of rank n over a PID, any basis of M has n elements.

Theorem 5. Let R be a PID and M an R-module whose rank is finite. If N is a submodule of M, then rank $N \leq$ rank M.

Proof. We let $\{y_1, \ldots, y_m\}$ be a minimal generating set of M, F the free module with $\{y_1, \ldots, y_m\}$ as basis and $p: F \to M$ the map defined in Theorem 4. Since N can be expressed as the quotient module of a submodule of F, namely $\{f \in F \,|\, p(f) \in N\}$, we may as well consider M to be free. We induct on the rank of M. If $m = 1$, M is isomorphic to R and the rank of any submodule of R is 0 or 1. Thus rank $N \leq 1$.

Let $A = \{a \in R \,|\, y - ay_1 \in Ry_2 + \cdots + Ry_m\}$. A is an ideal of R, so $A = Ra_1$ for some $a_1 \in A$. We let x be such that $x - a_1 y_1 \in Ry_2 + \cdots + Ry_m$ and $N_1 = N \cap (Ry_2 + \cdots + Ry_m)$. We claim that $N = N_1 + Rx$. For suppose $r_1 y_1 + \cdots + r_m y_m \in N$. Then $r_1 \in A$ so that $r_1 = ra_1$, $r \in R$. But then

$$r_1 y_1 + \cdots + r_m y_m - rx = r_1 y_1 + \cdots + r_m y_m - r(x - a_1 y_1) - r_1 y_1$$
$$\in N \cap (Ry_2 + \cdots + Ry_m) = N_1$$

so that $N \subset N_1 + Rx$. On the other hand, clearly $N_1 + Rx \subset N$. N_1 is a submodule of $Ry_2 + \cdots + Ry_m$, a module of rank $m - 1$. So by the induction hypothesis rank $N_1 = n - 1 \leq m - 1$ and rank $N \leq m$.

Corollary. Let R be a PID and M a free R-module of rank m. Then every submodule N of M is free of rank $n \leq m$.

Proof. From the theorem, N has a minimal generating set $\{x_1, \ldots, x_n\}$. We form a free module F with this set as basis and let $p: F \to N$ be defined as in Theorem 4. If kernel $p = (0)$, N is free. So suppose

$$0 \neq x = \sum r_i x_i \in \text{kernel } p.$$

Let $Rd = Rr_1 + \cdots + Rr_n$. Not all r_i are zero, so $d \neq 0$. Let $da_i = r_i$, $i = 1, \ldots, n$, so that $R = Ra_1 + \cdots + Ra_n$. Let $x' = \sum a_i x_i$. Now $p(x') \in M$, so let $p(x') = \sum c_i y_i$, where $\{y_1, \ldots, y_m\}$ is a basis for M. Then $\sum dc_i y_i = d(p(x')) = p(x) = 0$. Since M is free, $dc_i = 0$, $i = 1, \ldots, n$ and $c_i = 0$, $i = 1, \ldots, n$. Thus $p(x') = 0$. We can complete $\{x'\}$ to a basis $\{x', x'_2, \ldots, x'_n\}$ for F. Letting $F' = Rx'_2 + \cdots + Rx'_n$ we see that $p(F') = N$ so that N is generated by a set of $n - 1$ elements, contradicting the minimality of $\{x_1, \ldots, x_n\}$. Hence kernel p must be zero and N is free.

We next need to establish a relation between bases for free modules and bases for their submodules.

Theorem 6. *Let M be a free R-module of rank m, where R is a PID, and N a submodule of M. Then there is a basis $\{x_1, \ldots, x_m\}$ of M and $d_i \in R$, $i = 1, \ldots, m$, such that*

1) $d_i \,|\, d_{i+1}$, $i = 1, \ldots, m$, $d_n \neq 0$, $d_j = 0$, $j = n + 1, \ldots, m$,

and

2) $\{d_1 x_1, \ldots, d_n x_n\}$ is a basis for N.

Proof. From the corollary to Theorem 5 we know that N is free of rank $n \leq m$. We let $\{y_1, \ldots, y_n\}$ be a basis for N and $\{z_1, \ldots, z_m\}$ a basis for M. Then $y_i = \sum a_{jk} z_j$, $i = 1, \ldots, n$, $j = 1, \ldots, m$. We let d_1 be the gcd of the a_{ji}. Then $\sum Ra_{ji} = Rd_1$.

Suppose $\{y'_1, \ldots, y'_n\}$ is another basis for N and $\{z'_1, \ldots, z'_m\}$ another basis for M. Then $y'_i = \sum b_{ji} y_j$ and $z'_j = \sum c_{kj} z_k$. Since M is free, the determinant of (c_{kj}) must be nonzero, i.e., no basis element can be expressed as a linear combination with coefficients from R of the other elements of the same basis. Thus let

$$(c_{kj})^{-1}(a_{ji})(b_i) = (a'_{kl}),$$

and $a'_{kl} \in Rd_1, k = 1, \ldots, m, l = 1, \ldots, n$. But if $d'_1 = \gcd \{a'_{kl}\}$, by symmetry we obtain $a_{ji} \in Rd'_1$ so that $Rd_1 = Rd'_1$. Hence Rd_1 is independent of the choice of bases. Since $d_1 = 0$ if and only if (a_{ji}) is the zero matrix, in which case $N = (0)$ and we let $d_i = 0, i = 1, \ldots, m$, we may as well assume that $d_1 \neq 0$.

For any selection of bases for N and M we get a matrix (a_{jk}) connecting the two as above. Since R is a UFD, each entry in each such matrix has a unique factorization. Define the *length* of a matrix to be the minimum number of primes in the factorization of any entry of the matrix. Let (a_{jk}) be a matrix of minimum length among the matrices connecting the bases for N and M, and let $\{y_1, \ldots, y_n\}$ and $\{z_1, \ldots, z_m\}$ be the bases it connects. Some a_{ji} in (a_{ji}), say a_{11}, is the nonzero entry with the minimum number of primes in its factorization. We show that $a_{11} \mid a_{1i}, i = 1, \ldots, n$.

Suppose a_{11} does not divide some a_{1i}, say $a_{11} \nmid a_{12}$. We let

$$Ra_1 = Ra_{11} + Ra_{12}.$$

Then a_1 is the gcd of a_{11} and a_{12} and is a proper divisor of a_{11}, so that the number of primes in its factorization is less than the number of primes in the factorization for a_{11}. Letting $y'_1 = b_1 y_1 + b_2 y_2$, where $a_1 = b_1 a_{11} + b_2 a_{12}$, then since $R = Rb_1 + Rb_2$, we can construct a new basis for N which contains y'_1. But then

$$\begin{aligned}
y'_1 &= b_1 y_1 + b_2 y_2 \\
&= b_1 \sum a_{j1} z_j + b_2 \sum a_{j2} z_j \\
&= b_1 a_{11} z_1 + b_2 a_{12} z_1 + b_1 \sum_{j=2}^{m} a_{j1} z_j + b_2 \sum_{j=2}^{m} a_{j2} z_j \\
&= a_1 z_1 + b_1 \sum_{j=2}^{m} a_{j1} z_j + b_2 \sum_{j=2}^{m} a_{j2} z_j,
\end{aligned}$$

but this contradicts the minimality of a_{11}. So $a_{11} \mid a_{1i}$ for all $i = 1, \ldots, n$.

On the other hand, suppose a_{11} does not divide some a_{j1}, say $a_{11} \nmid a_{21}$. Then we form a new basis for M which includes $z'_1 = b'_1 z_1 + b'_2 z_2$, where $a_1 = b'_1 a_{11} + b'_2 a_{21}$ and obtain a contradiction as before.

Forming a basis for N such that $y'_1 = a_{11} z_1$ and

$$y'_i = \sum_{j=2}^{m} a_{ji} z_j, \qquad i = 2, \ldots, n,$$

finally we claim that $a_{11} \mid a_{ji}, i = 1, \ldots, n, j = 1, \ldots, m$. We consider the entry a_{kl} and form a new basis for N by replacing y'_1 by $y''_1 = y'_1 + y'_l$. Then

$$y''_1 = a_{11} z_1 + \cdots + a_{kl} z_k + \cdots + a_{nl} z_n,$$

so that $a_{11} \mid a_{kl}$ since a_{kl} is now in the $(j, 1)$ position.

Thus $u a_{11} = d_1$, where u is a unit; replacing z_1 by $u z_1$, we can assume that $d_1 = a_{11}$.

We now proceed by induction on m. If $m = 1$, $y_1 = a z_1$, and we are through. So suppose that the result holds whenever N is a submodule of a free module of rank $< m$. Thus we can assume that there is a basis $\{x_2, \ldots, x_m\}$ for

$$\sum_{i=2}^{m} Rz_i$$

such that $\{d_2x_2, \ldots, d_nx_n\}$ is a basis for

$$\sum_{i=2}^{n} Ry_i,$$

and $d_i \mid d_{i+1}, i = 2, \ldots, n - 1$. Now let $x_1 = z_1$ to complete the basis for M; since $a_{11} = d_1$ was independent of the choice of basis (up to multiplication by a unit) $d_1 \mid d_i, i > 1$, and $\{d_1x_1, \ldots, d_nx_n\}$ is a basis for N.

Theorem 7. *A finitely generated R-module M, where R is a PID, is the direct sum of a finite number of cyclic modules.*

Proof. Let $p: F \to M$ be the usual surjective map, F free. Then F has a basis $\{x_1, \ldots, x_n\}$ such that kernel p has as basis $\{d_1x_1, \ldots, d_nx_m\}$, $d_i \mid d_{i+1}$, $i = 1, \ldots, m - 1$. If $d_i \mid 1$, $\{x_1, \ldots, x_i\} \subset$ kernel p, and we may as well delete $\{x_1, \ldots, x_i\}$ from the bases. So we suppose that $d_1 \nmid 1$ and if $m < n$, $d_i = 0, i = m + 1, \ldots, n$. Then we claim

$$M \simeq \frac{Rx_1 \oplus \cdots \oplus Rx_n}{Rd_1x_1 \oplus \cdots \oplus Rd_nx_n} \simeq \frac{R}{Rd_1} \oplus \cdots \oplus \frac{R}{Rd_n}.$$

To see this we define

$$f: Rx_1 \oplus \cdots \oplus Rx_n \to R/Rd_1 \oplus \cdots \oplus R/Rd_n$$

by $f(r_1x_1 + \cdots + r_nx_n) = r_1 + Rd_1 + \cdots + r_n + Rd_n$. It is easy to see that this is a surjective module homomorphism. Suppose that

$$f(r_1x_1 + \cdots + r_nx_n) = Rd_1 + \cdots + Rd_n = 0.$$

Then $r_i = r_i'd_i$, for some $r_i' \in R$, $i = 1, \ldots, n$. But then $r_ix_i \in Rd_ix_i$, $i = 1, \ldots, n$. On the other hand, any element of $Rd_1x_1 \oplus \cdots \oplus Rd_nx_n$ goes onto the zero element, so kernel $f = Rd_1x_1 \oplus \cdots \oplus Rd_nx_n$ and we have the desired isomorphism. Finally we must show that R/Rd_i is cyclic. But that is obvious since it is generated by $1 + Rd_i, i = 1, \ldots, n$.

Corollary (Fundamental Theorem of Abelian Groups). Any finitely generated abelian group is the direct sum of cyclic groups.

Corollary. Any finite abelian group is the direct sum of cyclic groups of prime power order.

3. PROJECTIVE MODULES

Modules may be considered as a generalization of vector spaces; however, they turn out to be too general for many purposes. For example, for many results in the theory of vector spaces, we need the existence of a basis; hence we introduced the notion of free modules. This is a more restrictive condition than it is necessary that modules satisfy in order to enjoy certain properties analogous to those which vector spaces have. Hence we generalize the notion of a free module as follows: A module P is *projective* if whenever we have

with s surjective, there is a homomorphism $r:P \to B$ such that the diagram is commutative, that is, $sr = t$. In other words, given a surjective homomorphism $s:B \to C$, each module homomorphism $t:P \to C$ can be *lifted* to an $r:P \to B$ such that $sr = t$.

Theorem 8.   *Every free module is projective.*

Proof. We consider the diagram

$$
\begin{array}{c}
F \\
\downarrow {\scriptstyle t} \\
M \xrightarrow{\ s\ } N
\end{array}
$$

where F is a free module and s is surjective. We let $\{x_\alpha\}_{\alpha \in A}$ be a basis of F. For each α we let $y_\alpha = t(x_\alpha)$ and let $z_\alpha \in M$ be such that $s(z_\alpha) = y_\alpha$. We define $r:F \to M$ by

$$r(\textstyle\sum a_\alpha x_\alpha) = \sum a_\alpha z_\alpha.$$

This map is well defined and is a homomorphism because of the way the module operations in a free module are defined. Moreover,

$$sr(\textstyle\sum a_\alpha x_\alpha) = s(\sum a_\alpha z_\alpha) = \sum a_\alpha s(z_\alpha) = \sum a_\alpha y_\alpha$$
$$= \textstyle\sum a_\alpha t(x_\alpha) = t(\sum a_\alpha x_\alpha).$$

The converse is not true. For example, let $R = Z \oplus Z$. Then Z is an R-module which is not free, but it is projective, as shown by the following:

Theorem 9.   *An R-module P is projective if and only if it is a direct summand of a free R-module.*

Proof. We suppose that $p:F = P \oplus Q \to P$, with F free. Given

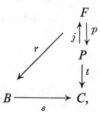

$tp:F \to C$ lifts to $r:F \to B$ with $sr = tp$ (since F is projective). Let

$$j:P \to P \oplus Q$$

be the injection. Then $s(rj) = tpj = t$, so t lifts to rj and P is projective.

Conversely, if P is projective, we have a surjective homomorphism $r:F \to P$ with F free. We lift $1_P:P \to P$ to $b:P \to F$ with $rb = 1$. We claim that F is the direct sum of $b(P) \simeq P$ and kernel r. Clearly kernel $r \cap b(P) = (0)$ since $rb = 1_P$. On the other hand, the elements of P generate F so that $b(P) + \text{kernel } r = F$.

We reverse the arrows in the definition of projectivity to get the following: A module Q is *injective* if whenever we have

$$
\begin{array}{ccc}
A & \xrightarrow{\ s\ } & B \\
{\scriptstyle t}\big\downarrow & & \\
Q & &
\end{array}
$$

with s injective, then there exists a homomorphism $r:B \to Q$ with $rs = t$, that is, every homomorphism from A to Q can be *extended* to a homomorphism from any module containing A to Q.

4. HOM

In this section we shall introduce a basic tool of homological algebra, the exact sequence, and use it in discussing the analog of the space of linear transformations of one vector space to another.

A sequence

$$K: \cdots \longrightarrow M_i \xrightarrow{\ f_i\ } M_{i+1} \xrightarrow{\ f_{i+1}\ } M_{i+2} \longrightarrow \cdots$$

of R-modules and module homomorphisms is *exact* if for each i, image $f_i = $ kernel f_{i+1}. If the sequence satisfies the weaker condition image $f_i \subset$ kernel f_{i+1}, or equivalently $f_{i+1}f_i = 0$ for each i, K is called a *complex*. We define

$$H_i(K) = (\text{kernel } f_i)/(\text{image } f_{i-1}),$$

and call the collection of quotient modules $\{H_i(K) \mid i \in Z\}$ the *homology* of the complex. Thus an exact sequence is a complex with zero homology.

The sequence

(*) $$0 \longrightarrow M \xrightarrow{\ f\ } N \xrightarrow{\ g\ } P \longrightarrow 0$$

is exact if and only if f is injective, g is surjective, and image $f = $ kernel g. A sequence of this type is called a *short exact sequence*.

An exact sequence (*) is a *split exact sequence* if image $f = $ kernel g is a direct summand of N.

Example $$0 \to Z_2 \to Z_6 \to Z_3 \to 0$$

splits, but $$0 \to Z_2 \to Z_4 \to Z_2 \to 0$$

does not (where the homomorphisms are the obvious ones). We note that splitting is defined only for exact sequences.

Theorem 10. *If*

$$0 \longrightarrow M \xrightarrow{f} N \xrightarrow{g} P \longrightarrow 0$$

is an exact sequence, then the following are equivalent:

1) *There exists a module homomorphism* $p: N \twoheadrightarrow M$ *such that* $pf = 1_M$.
2) *There exists a module homomorphism* $m: P \to N$ *such that* $gm = 1_P$.

If these conditions hold, we have

$$N = image\, f \oplus kernel\, p = kernel\, g \oplus image\, m \simeq M \oplus P,$$

so that the sequence splits.

Proof. We show that (1) implies the existence of the first direct sum decomposition and condition (2); that (2) gives the other decomposition and that (2) implies (1) are proved similarly. Then that $N \simeq M \oplus P$ follows.

Let $n \in N$. Then $n - f(p(n)) \in$ kernel p so that $N =$ kernel $p +$ image f. Suppose $f(m) = n \in$ kernel $p \cap$ image f. Then, $p(n) = p(f(m)) = m = 0$ so that $n = 0$, and the sum is direct.

We define $m: P \to N$ by

$$m(c) = n - f(p(n)), \qquad \text{where} \qquad g(n) = c.$$

We must check to see whether this is well defined. Suppose $g(n) = g(n') = c$. Then $n - n' \in$ kernel $g =$ image f and

$$n - f(p(n)) - n' + f(p(n')) \in \text{kernel } p \cap \text{image } f = (0).$$

Thus m is well defined and for $c \in P$, $g(m(c)) = g(n) = c$, since image $f =$ kernel g.

We let A and B be R-modules. The set

$$\text{Hom}_R(A, B) = \{f \,|\, f: A \to B\}$$

of all R-module homomorphisms of A into B is an abelian group under the addition defined for $f, g: A \to B$ by $(f + g)a = fa + ga$. If $A = B$, $\text{Hom}_R(A, A)$ is a ring under this addition and composition of homomorphisms; this ring is called the *ring of R-endomorphisms* of A. If (and only if) R is commutative, $\text{Hom}_R(A, B)$ may be regarded not as just a group but as an R module. $tf: A \to B$ is defined for $t \in R$ and $f: A \to B$ by $(tf)(a) = t(fa)$ for all $a \in A$. That this is an R-module homomorphism follows from

$$(tf)(ra) = t(fra) = tr(fa) = rt(fa) = r[(tf)a],$$

which uses the commutativity of R. We omit the subscript on Hom if confusion is not likely.

If R is a field, A and B vector spaces over R, $\text{Hom}_R(A, B)$ is, of course, the vector space of all linear transformations of the vector space A into the vector space B. If the range module is the base ring, then we obtain the *dual module*, $A^* = \text{Hom}_R(A, R)$, provided R is commutative. We focus our attention on $\text{Hom}(A, -)$ for a ring R and fixed module A.

We consider a module homomorphism $b: B \to B'$. Each $f \in \text{Hom}_R(A, B)$ determines a composite $bf: A \to B'$ and $b(f + g) = bf + bg$. Hence the correspondence $f \to bf$ is a homomorphism,

$$b_*: \text{Hom}_R(A, B) \to \text{Hom}_R(A, B')$$

of abelian groups, called the homomorphism *induced* by b. Explicitly, $b_*(f) = bf$. If b is an identity, so is b_*, that is,

$$(1_B)_* = 1_{\text{Hom}(A,B)}.$$

Moreover, $(bb')_* = b_* b'_*$ whenever bb' is defined.

Suppose we now vary the first argument in $\text{Hom}_R(A, B)$. For $a: A \to A'$, each $f: A' \to B$ determines a composite $fa: A \to B$ with $(f + g)a = fa + ga$. Hence $a^*(f) = fa$ defines an induced homomorphism

$$a^*: \text{Hom}_R(A', B) \to \text{Hom}_R(A, B)$$

of abelian groups. Again $(1_A)^*$ is an identity map. If $a: A \to A'$ and $a': A' \to A''$, the composite $a'a$ is defined and the induced maps are

$$\text{Hom}_R(A'', B) \xrightarrow{a'^*} \text{Hom}_R(A', B) \xrightarrow{a^*} \text{Hom}_R(A, B);$$

it is easy to show that $a^* a'^* = (a'a)^*$, that is, the order is reversed.

Using terminology which we introduce in Chapter 8 we may summarize the above by saying that $\text{Hom}_R(A, B)$ is a *functor covariant* in the second argument and *contravariant* in the first (from R-modules to abelian groups).

Now we vary both A and B, that is, we consider Hom_R as a function of two variables. Given $a: A \to A'$ and $b: B \to B'$, each $f: A' \to B$ determines a composite $bfa: A \to B'$; the correspondence $f \to bfa$ is a homomorphism

$$\text{Hom}(a, b): \text{Hom}(A', B') \to \text{Hom}(A, B')$$

of abelian groups with $a^* b_* = \text{Hom}(a, b) = b_* a^*$. It has the properties $\text{Hom}(1, 1') = 1_{\text{Hom}(A,B)}$ for 1 the identity of A and $1'$ the identity of B, and $\text{Hom}(aa', bb') = \text{Hom}(a', b)\text{Hom}(a, b')$, whenever the composites aa' and bb' are defined.

Since we have both modules and homomorphisms produced by the application of Hom, we can consider forming new sequences from a given sequence of modules and homomorphisms. The question of the preservation of exactness is an important one.

Theorem 11. *For any R-module D and any sequence of R-modules*

$$0 \longrightarrow A \xrightarrow{f} B \xrightarrow{g} C$$

exact at A and B, the induced sequence

$$0 \longrightarrow \operatorname{Hom}_R(D, A) \xrightarrow{f_*} \operatorname{Hom}_R(D, B) \xrightarrow{g_*} \operatorname{Hom}_R(D, C)$$

of Z-modules is exact.

Proof. To show that f_* is injective we suppose that $h: D \to A$ is an R-module homomorphism with $f_* h = 0$. For each $d \in D$, $f_* hd = fhd = 0$; since f is injective, each $hd = 0$ so $h = 0$.

Clearly $g_* f_* = (gf)_* = 0_* = 0$ so that image $f_* \subset$ kernel g_*. For the other inclusion, we suppose that $h: D \to B$ with $g_* h = 0$. Then $ghd = 0$ for each $d \in D$. But kernel $g =$ image f by the given exactness, so there is an a in A with $fa = hd$, unique because f is injective. Then $kd = a$ defines a homomorphism $k: D \to A$ with $f_* k = h$. Thus image $f_* \supset$ kernel g_*, which completes the proof.

Theorem 12. *If*

$$A \xrightarrow{f} B \xrightarrow{g} C \longrightarrow 0$$

is exact, and D is any module, the induced sequence

$$0 \longrightarrow \operatorname{Hom}_R(C, D) \xrightarrow{g_*} \operatorname{Hom}_R(B, D) \xrightarrow{f_*} \operatorname{Hom}_R(A, D)$$

is exact.

The proof, which proceeds as for Theorem 11, is left to the reader. Now suppose we have an exact sequence of R-modules,

$$0 \longrightarrow A \xrightarrow{f} B \xrightarrow{g} C \longrightarrow 0;$$

can we conclude that the following sequences, with D an arbitrary R-module, are exact with a zero added on the right?

1) $0 \longrightarrow \operatorname{Hom}_R(D, A) \xrightarrow{f_*} \operatorname{Hom}_R(D, B) \xrightarrow{g_*} \operatorname{Hom}_R(D, C) \longrightarrow$

2) $0 \longrightarrow \operatorname{Hom}_R(C, D) \xrightarrow{g_*} \operatorname{Hom}_R(B, D) \xrightarrow{f_*} \operatorname{Hom}_R(A, D) \longrightarrow$

For example, exactness of (1) at the right would assert that each $h: D \to C$ has the form $h = gh'$ for some $h': D \to B$, that is, that each map h into $C = B/(\text{image } f)$ could be lifted to a map h' into B, as would be the case if D were projective. We note, however, that projectivity of D is not a necessary condition for the sequence to be exact for a particular choice of D, A, B, and C. On the other hand, the induced sequence is not always exact: if we take

$R = Z$ and $D = Z_m$ and the short exact sequence

$$0 \longrightarrow Z \xrightarrow{f} Z \xrightarrow{g} Z_m \longrightarrow 0,$$

with f the operation of multiplication by m and g the canonical projection, (1) becomes

$$0 \to 0 \to 0 \to \mathrm{Hom}(Z_m, Z_m) \to 0,$$

which is certainly not exact.

Similarly, (2) need not be exact since for modules $A \subset B$ a homomorphism $f: A \to D$ cannot in general be extended to one of B into D. We do have the following result:

Theorem 13. *The following properties of a module D are equivalent:*

1) *D is projective,*

2) *For each surjective homomorphism $s: B \to C$,*

$$s_*: \mathrm{Hom}_R(D, B) \to \mathrm{Hom}_R(D, C)$$

   is surjective.

3) *If $0 \to A \xrightarrow{f} B \xrightarrow{g} C \to 0$ is a short exact sequence, so is*

$$0 \longrightarrow \mathrm{Hom}_R(D, A) \xrightarrow{f_*} \mathrm{Hom}_R(D, B) \xrightarrow{g_*} \mathrm{Hom}_R(D, C) \longrightarrow 0.$$

4) *Every short exact sequence*

$$0 \longrightarrow A \xrightarrow{f} B \xrightarrow{s} D \longrightarrow 0$$

   splits.

Proof

$(1) \Leftrightarrow (2)$. In (2) the statement that s_* is a surjective homomorphism means that each $t: D \to C$ can be factored as $t = sr$, $r: D \to B$; this is exactly the definition of projectivity for D.

$(2) \Leftrightarrow (3)$. This equivalence follows from Theorem 8.

$(1) \Rightarrow (4)$. If D is projective and $s: B \to D$ is surjective, the homomorphism $1_D: D \to D$ lifts to a homomorphism $r: D \to B$, with $sr = 1_D$, so the sequence splits.

$(4) \Rightarrow (1)$. We write D as the image of $r: F \to D$ for some free module F. Then

$$0 \to \mathrm{kernel}\ r \to F \to D \to 0$$

splits. But then $F \simeq \mathrm{kernel}\ r \oplus D$ and D, being a direct summand of a free module, is projective.

We close this section with a theorem which illustrates how looking at the modules over a ring can give us information about the ring's internal structure.

Theorem 14. *If R is a ring with identity, the following statements are equivalent:*

1) *R is semisimple.*

2) *Every R-module is projective.*

3) *Every short exact sequence of R-modules splits.*

4) *Every R-module is injective.*

Proof. $(2) \Leftrightarrow (3)$ follows from Theorem 13, and $(3) \Leftrightarrow (4)$ is a consequence of Problem 6.

$(1) \Rightarrow (3)$. Suppose that R is semisimple. To show that any short exact sequence splits, it is clearly sufficient to show that M is completely reducible. But this follows from Theorem 3.

$(3) \Rightarrow (1)$. We first show that R has minimal left ideals. We let $\mathfrak{A}$ be the set of all proper left ideals of R, partially ordered by set inclusion. Then $\mathfrak{A}$ has a maximal element, say J, by Theorem 1, Chapter 1. We have the exact sequence

$$0 \to J \to R \to R/J \to 0,$$

which splits. Hence J is a direct summand of R, $R = I \oplus J$, I a left ideal of R. Now suppose that there is a left ideal I' of R such that $0 \subsetneq I' \subsetneq I$. Then we have the exact sequence

$$0 \to I' \to I \to I/I' \to 0$$

which splits. Hence I' is a direct summand of I, $I = I' \oplus I''$, I'' a nonzero left ideal of R. Then $R = I' \oplus (I'' \oplus J)$. Since $I' \neq (0)$, $I'' \oplus J \neq R$, and $I'' \oplus J \in \mathfrak{A}$, contradicting the maximality of J. This proof can also be applied to show that any nonzero left ideal of R has a minimal left ideal.

Now let $\mathfrak{S}$ be the set of all finite sums of minimal ideals of R. We have shown that $\mathfrak{S}$ is not empty and we can apply Zorn's lemma to obtain a maximal element, say

$$R' = I_1 \oplus \cdots \oplus I_n,$$

I_i a minimal left ideal of R, $i = 1, \ldots, n$. Suppose $R' \neq R$. Then since the sequence

$$0 \to R' \to R \to R/R' \to 0$$

splits, we can write R as

$$R = R' \oplus I,$$

I a nonzero left ideal of R. We can proceed as above to show that I has a minimal left ideal, say I', which is also a minimal left ideal of R, since I is a direct summand. Thus $R' \oplus I' \in \mathfrak{S}$, contradicting the maximality of R'. Hence $R = R'$. Each I_i, being a minimal left ideal of R, is left Artinian. Write $1 = \sum e_i$. Then $1 = 1^2 = \sum e_i^2$ so that $e_i = e_i^2$, $i = 1, \ldots, n$. Therefore for each $i = 1, \ldots, n$, $I_i^2 \neq (0)$ and each I_i is simple. Thus by Theorem 17, Chapter 2, R is semisimple.

5. TENSOR PRODUCTS

The topic we now introduce is in some senses a complementary concept to
Hom. Tensor products are also a way of constructing new modules from those
given; their importance in homological algebra comes, as we shall see, from
their factorization properties. Throughout this section we shall consider only
unital modules over commutative rings with identity.

If $A_1, \ldots, A_n$, B are R-modules, a function

$$f: A_1 \times \cdots \times A_n \to B,$$

which is linear in each variable, i.e., for each $i = 1, \ldots, n$,

$$f(a_1, \ldots, a_i + a_i', \ldots, a_n) = f(a_1, \ldots, a_i, \ldots, a_n) + f(a_1, \ldots, a_i', \ldots, a_n)$$

and

$$f(a_1, \ldots, ra_i, \ldots, a_n) = rf(a_1, \ldots, a_i, \ldots, a_n), \qquad a_i \in A_i, \quad r \in R,$$

is an *n-multilinear map*. The set of all multilinear functions from $A_1 \times \cdots \times A_n$
to B can be made into an R-module in the usual way.

If T is a module such that all multilinear maps from $A_1 \times \cdots \times A_n$ factor
uniquely through T, that is, if there is a multilinear map $g: A_1 \times \cdots \times A_n \to T$
such that whenever $f: A_1 \times \cdots \times A_n \to B$ is multilinear, then there is a unique
module homomorphism $\bar{f}: T \to B$ such that

$$A_1 \times \cdots \times A_n \xrightarrow{\;g\;} T$$
$$\Big\downarrow{\scriptstyle \bar{f}}$$
$$f \searrow\quad B$$

is commutative, that is, $\bar{f}g = f$, then T is called a *tensor product* of the
$A_1, \ldots, A_n$.

We can show that any two tensor products of the modules $A_1, \ldots, A_n$
are isomorphic. For suppose T and T' are such. Then we have factorizations
of the identity of T and of the identity of T':

$$A_1 \times \cdots \times A_n \xrightarrow{\;g\;} T \qquad \text{and} \qquad A_1 \times \cdots \times A_n \xrightarrow{\;g'\;} T'$$
$$\Big\downarrow{\scriptstyle 1_T} \qquad\qquad\qquad\qquad\qquad\qquad \Big\downarrow{\scriptstyle 1_{T'}}$$
$$g \searrow\; T \qquad\qquad\qquad\qquad\qquad g' \searrow\; T'$$

From the definition of tensor product we also have that there exist $\bar{g}$ and $\bar{g}'$
such that

$$A_1 \times \cdots \times A_n \xrightarrow{\;g\;} T \qquad \text{and} \qquad A_1 \times \cdots \times A_n \xrightarrow{\;g'\;} T'$$
$$\Big\downarrow{\scriptstyle \bar{g}'} \qquad\qquad\qquad\qquad\qquad\qquad \Big\downarrow{\scriptstyle \bar{g}}$$
$$g' \searrow\; T' \qquad\qquad\qquad\qquad\qquad g \searrow\; T$$

are commutative. Thus

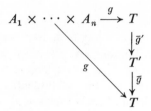

is commutative, so by the uniqueness requirement $\bar{g}\bar{g}' = 1_T$. Similarly $\bar{g}'_i\bar{g} = 1_{T'}$ and $\bar{g}$, $\bar{g}'$ and their composition are isomorphisms (see Problem 1).

Now the problem is to construct a module which does in fact have this factorization property.

Let F be the free module generated by the set $A_1 \times \cdots \times A_n$, so that elements of F are of the form $\sum r_\alpha x_\alpha$, where x_α runs through all elements of the form $(a_1, \ldots, a_n)$, $a_i \in A_i$, and $r_\alpha \in R$. Let N be the submodule of F generated by all elements of the following types:

$$(a_1, \ldots, a_i + a_i', \ldots, a_n) - (a_1, \ldots, a_i, \ldots, a_n) - (a_1, \ldots, a_i', \ldots, a_n)$$

and

$$(a_1, \ldots, ra_i, \ldots, a_n) - r(a_1, \ldots, a_n), \qquad a_i \in A_i, \quad r \in R.$$

We observe that, for example,

$$(a_1, \ldots, ra_i, \ldots, a_n) \quad \text{and} \quad r(a_1, \ldots, a_i, \ldots, a_n), \qquad a_i \in A_i, \quad 1 \neq r \in R,$$

are not the same element of F. The first is a formal sum with $r_\alpha = 0$ for $x_\alpha \neq (a_1, \ldots, ra_i, \ldots, a_n)$ and $r_\alpha = 1$ for $x_\alpha = (a_1, \ldots, ra_i, \ldots, a_n)$, whereas $r(a_1, \ldots, a_i, \ldots, a_n)$ is a formal sum with $r = 0$ for

$$x_\alpha \neq (a_1, \ldots, a_i, \ldots, a_n)$$

and $r_\alpha = r$ for $x_\alpha = (a_1, \ldots, a_i, \ldots, a_n)$.

We claim that F/N is a tensor product.

First of all we have a map $g : A_1 \times \cdots \times A_n \to F/N$ given by the composition of the injection $A_1 \times \cdots \times A_n \to F$ and the projection $F \to F/N$. That g is multilinear follows from the definition of F/N. Thus if

$$f : A_1 \times \cdots \times A_n \to B$$

is multilinear, then we need only the existence of a unique module homomorphism $F/N \to B$ with the proper commutativity property.

Since F is free on $A_1 \times \cdots \times A_n$, there is a unique induced homomorphism $F \to B$ such that

$$A_1 \times \cdots \times A_n \longrightarrow F$$
$$\underset{f}{\searrow} \quad \downarrow$$
$$B$$

is commutative. But since f is multilinear, N is contained in the kernel of the induced homomorphism. Hence it can be factored through F/N. Thus we have an induced homomorphism $\bar{f}$ such that

$$
\begin{array}{ccc}
A_1 \times \cdots \times A_n & \xrightarrow{\;g\;} & F/N \\
& \searrow{\scriptstyle f} & \downarrow{\scriptstyle \bar{f}} \\
& & B
\end{array}
$$

is commutative. But the image of g generates F/N so that $\bar{f}$ must be uniquely determined.

We denote F/N by $A_1 \otimes \cdots \otimes A_n$ and since all tensor products are isomorphic, we call it *the* tensor product of the A_i. When necessary we shall distinguish a tensor product over R, that is, the tensor product of modules as R-modules, by $\otimes_R$.

If $(a_1, \ldots, a_n) \in A_1 \times \cdots \times A_n$, we write $g(a_1, \ldots, a_n)$ as $a_1 \otimes \cdots \otimes a_n$. We observe that these symbols satisfy the relations

$$
a_1 \otimes \cdots \otimes ra_i \otimes \cdots \otimes a_n = r(a_1 \otimes \cdots \otimes a_n)
$$

and

$$
a_1 \otimes \cdots \otimes (a_i + a_i') \otimes \cdots \otimes a_n
$$
$$
= (a_1 \otimes \cdots \otimes a_i \otimes \cdots \otimes a_n) + (a_1 \otimes \cdots \otimes a_i' \otimes \cdots \otimes a_n),
$$

for $a_i, a_i' \in A_i$, $r \in R$. It is important to note that the symbols $a_1 \otimes \cdots \otimes a_n$, $a_i \in A_i$, merely generate the tensor product. Thus a typical element must be written as a linear combination of elements represented by the symbols $a_1 \otimes \cdots \otimes a_n$. A word of caution:

$$
(a_1 \otimes \cdots \otimes a_n) + (a_1' \otimes \cdots \otimes a_n')
$$

cannot be reduced to

$$
(a_1 + a_1') \otimes \cdots \otimes (a_n + a_n').
$$

For example, $(r_1 \otimes r_2) + (r_1 \otimes r_2') = r_1 \otimes (r_2 + r_2')$, which is not the same as $(r_1 + r_1) \otimes (r_2 + r_2')$, unless $r_1 = 0$.

However, we can define a homomorphism whose domain is a tensor product by specifying its value on the generators and requiring linearity, as when defining a linear transformation on a vector space by giving its values on a basis.

Examples

1. The tensor product of an R-module A with the ring R, considered as a module over itself, is isomorphic to A.

2. Considering Z_m, Z_n, n, m relatively prime, as Z-modules, we can form $Z_n \otimes Z_m$. The elements of $Z_n \otimes Z_m$ can be written as sums of terms $x \otimes y$, $x \in Z_n$, $y \in Z_m$.

However,

$$n(x \otimes y) = nx \otimes y = 0 \otimes y = 0$$

and

$$m(x \otimes y) = x \otimes my = x \otimes 0 = 0.$$

But then $x \otimes y = 0$ since $(n, m) = 1$, and $Z_n \otimes Z_m = (0)$.

3. Suppose A and B are finite-dimensional vector spaces over a field K. If $\{v_1, \ldots, v_n\}$ and $\{w_1, \ldots, w_n\}$ are bases for A and B, respectively, then any element of $A \otimes B$ can be represented as

$$x = \sum k_{ij}(x_i \otimes y_j) = \sum k_{ij}(\sum a_{ki}v_{ki} \otimes \sum b_{lj}w_{lj}),$$

for $k_{ij}, a_{ki}, b_{lj} \in K, x_i \in A, y_j \in B$. But by linearity of the tensor product this reduces to

$$x = \sum c_{ij}(v_i \otimes w_j), \qquad c_{ij} \in K.$$

Thus $v_i \otimes w_j$ is a basis for $A \otimes B$, which is a vector space of dimension nm.

The same result holds for free modules over an arbitrary commutative ring with identity, i.e., if F and F' are free with bases $\{v_i\}_{i \in I}$, $\{y_j\}_{j \in J}$, respectively, then $F \otimes F'$ is free with basis $\{v_i \otimes y_j\}$ and rank $(F \otimes F') = $ rank $F \times$ rank F'.

The tensor product is additive in the following sense:

Theorem 15. *If $A_1, \ldots, A_n$ and B are R-modules, then*

$$B \otimes \left(\sum_1^n A_i \right) \simeq \sum_1^n (B \otimes A_i),$$

where the sum is direct.

Proof. We define

$$f: B \times \left(\sum A_i \right) \to \sum (B \otimes A_i)$$

by $f(b, (a_1, \ldots, a_n)) = (b \otimes a_1, \ldots, b \otimes a_n)$. This is bilinear as a function of b and $(a_1, \ldots, a_n)$ and hence factors uniquely through $B \otimes \sum A_i$ with the module homomorphism $\bar{f}: B \otimes \sum A_i \to \sum (B \otimes A_i)$ taking $(b \otimes (a_1, \ldots, a_n))$ to $(b \otimes a_1, \ldots, b \otimes a_n)$. To show that this is an isomorphism we define an inverse for it by

$$\bar{f}^{-1}(b \otimes a_1, \ldots, b \otimes a_n) = \sum b \otimes (0, \ldots, a_i, \ldots, 0)$$

and linearity.

Theorem 16. *If $A, B,$ and C are R-modules, then*

$$Hom(A \otimes B, C) \simeq Hom(A, Hom(B, C)).$$

Proof. We define a homomorphism $f: Hom(A \otimes B, C) \to Hom(A, Hom(B, C))$ by

$$((fg)(a))(b) = g(a \otimes b),$$

for $g: A \otimes B \to C$, $a \in A$, $b \in B$. $(fg)(a)$ as a function of b is a module homomorphism, since g is a homomorphism and the tensor product is linear. Moreover, f as a function of a is a module homomorphism with range $\text{Hom}(B, C)$. Finally, f is a module homomorphism as a function of g.

As in the preceding theorem, we show that f is an isomorphism by finding an inverse. For any $g: A \to \text{Hom}(B, C)$ we consider $(ga)(b): A \times B \to C$. This is a bilinear map and thus factors uniquely through $A \otimes B$, giving a homomorphism f' such that

$$(f'g)(a \otimes b) = (ga)(b).$$

But then $f'f$ and ff' are identities.

Corollary. If P and P' are projective, then $P \otimes P'$ is projective.

Proof. By Theorem 13, P' projective implies that if $B \to C$ is surjective, then the induced homomorphism $\text{Hom}(P', B) \to \text{Hom}(P', C)$ is surjective. The projectivity of P implies that

$$\text{Hom}(P, \text{Hom}(P', B)) \to \text{Hom}(P, \text{Hom}(P', C))$$

is surjective. Then

$$\text{Hom}(P \otimes P', B) \simeq \text{Hom}(P, \text{Hom}(P', B))$$

and

$$\text{Hom}(P, \text{Hom}(P', C)) \simeq \text{Hom}(P \otimes P', C)$$

so that whenever $B \to C$ is surjective, the induced homomorphism $\text{Hom}(P \otimes P', B) \to \text{Hom}(P \otimes P', C)$ is surjective and $P \otimes P'$ is projective.

We shall now examine another way in which the tensor product complements Hom, this time in connection with the preservation of the exactness of sequences. First we introduce a convenient notation. If $f: A \to C$ and $g: B \to D$, we define $f \otimes g: A \otimes B \to C \otimes D$ to be the map such that

$$(f \otimes g)(a \otimes b) = fa \otimes gb,$$

that is, $f \otimes g$ is the homomorphism given by the factorization of (f, g) through the tensor product of A and B. The same notation is used to denote an element of $\text{Hom}(A, C) \otimes \text{Hom}(B, D)$, but the meaning will be clear from the context.

Theorem 17. *If*

$$0 \longrightarrow A \overset{f}{\longrightarrow} B \overset{g}{\longrightarrow} C \longrightarrow 0$$

is an exact sequence of R-modules and D is an arbitrary R-module, then

$$D \otimes A \overset{1 \otimes f}{\longrightarrow} D \otimes B \overset{1 \otimes g}{\longrightarrow} D \otimes C \longrightarrow 0$$

is an exact sequence of R-modules.

Proof. For $d \in D$, $c \in C$, there exists $b \in B$ such that $g(b) = c$ and

$$(1 \otimes g)(d \otimes b) = d \otimes c.$$

But elements of this type generate $D \otimes C$, so that $1 \otimes g$ is surjective. It is clear that $(1 \otimes g)(1 \otimes f) = 0$, that is, image$(1 \otimes f) \subset$ kernel$(1 \otimes g)$.

Let $I = $ image$(1 \otimes f)$ and suppose we replace $D \otimes C$ by $(D \otimes B)/I$, and let $p':(D \otimes B)/I \to D \otimes C$ be the induced homomorphism. We define $p:D \times C \to (D \otimes B)/I$ by

$$p'(d, c) = (d \otimes b) + I,$$

where $g(b) = c$. This map is well defined, for suppose $g(b) = g(b')$. Then $g(b - b') = 0$ so that by the exactness of the original sequence there exists $a \in A$ such that $f(a) = b - b'$. Thus we have $d \otimes b - d \otimes b' = d \otimes f(a) \in I$. Moreover, the map is bilinear and therefore factors through $D \otimes C$, by a homomorphism $\bar{p}$. Then $p\bar{p}$ is the identity on the generators $d \otimes c$. Thus p is injective, and since $D \otimes C \simeq (D \otimes B)/$kernel$(1 \otimes g)$, kernel$(1 \otimes g) \subset$ image $1 \otimes f$.

If

(*) $0 \longrightarrow A \overset{f}{\longrightarrow} B \overset{g}{\longrightarrow} C \longrightarrow 0$

is exact, we cannot in general conclude that

(**) $0 \longrightarrow D \otimes A \overset{1 \otimes f}{\longrightarrow} D \otimes B \overset{1 \otimes g}{\longrightarrow} D \otimes C \longrightarrow 0$

is exact. For example, we consider the Z-modules $A = nZ$, $B = Z$, $C = Z_n$, $D = Z_n$. Then $Z_n \otimes nZ$ is a cyclic group of order n with generator $1 \otimes n$, but $(1 \otimes f)(1 \otimes n) = 1 \otimes n = n \otimes 1 = 0 \otimes 1 = 0$, that is, in the resulting sequence, $1 \otimes f$ is the zero homomorphism rather than being injective.

If a module D is such that for any exact sequence (*) the resulting sequence (**) is exact, D is said to be *flat*. It is not hard to show that a projective module must be flat, but the converse is not true. For example, any torsion-free abelian group is a flat Z-module, but only free abelian groups are projective.

6. ALGEBRAS

If K is a commutative ring with identity, a *K-algebra A* is a ring which is also a K-module such that always

$$k(a_1 a_2) = (ka_1)a_2 = a_1(ka_2), \qquad k \in K, \quad a_i \in A.$$

In this section we are concerned with algebras with identity. If 1_A is the identity of A, then $I(k) = k1_A$ defines a ring homomorphism $I:K \to A$.

The ring product $a_1 a_2$ is left and right distributive and so is a K-bilinear function. Hence $\pi(a_1 \otimes a_2) = a_1 a_2$ determines a K-module homomorphism $\pi:A \otimes A \to A$. Thus we may describe a K-algebra with identity as a K-module

A equipped with two homomorphisms,

$$\pi: A \otimes A \to A, \qquad I: K \to A,$$

of K-modules such that the diagrams

$$
\begin{array}{ccc}
A \otimes A \otimes A & \xrightarrow{\pi \otimes 1} & A \otimes A \\
{\scriptstyle 1 \otimes \pi} \downarrow & & \downarrow {\scriptstyle \pi} \\
A \otimes A & \xrightarrow{\pi} & A
\end{array}
\qquad \text{and} \qquad
\begin{array}{ccccc}
K \otimes A & \simeq & A & \simeq & A \otimes K \\
{\scriptstyle I \otimes 1} \downarrow & & \| & & \downarrow {\scriptstyle 1 \otimes I} \\
A \otimes A & \xrightarrow{\pi} & A & \xleftarrow{\pi} & A \otimes A
\end{array}
$$

are commutative. The first diagram asserts that the product is associative, while the left and right halves of the second diagram state that 1 is a left and right identity for the product in A and that $\pi(Ik \otimes a) = ka = \pi(a \otimes Ik)$.

By reversing the arrows in the diagrams we can define a coalgebra. We have: a K-module W is a K-*coalgebra* if it is equipped with two module homomorphisms:

$$\psi: W \to W \otimes W \qquad \text{and} \qquad \varepsilon: W \to K \quad \text{(comultiplication and counit)}$$

such that

$$
\begin{array}{ccc}
W & \xrightarrow{\psi} & W \otimes W \\
{\scriptstyle \psi} \downarrow & & \downarrow {\scriptstyle 1 \otimes \psi} \\
W \otimes W & \xrightarrow{\psi \otimes 1} & W \otimes W \otimes W
\end{array}
\qquad \text{and} \qquad
\begin{array}{ccccc}
W \otimes W & \xleftarrow{\psi} & W & \xrightarrow{\psi} & W \otimes W \\
{\scriptstyle \varepsilon \otimes 1} \downarrow & & \| & & \downarrow {\scriptstyle 1 \otimes \varepsilon} \\
K \otimes W & \simeq & W & \simeq & W \otimes K
\end{array}
$$

are commutative.

A *homomorphism* of K-algebras (of K-algebras with identity) is a module homomorphism $f: A \to B$ such that $(*)$ commutes $((*)$ and $(**)$ commute):

$$
(*) \qquad
\begin{array}{ccc}
A \otimes A & \xrightarrow{\pi_A} & A \\
{\scriptstyle f \otimes f} \downarrow & & \downarrow {\scriptstyle f} \\
B \otimes B & \xrightarrow{\pi_B} & B
\end{array}
\qquad\qquad
(**) \qquad
\begin{array}{ccc}
K & \xrightarrow{I_A} & A \\
\| & & \downarrow {\scriptstyle f} \\
K & \xrightarrow{I_B} & B
\end{array}
$$

A homomorphism of coalgebras is defined by commutativity of the appropriate diagrams.

A *Hopf algebra* V is a K-module V which is both a K-algebra with product $\pi: V \otimes V \to V$ and unit $I: K \to V$ and a K-coalgebra with comultiplication ψ and counit ε and such that

1) $I: K \to V$ is a homomorphism of coalgebras.

2) $\varepsilon: V \to K$ is a homomorphism of algebras.

3) $\pi: V \otimes V \to V$ is a homomorphism of coalgebras.

3') (equivalent to 3) $\psi: V \to V \otimes V$ is a homomorphism of algebras.

Condition (3) or (3′) states that the following diagram is commutative:

$$
\begin{array}{ccc}
V \otimes V & \xrightarrow{\ \psi \otimes \psi\ } & V \otimes V \otimes V \otimes V \xrightarrow{\ 1 \otimes \tau \otimes 1\ } V \otimes V \otimes V \otimes V \\
\downarrow{\scriptstyle \pi} & & \hspace{3cm} \downarrow{\scriptstyle \pi \otimes \pi} \\
V & \xrightarrow{\hspace{5cm}\psi\hspace{5cm}} & V \otimes V
\end{array}
$$

where τ is the isomorphism $A \otimes B \simeq B \otimes A$ given by $\tau(a \otimes b) = (b \otimes a)$. Construction of the proper diagrams for the defininition of a Hopf algebra homomorphism is left to the reader

A *subalgebra* S of an algebra A is a submodule of A such that $1_A \in S$ and $s, s' \in S$ imply $ss' \in S$. A *left ideal* L in A is a submodule of A such that $a \in A$ and $m \in L$ imply $am \in L$. Similarly, we define right ideal and ideal.

Examples

1. In case $K = Z$, a Z-algebra is simply a ring with identity.

2. A commutative ring K with identity is an algebra, coalgebra, and Hopf algebra over itself.

3. $A = F[x]$, the ring of polynomials in an indeterminate x over a field F, is an F-algebra with the usual multiplication of polynomials as product. It is also a Hopf algebra with

$$\varepsilon x = 0 \quad \text{and} \quad xx = x \otimes 1 + 1 \otimes x.$$

4. The ring of $n \times n$ matrices over a commutative ring with identity, with the usual operations, is an algebra.

5. If G is a group written multiplicatively, we let $Z(G)$ be the free abelian group generated by the elements of G, that is, $Z(G) = \{\sum m_g g \mid m_g \in Z, g \in G\}$, where the sums are finite.

The product of G induces a product on $Z(G)$

$$\left(\sum_g m_g g\right)\left(\sum_h n_h h\right) = \sum_{g,h} m_g n_h gh,$$

which makes $Z(G)$ into a ring, called the *group ring of G*. We define

$$\varepsilon : Z(G) \to Z$$

by $\varepsilon(\sum_g m_g g) = \sum_g m_g$ and a comultiplication by letting

$$\psi(g) = g \otimes g \quad \text{for} \ \ g \in G,$$

and requiring linearity. Letting $I : Z \to Z(G)$ be the injection, we have that $Z(G)$ is a Hopf algebra over Z. Also, a homomorphism of groups $G \to G'$ induces a Hopf algebra homomorphism $Z(G) \to Z(G')$.

Similarly, for any commutative ring K we define the *group algebra* of G with respect to K to be $K \otimes_Z Z(G)$, that is, the free module over K generated by elements of g with product induced by the product of G. Again it is a Hopf algebra with coproduct given by $\psi(g) = g \otimes g$. We denote this algebra by $K(G)$.

6. We look briefly at another commonly encountered algebra. The *tensor algebra* $T(M)$ of a K-module M is the K-module $\sum T_n(M)$, where the sum is direct, and

$$T_0(M) = K, \qquad T_n(M) = M^n = M \otimes \cdots \otimes M \qquad (n \text{ factors}),$$

with product given by the identification map $\pi: M^p \otimes M^q \simeq M^{p+q}$. In other words, the product is formed by juxtaposition, as in

$$(m_1 \otimes \cdots \otimes m_p)(m_1' \otimes \cdots \otimes m_q') = m_1 \otimes \cdots \otimes m_p \otimes m_1' \otimes \cdots \otimes m_q'.$$

The algebra $T(M)$ with the obvious K-module injection $M \to T(M)$ is characterized up to isomorphism by the following property:

> **Theorem 18.** *If M is a module and A an algebra over a commutative ring K with identity, each module homomorphism $g: M \to A$ extends to a unique algebra homomorphism $f: T(M) \to A$.*

Proof. We let $f(m_1 \otimes \cdots \otimes m_p) = (gm_1) \cdots (gm_p)$ and require linearity. This defines f on all of $T(M)$, since it is generated by elements of this form.

Thus any algebra with this factorization property for M must be isomorphic to $T(M)$. In particular, if M is the free K-module F with basis $\{x_1, \ldots, x_n\}$, $T(F)$ is the free algebra on these generators in the sense that any set map $f: \{x_1, \ldots, x_n\} \to A$ extends to a unique algebra homomorphism $T(F) \to A$. When F has just one generator x, $T(F)$ is the polynomial algebra in the indeterminate; when V is a vector space over a field K, $T(V)$ is the tensor algebra of V over K, consisting of all covariant tensors in any number of indices. We recall from Section 5 that if V, W have bases $\{v_1, \ldots, v_m\}$ and $\{w_1, \ldots, w_n\}$, respectively, over a field K, then $V \otimes W$ has a basis of mn vectors $v_i \otimes w_j$ and in particular, any vector u in $V \otimes V$ (a twice covariant tensor) has a unique expression as

$$u = \sum x^{ij}(v_i \otimes v_j),$$

where the m^2 constants $x^{ij} \in K$ are known as the *components of the tensor u* relative to the basis $\{v_1, \ldots, v_m\}$.

The *tensor product* of two K-algebras with identities A and B is the tensor product $A \otimes_K B$ as K-modules, with product map defined as the composite

$$(A \otimes B) \otimes (A \otimes B) \xrightarrow{1 \otimes \tau \otimes 1} A \otimes A \otimes B \otimes B \xrightarrow{\pi_A \otimes \pi_B} A \otimes B,$$

where τ is as before the isomorphism $B \otimes A \simeq A \otimes B$ given by $\tau(b \otimes a) = a \otimes b$, and with identity element map given by $I \otimes I: K = K \otimes K \to A \otimes B$. In terms of elements, the product is given by

$$(a \otimes b)(a' \otimes b') = aa' \otimes bb',$$

and the identity of $A \otimes B$ is $1_A \otimes 1_B$. It is easy to verify that the tensor product of K-algebras is a K-algebra. If $f: A \to A'$ and $g: B \to B'$ are algebra homomorphisms, so is $f \otimes g: A \otimes B \to A' \otimes B'$. Also, $a \to a \otimes 1_B$, $b \to 1_A \otimes b$

define algebra homomorphisms. With these mappings, the tensor product $A \otimes B$ is characterized up to isomorphism by the following property:

Theorem 19. *If $f: A \to B$ and $g: C \to B$ are algebra homomorphisms, A, B, C algebras with identity, such that always*

$$(*) \qquad\qquad (fa)(gc) = (gc)(fa),$$

then there is a unique algebra homomorphism $h: A \otimes C \to B$ with

$$h(a \otimes 1) = fa, \ h(1 \otimes c) = gc.$$

Proof. We let h be defined by

$$h(a \otimes c) = (fa)(gc).$$

We note that if the multiplication in B is commutative, then condition $(*)$ holds automatically. We also observe that it is possible to define the tensor product of rings with identity as Z-modules and that the resulting ring has the unique factorization property if $(*)$ holds.

The tensor product of algebras is, as we have noted, commutative, that is, $A \otimes B \simeq B \otimes A$, and associative, that is, $A \otimes (B \otimes C) \simeq (A \otimes B) \otimes C$, and $K \otimes A \simeq A$. The tensor product of algebras is sometimes called their *Kronecker product* and was formerly known as their *direct product*.

PROBLEMS

1. Show that if $f: M \to N$ and $g: N \to M$ are module homomorphisms such that $gf = 1_M$ and $fg = 1_N$, then they are isomorphisms.

2. Prove Zassenhaus' lemma: If M_1, M_2, M_3, and M_4 are submodules of an R-module M, $M_1 \subset M_2$, $M_3 \subset M_4$, then

$$\frac{M_1 + (M_2 \cap M_4)}{M_1 + (M_2 \cap M_3)} \simeq \frac{M_3 + (M_4 \cap M_2)}{M_3 + (M_4 \cap M_1)}.$$

3. Prove the modular law: if M_1, M_2, and M_3 are submodules of an R-module M, then $M_1 \cap (M_2 \oplus M_3) = (M_1 \oplus M_2) \cap M_3$.

4. We can define ascending and descending chain conditions for modules analogously to the definitions for rings. Prove that an R-module M has a composition series if and only if it satisfies both the acc and the dcc.

5. Let M be the additive group of those rational numbers whose denominators are powers of a fixed prime p modulo the subgroup consisting of the integers. Show that M satisfies the dcc as a Z-module, but not the acc. Show that every proper submodule of M is finite. Find the maximal and minimal submodules of M.

6. If M is a finitely generated module over a left Artinian ring, show that the submodules of M are left Artinian.

7. State and prove a theorem about injectiveness which is similar to Theorem 13.

8. Prove Theorem 12.

9. Show that the injective Z-modules are precisely the divisible abelian groups. Characterize projective Z-modules similarly.

10. If M is a left A-module, A a ring with identity, M is *divisible* if for each nonzero a in A, $aM = M$. Prove that an injective module is divisible. Find a condition on A which gives the converse.

11. Show that a module $P = P_1 \oplus \cdots \oplus P_n$ is projective if and only if P_i is projective, $i = 1, \ldots, n$.

12. Show that if Q is an injective R-module, then for each left ideal of R and each module homomorphism $f: I \to Q$ there is an element $a \in Q$ such that $f(r) = ra$ for all $r \in I$.

13. Show that every R-module can be embedded in an injective R-module.

14. Show that an R-module M is injective if and only if $M \subset N$ implies that M is a direct summand of N.

15. Show that for R-modules M, M', N, N'
$$\text{Hom}(M \oplus M', N) \simeq \text{Hom}(M, N) \oplus \text{Hom}(M', N)$$
and
$$\text{Hom}(M, N \oplus N') \simeq \text{Hom}(M, N) \oplus \text{Hom}(M, N').$$

16. If R is a left Artinian ring with identity and $W(R)$ is its radical, show that an R-module M is completely reducible if and only if $W(R)M = (0)$.

17. Describe the construction of the tensor product of modules over a noncommutative ring.

18. Describe $Z_n \otimes_Z Z_m$ for $(n, m) \neq 1$.

19. If M, N are vector spaces over a field K, show that if $m_1, \ldots, m_r$ are linearly independent in M, then for $n_i \in N$, $\sum m_i \otimes n_i = 0$ implies $n_1 = \cdots = n_r = 0$.

20. If I is an ideal of a commutative ring R with identity and A is an R-module, show that
$$(R/I) \otimes A \simeq A/IA.$$

21. Show that if the exact sequence of R-modules
$$0 \to A \to B \to C \to 0$$
splits, then for any R-module D
$$0 \to D \otimes A \to D \otimes B \to D \otimes C \to 0$$
is exact.

22. Restate the definition of algebra homomorphism (given in Section 6) in terms of elements.

23. Show the equivalence of (3) and (3′) in the definition of Hopf algebra.

24. Reformulate some of the results of Chapter 1 by replacing rings by algebras and check to see whether they hold.

25. Let R be a simple ring with identity and I any nonzero left ideal in R, considered as a left R-module. Let $R' = \text{Hom}_R(I, I)$ and $R'' = \text{Hom}_{R'}(I, I)$. Then prove that $R \simeq R''$.

26. Show that if A is a K-algebra,
$$Z(A) = \{z \in A \mid za = az\}$$
is a subalgebra of A, called the *center* of A.

27. If M is a completely reducible A-module, where A is an algebra over a field K, show that $\mathrm{Hom}_A(M, M) = K$ implies that M is irreducible. Show that complete reducibility is a necessary condition for this result by letting A be the upper triangular matrices over K and M a two-dimensional vector space over K.

28. Let K be a field and G a finite group such that the characteristic of K divides the order of G. Let n be the element of the group algebra $K(G)$ given by

$$n = \sum_{x \in G} x.$$

Prove that $K(G)n$ is a submodule of $K(G)$, but not a direct summand.

29. Show that

$$N = \left\{ \sum_{x \in G} \alpha_x x \ \middle|\ \alpha_x \in K, \sum_{x \in G} \alpha_x = 0 \right\}$$

is a $K(G)$-(ring)submodule of $K(G)$. Discuss the structure of $K(G)/N$.

30. Show that for groups G_1, G_2

$$K(G_1 \oplus G_2) \simeq K(G_1) \otimes K(G_2).$$

CHAPTER 4

The Jacobson Radical

While the theory of Chapter 2 characterizes completely the structure of rings with minimal condition, it leaves out many important examples of rings, e.g., the integers. Hence there has been a series of efforts to generalize the Wedderburn-Artin structure theorems. These have had two major goals:

1) To find an analogue of the classical radical and related structure theorems for a general ring.

2) To define a "radical" for other algebraic structures: groups, near-rings, algebras, nonassociative rings, etc.

It is clear that any generalization must satisfy several requirements. First, the extended definition must coincide with the classical in the presence of a minimal condition. Second, it must have at least some of the properties of its ancestor—the ring modulo the radical should have zero radical, it should lead to a satisfactory structure theorem for "semisimple" rings, etc. We consider such "radical properties" in Chapter 5.

In this chapter we shall examine the most commonly employed definition of radical which can be applied in any ring; there are several equivalent characterizations of this radical, due to Perlis, Chevalley, and Jacobson. We shall discuss these characterizations, but not in the chronological order of their development. The earliest definitions of this radical, which were given in the 1940's, did not employ modules, but since the theory of rings has been so revolutionized by the use of modules, the current commonly used definition is in terms of modules, and it is this that we introduce first.

1. DEFINITION OF THE JACOBSON RADICAL

Let R be an arbitrary ring. If there exist irreducible R-modules, we let

$$J(R) = \bigcap_{\substack{M \text{ an irreducible} \\ R\text{-module}}} A(M),$$

where $A(M)$ is the annihilator of M in R. If R has no irreducible R-modules, we set $J(R) = R$. $J(R)$ is called the *Jacobson radical* of R. If $J(R) = R$, we say that R is a *radical ring*. We note that since we use module to mean left module, the definition is given in terms of left modules. The analogous ideal could be defined by using right R-modules. However, we shall see later that both definitions lead to the same ideal of R.

In order to establish the properties of the Jacobson radical, it will be useful to have alternative characterizations. To give the equivalent definitions, we need to devote more attention to the ideals of the ring R.

Lemma 1. Let M be an irreducible R-module. Then $M \simeq R/P$, where P is a maximal left ideal of R. Furthermore, there is an $a \in R$ such that $R(1 - a) = \{x - xa \mid x \in R\} \subset P$. (This definition is independent of the existence of an identity in R.)

Proof. By Theorem 1, Chapter 3, M is cyclic, say $M = Rm$. We define $f : R \to M$ by $f(r) = rm$. f is a surjective module homomorphism, and so $R/P \simeq M$, where P is the kernel of f.

Now let P' be a left ideal of R such that $P \subsetneq P' \subset R$. Then P'/P is isomorphic to a nonzero submodule of M, that is, $P'/P \simeq M$. Therefore $P' = R$, and P is maximal.

Since $Rm = M$, there is an $a \in R$ such that $am = m$. Then for each $x \in R$, $(x - xa)m = xm - xam = xm - xm = 0$ so $x - xa \in P$. Thus

$$R(1 - a) \subset P.$$

A left ideal P of R is called a *regular* (or *modular*) ideal if there is an $a \in R$ such that $R(1 - a) \subset P$.

Lemma 2. Every regular proper left ideal of R is contained in a maximal regular left ideal of R.

Proof. Let P be a regular proper left ideal of R and let $a \in R$ be such that $R(1 - a) \subset P$. Suppose $a \in P$ and let $x \in R$. Then $x - xa \in P$ and $xa \in P$. Hence $x \in P$ and $R \subset P$, a contradiction. Thus $a \notin P$.

By Zorn's lemma, there is an ideal P' maximal with respect to the properties:

1. $P \subset P'$,

2. $a \notin P'$.

We claim P' is actually a maximal ideal of R. For suppose $P' \subsetneq P'' \subset R$. Then $a \in P''$ and furthermore $x - xa \in P''$, $xa \in P''$. Hence $x \in P''$ and $P'' = R$.

Finally P' is a regular ideal since $R(1 - a) \subset P \subset P'$.

If P is a left ideal of a ring R, we extend the definition of the quotient of ideals:

$$R:P = \{x \in R \mid xR \subset P\}.$$

It is easy to verify that $R:P$ is also a left ideal of R. Then we have the following characterization of the Jacobson radical:

Theorem 1. $J(R) = \cap (R:P)$, where P ranges over all maximal regular left ideals of the ring R.

Proof. By Lemma 1 and the definition of $J(R)$,

$$J(R) = \cap\, A(R/P),$$

where P ranges over all maximal regular left ideals of R. We have

$$A(R/P) = \{x \in R \mid x(R/P) = (0)\}$$
$$= \{x \in R \mid xR \subseteq P\}$$
$$= R{:}P.$$

We can obtain an even simpler characterization.

Theorem 2. $J(R) = \cap\, P$, *where the intersection is over all maximal regular left ideals of the ring* R.

Proof. We let $x \in J(R)$ and let P be a maximal regular left ideal of R. Then $R(1 - a) \subset P$ for some $a \in R$. Thus $x - xa \in P$. Since $x \in J(R)$, we have $x \in R{:}P$, that is, $xR \subset P$. Hence $xa \in P$ and so $x \in P$. Thus $J(R) \subset \cap\, P$.

Now we suppose that $x \in \cap P$. $R(1 + x)$ is a regular left ideal of R. If it is proper, it is contained in a maximal regular left ideal, say P'. But $x \in P'$ and thus for all $y \in R$, $yx \in P'$, and $y + yx - yx = y \in P'$. Hence, $P' = R$, a contradiction. Therefore we have $R(1 + x) = R$, so that $-x \in R(1 + x)$, that is, there is a $y \in R$ such that $x + y + yx = 0$.

We let M be an irreducible R-module and suppose $\cap P \not\subseteq A(M)$. Then $(\cap P)M \neq (0)$ and $(\cap P)m \neq (0)$ for some $m \in M$. But then $(\cap P)m = M$. Hence $pm = -m$ for some $p \in \cap P$. We now let $s \in R$ be such that $p + s + sp = 0$. Then

$$0 = (p + s + sp)m = pm + sm + spm$$
$$= -m + sm - sm = -m,$$

so that $(\cap P)m = (0)$, a contradiction. Thus $\cap P \subset A(M)$ and hence $\cap P \subset J(R)$.

Corollary. If R is a commutative ring with identity, then $J(R) = \cap M$, where M is a maximal ideal of R.

Example. $J(Z) = \cap(p) = (0)$, p a prime.

2. PROPERTIES

The early attempts at generalization of the Wedderburn theory took the approach of investigating some property roughly similar to nilpotency and establishing the existence of a maximal ideal, a "radical" having the same relationship to this property that the classical radical has to nilpotency, namely, all one-sided ideals with the property would be contained in the "radical," the quotient ring modulo the "radical" would have no ideals with the property, etc. In connection with the Jacobson radical we shall now discuss such a property, which was used in the original characterization.

In fact we give a name to a property of elements of regular ideals which we used in the proof of the last theorem. An element $a \in R$ is *left quasi-regular* if there is an element $a' \in R$ such that $a + a' + a'a = 0$. a' is called a *left quasi-inverse* of a. A left ideal P of R is *left quasi-regular* if each of its elements is left quasi-regular. We can define right quasi-regularity similarly; an element a is *quasi-regular* if there exists $a' \in R$ such that

$$a + a' + aa' = a + a' + a'a = 0.$$

We note that if P is a left quasi-regular ideal of a ring R and a' a left quasi-inverse of $a \in P$, then $a + a' + a'a = 0$ so that $a' = -a - a'a \in P$.

We can define a binary operation on a ring R by

$$a \circ b = a + b + ba \quad \text{for} \quad a, b \in R.$$

This is associative, so R is a semigroup under this operation. The quasi-regular elements, i.e., the set of all $a \in R$ such that there exists $a' \in R$ with

$$a \circ a' = a' \circ a = 0,$$

are exactly the elements with two-sided inverses with respect to $\circ$. If we can show that this subset is closed under $\circ$, we will have that it is a group. But

$$(a \circ b) \circ (b' \circ a') = (a \circ (b \circ b')) \circ a' = a \circ a' = 0,$$

and similarly on the left, so $b' \circ a'$ is a quasi-inverse for $a \circ b$.

Theorem 3. *$J(R)$ is a left quasi-regular ideal of R and contains every left quasi-regular left ideal of R.*

Proof. Let P be a left quasi-regular left ideal of R. Let M be an irreducible R-module. Suppose $PM \neq (0)$. Then there exists $m \in M$ such that $Pm = M$. Hence there exists an $a \in P$ such that $am = -m$. Let $a' \in P$ be a left quasi-inverse of a. Then $0 = (a + a' + a'a)m = am + a'm + a'am = -m + a'm - a'm = -m$. Thus $Pm = (0)$, a contradiction. Thus $PM = (0)$, that is, $P \subset A(M)$. Therefore $P \subset J(R)$.

That $J(R)$ is left quasi-regular follows from the proof of Theorem 2.

One of the properties it is desirable for a radical to possess is that the homomorphic image of the radical of a ring be contained in the radical of the homomorphic image of the ring. But clearly left quasi-regularity is preserved under homomorphisms, so we have:

Corollary. Let f be a ring homomorphism $f: R \to R'$. Then

$$f(J(R)) \subset J(f(R)).$$

We recall from Chapter 2 that for rings with minimal condition, the maximum left, right, and two-sided nilpotent ideals coincide. We show that the analogous result holds for quasi-regular ideals in a general ring.

Lemma 1. If an element a of a ring R has a left quasi-inverse c and a right quasi-inverse b, then $b = c$.

Proof. We have $a + c + ca = 0$ and $a + b + ab = 0$. Thus

$$ab + cb + cab = 0 = ca + cb + cab,$$

so that $ab = ca$. Therefore

$$c - b = c - b + a - a + ca - ab$$
$$= (a + c + ca) - (a + b + ab) = 0.$$

Lemma 2. Every element of $J(R)$ is right quasi-regular.

Proof. Let $a \in J(R)$. Then there is an $a' \in J(R)$ such that $a + a' + a'a = 0$. Then $a' \in J(R)$ so a' has a left quasi-inverse, say a''. But a is a right quasi-inverse of a' and so by Lemma 1, $a = a''$. Thus $a + a' + aa' = 0$, that is, a' is a right quasi-inverse of a.

The lemmas give us immediately:

Theorem 4. *$J(R)$ is a right quasi-regular ideal and thus a quasi-regular ideal of R.*

If in our original exposition we replace left by right, we are led to a radical, say $J'(R)$, which contains every right quasi-regular right ideal, that is,

$$J(R) \subset J'(R).$$

But also $J'(R)$ is a left quasi-regular ideal so that $J'(R) \subset J(R)$. Hence the Jacobson radical is independent of the choice of right or left in the definition.

We have another characterization of the Jacobson radical:

Theorem 5. *$J(R) = \{z \in R \mid bza$ is quasi-regular for all $a, b \in R\}$.*

Proof. Since $J(R)$ is an ideal, if $z \in J(R)$, then $bza \in J(R)$ for all $a, b \in R$. Since $J(R)$ is a quasi-regular ideal, bza is quasi-regular. Conversely, let z be an element of R such that bza is quasi-regular for all $a, b \in R$. Let M be an irreducible R-module. Then as in the proof of Theorem 3, $za \in A(M)$ for all $a \in R$. If $0 \neq u \in M$, then $M = Ru$ and $zM = zRu = (0)$ so that $z \in A(M)$. Hence $z \in J(R)$.

We now use quasi-regularity to show that the Jacobson radical has another of the desirable properties of radicals.

Theorem 6. *$J(R/J(R)) = (0)$.*

Proof. Let $\bar{P}$ be a left quasi-regular left ideal in $R/J(R)$. Let P be its inverse image in R. Let $a \in P$, $\bar{a} = a + J(R)$. Let $b \in P$ be such that $\overline{a + b + ba} = \bar{a} + \bar{b} + \bar{b}\bar{a} = 0$. Then $a + b + ba \in J(R)$ and so is left quasi-regular. Let c be such that $a + b + ba + c + c(a + b + ba) = 0$. Then

$$a + (b + c + cb) + (b + c + cb)a = 0,$$

and thus a is left quasi-regular. Thus P is a left quasi-regular left ideal of R, and so $P \subset J(R)$, that is, $\bar{P} = (0)$. But $J(R/J(R))$ is a left quasi-regular left ideal of $R/J(R)$ so $J(R/J(R)) = (0)$.

A ring R is called (Jacobson) *semisimple* if $J(R) = (0)$.

We now look at the relation between the Jacobson and the classical radical of a ring.

Theorem 7. *Every nil left ideal (and hence every nilpotent ideal) of a ring R is contained in $J(R)$.*

Proof. If $a^n = 0$, then

$$a + (-a + a^2 - a^3 + \cdots + (-1)^{n-1}a^{n-1})$$
$$+ (-a + a^2 - a^3 + \cdots + (-1)^{n-1}a^{n-1})a = 0.$$

Hence every nil left ideal is left quasi-regular.

Theorem 8. *If R is left Artinian, then $J(R)$ is a nilpotent ideal.*

Proof. Let $J = J(R)$. Then

$$J \supset J^2 \supset J^3 \supset \cdots,$$

and so there is a positive integer n such that

$$J^n = J^{n+1} = \cdots = J^{2n} = \cdots.$$

Thus if $xJ^{2n} = (0)$, then $xJ^n = (0)$. Let $I = \{x \in J \mid xJ^n = (0)\}$. If $I \supset J^n$, then $J^{2n} = (0)$ and so $J^n = (0)$ and we are through.

Thus we suppose that $I \not\supseteq J^n$. Further suppose that $\overline{xJ^n} = (0)$ in R/I. Then $xJ^n \subset I$ and so $xJ^{2n} = (0)$. Hence $xJ^n = (0)$ and $x \in I$.

If $\overline{J^n} \neq (0)$ in R/I, since R and therefore R/I is left Artinian, $\overline{J^n}$ contains a minimal left ideal $\bar{P}$ of R/I. Either $\bar{P}\overline{J^n} = (0)$ or $\bar{P}$ is an irreducible R/I module. But in the second case we also have $\bar{P}\overline{J^n} = (0)$, since anything in J annihilates all irreducible R/I-modules. Let P be the inverse image of $\bar{P}$ in R under the canonical projection. Then by the above remarks, $P \subset I$. Hence $\bar{P} = (0)$, a contradiction. Thus we must have $\overline{J^n} = (0)$. Therefore $J^n \subset I$, and $J^n = (0)$.

Corollary. If R is left (right) Artinian, then $J(R) = W(R)$.

An element a of a ring R is *regular* (in the sense of von Neumann) if there exists an element u in R such that $aua = a$; u is called a *relative inverse* for a. If every element of a ring R is regular, R is a *regular ring*.

Example. If V is a vector space over a field K, the ring $\text{Hom}_K(V, V)$ of linear transformations of V under addition and composition is regular.

Theorem 9. *Any regular ring is semisimple.*

Proof. Suppose $a \in J(R)$, R a regular ring. Then a has a relative inverse u. Then $-ua$ has a quasi-inverse v such that $-ua + v - uav = 0$. Hence

$$0 = -aua + av - auav$$

$$= -a + av - av$$

$$= -a.$$

3. JACOBSON RADICALS OF RELATED RINGS

We recall that a classically semisimple ring must have an identity element. We have a related result for Jacobson semisimplicity. First we note (Problem 16, Chapter 1) that if R is an arbitrary ring, it can be embedded in a ring R^* with identity 1 such that $R^* = R \oplus (1)$, where (1), the ring generated by the identity, is isomorphic to Z.

Theorem 10. *Let R be an arbitrary ring and $R^* = R + (1)$, 1 an identity for R^*. Then $J(R) = J(R^*) \cap R$. If in addition $R \cap (1) = (0)$ and $(1) \simeq Z$, then $J(R) = J(R^*)$.*

Proof. Let $z \in J(R^*) \cap R$. Then z has a quasi-inverse $z' \in R^*$. Since $z' = -z - z'z$, z' is in R and z is quasi-regular in R. Hence $J(R^*) \cap R \subset J(R)$. Since $R^* = R + (1)$, any left ideal of R is a left ideal of R^*. Hence

$$J(R) \subset J(R^*) \cap R.$$

Suppose now that $R \cap (1) = (0)$ and $(1) \simeq Z$. Then if $z^* \in J(R^*)$, the coset $\bar{z}^*$ of z^* in R^*/R is in the radical of the quotient ring. But $J(Z) = (0)$, being the intersection of the maximal ideals of Z, so $\bar{z}^* = 0$ and $z^* \in R$. Therefore $J(R^*) \subset R$ and $J(R) = J(R^*)$.

Corollary. If R is semisimple, R can be embedded in a semisimple ring with identity.

Suppose we have a ring R' related to another ring R in some natural manner. We would like to have a method for finding the radical of R' in terms of that of R. An example of such a situation is the preceding theorem. We also consider the following cases:

1) R' is an ideal of R,

2) $R' = R_n$, the ring of $n \times n$ matrices over R,

3) $R' = R[x]$, the ring of polynomials in an indeterminate x with coefficients in R,

4) $R' = eRe$, where e is an idempotent in R.

Theorem 11. *If A is a (two-sided) ideal in a ring R, then $J(A) = A \cap J(R)$. In particular, if R is semisimple, then A is semisimple.*

Proof. Since every element of $A \cap J(R)$ is left quasi-regular, we have

$$A \cap J(R) \subset J(A).$$

The proof for the converse is similar to that of Theorem 6, Chapter 2. We suppose first that $J(R) = (0)$. Let $P = \{x \in R \mid Ax = (0)\}$. P is clearly a right ideal of R. $AJ(A)$ is a left ideal of R and $AJ(A) \subset J(A)$ and so $AJ(A)$ is left quasi-regular. Thus $AJ(A) \subset J(R) = (0)$. Then $J(A) \subset P \cap A$. But if $x \in P \cap A$, $x^2 = 0$ and so by the proof of Theorem 7, $x \in J(A)$. Hence $J(A) = P \cap A$. Therefore, $J(A)$ is a right ideal of R. But every element of $J(A)$ is right quasi-regular as an element of A and hence as an element of R; therefore $J(A)$ is a right quasi-regular right ideal of R. Thus $J(A) \subset J(R) = (0)$.

Now we consider the general case. $(A + J(R))/J(R)$ is an ideal in the semi-simple ring $R/J(R)$. Therefore, $J((A + J(R))/J(R)) = (0)$ and so

$$J(A/A \cap J(R)) = (0).$$

Hence $J(A) \subset A \cap J(R)$ and thus they are equal.

Theorem 12. *If $J(R)$ is the radical of a ring R, then the radical of R_n is $J(R)_n$.*

Proof. Consider a matrix of the form

$$A = \begin{pmatrix} a_{11} & 0 & \cdots & 0 \\ \cdot & & & \cdot \\ \cdot & & & \cdot \\ \cdot & & & \cdot \\ a_{n1} & 0 & \cdots & 0 \end{pmatrix},$$

where a_{11} is left quasi-regular. Then there exists a'_{11} such that $a_{11} + a'_{11} + a'_{11}a_{11} = 0$. Moreover $R(1 - a_{11}) = R$ so that there exist a'_{i1}, $i = 2, \ldots, n$, such that $a'_{i1} - a'_{i1}a_{11} = -a_{i1}$. Then if

$$A' = \begin{pmatrix} a'_{11} & 0 & \cdots & 0 \\ \cdot & & & \cdot \\ \cdot & & & \cdot \\ \cdot & & & \cdot \\ a'_{n1} & 0 & \cdots & 0 \end{pmatrix},$$

$A + A + A'A = 0$; thus A is left quasi-regular.

Now let J_j be the set of elements $A \in R_n$ with all entries except possibly the jth column zero and the jth column consisting of elements of $J(R)$. Each J_j is a left ideal and by arguments analogous to the one above for $j = 1$, they are left quasi-regular. Hence $J_j \subset J(R_n)$, for $j = 1, \ldots, n$. Thus

$$J(R)_n = J_1 + \cdots + J_n \subset J(R_n).$$

On the other hand, let $C = (c_{ij})$ belong to $J(R_n)$. If $a \in R$, let A_{pq} be the matrix with a in the (p, q) position and zeros elsewhere. Let a, b be arbitrary elements of R. Form

$$\sum A_{kp} CB_{qk} = \begin{pmatrix} ac_{pq}b & 0 & \cdots & & 0 \\ 0 & & & & \\ & & \ddots & & \vdots \\ \vdots & & & \ddots & \\ & & & & 0 \\ 0 & \cdots & & 0 & ac_{pq}b \end{pmatrix}$$

But $C \in J(R_n)$ and hence $\sum A_{kp} CB_{qk} \in J(R_n)$. Let (c'_{ij}) be the quasi-inverse of $\sum A_{kp} CB_{qk}$, so that

$$ac_{pq}b + c'_{11} + c'_{11}ac_{pq}b = 0$$

$$= ac_{pq}b + c'_{11} + ac_{pq}bc'_{11}.$$

Thus $ac_{pq}b$ is quasi-regular for all $a, b \in R$. But then by Theorem 5, $c_{pq} \in J(R)$. Thus $J(R_n) \subset J(R)_n$ and hence $J(R_n) = J(R)_n$.

Unfortunately the results in the case of polynomial rings are not so straight-forward. We shall need the following:

Lemma. Let I be a nonzero ideal in $R[x]$ and

$$p(x) = a_0 + a_1 x + \cdots + a_n x^n, \quad a_n \neq 0,$$

be a polynomial of least degree belonging to I. Suppose $r(x)$ is a polynomial such that $a_n^m r(x) = 0$, $m \geq 1$. Then $a_n^{m-1} p(x) r(x) = 0$.

Proof. That $a_n^m r(x) = 0$ is equivalent to $a_n^m r_i = 0$, $0 \leq i \leq$ degree $r(x)$, where r_i is the coefficient of x^i in $r(x)$, is clear. Thus it is sufficient to consider the case degree $r(x) = 0$. But then $a_n^{m-1} p(x) r$ has $a_n^m r$ ($= 0$) as the coefficient of x^n. But since I is an ideal, $a_n^{m-1} p(x) r \in I$; it cannot be a polynomial of degree $< n$, so we must have $a_n^{m-1} p(x) = 0$.

Now we can prove:

Theorem 13. *If a ring R has no nonzero nil ideals, then $R[x]$ is semisimple.*

Proof. Let M be the set of nonzero polynomials of least degree belonging to $J(R[x])$. Consider the ideal N formed by the leading coefficients of these polynomials. We shall show that N is a nil ideal.

Let $p(x) = a_0 + a_1 x + \cdots + a_n x^n \in M$. Then $xp(x)a_n$ is quasi-regular, so there exists $q(x)$ such that

$$xp(x)a_n + q(x) + xp(x)a_n q(x) = 0$$

and

$$xp(x)a_n + q(x) + q(x)xp(x)a_n = 0.$$

But then the constant term of $q(x)$ must be zero. Let $t(x)$ be the polynomial obtained by replacing x^{i+1} by x^i in the expression for $q(x)$. Then we have

$$(*) \qquad p(x)a_n + t(x) + xp(x)a_n t(x) = 0$$

and

(∗∗) $$p(x)a_n + t(x) + t(x)xp(x)a_n = 0.$$

We now show that

$$a_n^k t(x) = 0 \qquad \text{for sufficiently large } k.$$

Assume that $a_n^k t(x) \neq 0$ for $k = 1, 2, \ldots$. Let m be the least degree of these polynomials and write

$$t(x) = t_1(x) + x^{m+1}t_2(x),$$

where $t_1(x), t_2(x) \in R[x]$, and $t_1(x) = b_0 + b_1 x + \cdots + b_m x^m$. Then

$$a_n^k t_2(x) = 0 \qquad \text{for sufficiently large } k,$$

but

$$a_n^k b_m \neq 0, \qquad k = 1, 2, \ldots.$$

By the lemma and the fact that $p(x)a_n$ has leading coefficient a_n^2, we obtain

$$a_n^j t_2(x) = 0 = a_n^j p(x)a_n t_2(x)$$

for a suitable j. Multiplying (∗) by a_n^j gives

$$a_n^j p(x)a_n + a_n^j t_1(x) + a_n^j x p(x)a_n t_1(x) = 0.$$

We note that the coefficient of x^{n+m+1} is $a_n^{j+2}b_m$. Hence $a_n^{j+2}b_m = 0$, which contradicts the fact that $a_n^k b_m \neq 0$ for all k. Thus $a_n^i t(x) = 0$ for some i.

Multiplying (∗∗) on the left by a_n^i now gives

$$a_n^i p(x)a_n = 0.$$

Hence $a_n^{i+2} = 0$. But a_n was an arbitrary element of N, so N is a nil ideal; therefore $N = (0)$ and so there are no nonzero polynomials in $J(R[x])$, that is, $R[x]$ is semisimple.

There are rings which are not semisimple but which contain no nonzero nil ideals. For example, the ring $F\langle x \rangle$ of formal power series in one indeterminate with coefficients in a field F; the nonunits of $F\langle x \rangle$ are the elements of the ideal (x), which is the radical of $F\langle x \rangle$. For such a ring R, $R[x]$ is semisimple even though R is not.

If R is a commutative ring, then the radical of $R[x]$ is a nil ideal which contains all nil ideals of $R[x]$. Since

$$R[x]/J(R)[x] \simeq (R/J(R))[x]$$

and $R/J(R)$ has no nonzero nil ideal, we can apply the preceding theorem to get that the radical of $R[x]$ is $J(R)[x]$.

We have previously encountered idempotent elements in the discussion of the structure of rings with minimal condition, particularly semisimple Artinian rings. However, idempotents are also useful in the study of general rings.

Let R be a ring, e an idempotent in R. Since any element $r \in R$ can be written as

$$r = er + (r - er),$$

we have $R = eR + (1 - e)R$, where $(1 - e)R = \{r - er \mid e \in R\}$ as before. But $eb = b$ for all $b \in eR$ and $eb = 0$ for all $b \in (1 - e)R$, so that

$$eR \cap (1 - e)R = (0)$$

and thus

$$R = eR \oplus (1 - e)R$$
$$= Re \oplus R(1 - e).$$

We can also write

$$R = eRe \oplus eR(1 - e) \oplus (1 - e)Re \oplus (1 - e)R(1 - e).$$

These representations are called the right, left, and two-sided *Peirce decompositions of R relative to e*, respectively. We note that the terms of the first two are right and left ideals, respectively, while those of the third are subrings of R. Moreover,

$$eRe = eR \cap Re,$$
$$eR(1 - e) = eR \cap R(1 - e),$$
$$(1 - e)Re = (1 - e)R \cap Re,$$
$$(1 - e)R(1 - e) = (1 - e)R \cap R(1 - e).$$

Theorem 14. *Let R be an arbitrary ring, $J(R)$ its Jacobson radical. Then $eJ(R)e = eRe \cap J(R)$ is the radical of eRe and $(1 - e)J(R)(1 - e) = (1 - e)R(1 - e) \cap J(R)$ is the radical of $(1 - e)R(1 - e)$.*

Proof. It is clear that $eRe \cap J(R) = eJ(R)e$ and that this is a quasi-regular ideal in eRe. Hence $eJ(R)e \subset J(eRe)$. Suppose $z \in J(eRe)$. Using the two-sided Peirce decomposition of R, we write $r \in R$ as

$$r = r_{11} + r_{10} + r_{01} + r_{00},$$

where $r_{11} \in eRe$, $r_{10} \in eR(1 - e)$, $r_{01} \in (1 - e)Re$, and $r_{00} \in (1 - e)R(1 - e)$. Then

$$zr = zr_{11} + zr_{10},$$

since

$$zr_{01} = zer_{01} = zr_{00} = zer_{00} = 0.$$

Now zr_{11} has a quasi-inverse, say z', in eRe. Since $zr_{10}z' = 0$, we have

$$zr + z' + zrz' = zr_{10}.$$

Moreover, $(zr_{10})^2 = 0$ and hence by Theorem 7, zr_{10} is quasi-regular. Therefore zr is quasi-regular for every $r \in R$, since the quasi-regular elements of R form a group under the circle composition. Thus $zR \subset J(R)$. Hence bza is quasi-regular for every $a, b \in R$. But then $z \in J(R)$ and $z \in eRe \cap J(R) = eJ(R)e$. Thus $J(eRe) = eJ(R)e$. The proof for $(1 - e) R(1 - e)$ is analogous.

4. PRIMITIVE RINGS

We are now faced with finding an analogous property to simplicity in rings; we want a type of ring to use as a building block in a construction, similar to direct sum, which will give us a characterization of radical-free rings. Also, we need a generalization of matrix rings in order to develop a complete structure theory analogous to that for rings with minimal condition. The required notions are those of primitivity and of a dense ring of linear transformations.

An R-module M is *faithful* if $aM = (0)$ for $a \in R$ implies that $a = 0$. A ring R is *primitive* if it has a faithful, irreducible module. An ideal P of R is *primitive* if the ring R/P is primitive.

We now connect this concept with the notion of radical we have developed for a general ring.

Lemma. An ideal P in a ring R is primitive if and only if $P = R:Q$, where Q is a maximal regular left ideal of R.

Proof. Let Q be a maximal regular left ideal of R. Then R/Q is clearly a faithful, irreducible $R/(R:Q)$-module, so $R:Q$ is primitive.

On the other hand, let P be a primitive ideal of R and let M be a faithful, irreducible (R/P)-module. Then M is an R-module and, in fact, is an irreducible R-module. As an (R/P)-module M is faithful, so its annihilator is the zero submodule of R/P. Thus the annihilator of M, considering M as an R-module, is P. Then as in the proof of Theorem 1, $P = R:Q$, where Q is a maximal regular left ideal of R.

Corollary. $J(R) = \cap P$, where P ranges over all primitive ideals of R (the empty intersection is taken to be all of R).

Theorem 15. *A commutative ring is primitive if and only if it is a field.*

Proof. Let R be a commutative primitive ring and I a maximal regular left ideal such that $R:I = (0)$. But R is commutative, so I is a two-sided ideal and $I = R:I = (0)$, that is, (0) is a maximal regular left ideal of R, so that R is simple. Since I is regular, R has an identity. But a commutative simple ring with identity is a field.

Actually a stronger converse holds, namely: any division ring R is primitive since it is itself a faithful, irreducible R-module.

Theorem 16. *If R is primitive, then eRe and $(1 - e)R(1 - e)$ are primitive.*

Proof. Our proof will be for eRe; that for $(1 - e)R(1 - e)$ is similar.

Let M be a faithful, irreducible R-module and write

$$M = eM \oplus (1 - e)M.$$

Then eM is clearly an eRe-module. Since $ere(1 - e)M = (0)$, if $ereeM = (0)$, then $ere \in A(M)$. Hence eM is faithful as an eRe-module.

Now we let $ex \neq 0$ and $ey \in eM$. There exists $r \in R$ such that $r(ex) = ey$. But then $(ere)(ex) = ey$ and eM is eRe-irreducible, since any nonzero element generates all of eM.

5. THE DENSITY THEOREM

Let M be an R-module and let $E(M)$ be the ring of all the endomorphisms of the additive group of M with the obvious addition and multiplication. If $r \in R$, we define $T_r \in E(M)$ by $T_r m = rm$. The set

$$C_R(M) = \{f \in E(M) \,|\, fT_r = T_r f \text{ for all } r \in R\}$$

is a subring of $E(M)$ called the *commuting ring* of R on M.

Theorem 17 (Schur's Lemma). *If M is an irreducible R-module, then $C_R(M)$ is a division ring.*

Proof. Let $f \in C_R(M)$ and suppose $f \neq 0$. Then $f(M)$ is a submodule of M. But $f \neq 0$ so $f(M) = M$. Now let $N = \text{kernel } f$. N is a submodule of M so $N = (0)$ or $N = M$. But $f(M) \neq (0)$ so $N = (0)$. Thus f is an automorphism and has an inverse in $E(M)$. But this inverse is clearly also in $C_R(M)$.

If R is a primitive ring and M a faithful, irreducible R-module, then M can be regarded as a left vector space over the division ring $C_R(M)$.

R is a *dense ring of linear transformations* on M if, given any $v_1, \ldots, v_n \in M$ which are linearly independent over $C_R(M)$ and any $w_1, \ldots, w_n \in M$, there is an $r \in R$ such that $rv_i = w_i$, $i = 1, \ldots, n$. We sometimes say simply that R is *dense* on M.

Theorem 18 (Jacobson Density Theorem). *Let R be a ring and M be an irreducible R-module. Then, considering M as a left vector space over $C_R(M)$, R is a dense ring of linear transformations on M.*

Proof. It is sufficient to prove the following:

(∗) if V is a finite-dimensional subspace of M over $C_R(M)$ and if $m \in M$, $m \notin V$, then there is an $r \in R$ such that $rV = (0)$ but $rm \neq 0$.

For suppose we can always find such an r. Since $rm \neq 0$, we can apply the statement to the 0-subspace and rm. Thus we can find $r_1 \in R$ such that $r_1 rm \neq 0$. Since $Rrm \neq (0)$, we must have $Rrm = M$. Thus, given any $m_1 \in M$, we can find $s \in R$ such that $srV = (0)$ and $srm = m_1$.

If we are given $v_1, \ldots, v_n \in M$, linearly independent over $C_R(M)$ and $w_1, \ldots, w_n \in M$, we can, by virtue of the above argument, find $r_1, \ldots, r_n \in R$ such that

$$r_i v_j = \begin{cases} 0 & \text{if } j \neq i, \\ w_i & \text{if } j = i. \end{cases}$$

Let $r = r_1 + \cdots + r_n$. Then for $i = 1, \ldots, n$,

$$rv_i = (r_1 + \cdots + r_n)v_i = r_1v_i + \cdots + r_nv_i$$
$$= r_iv_i = w_i.$$

Thus R is dense on M.

We now establish (∗) by induction on the dimension of V.

First suppose dim $V = 0$, and let $m \in M$, $m \neq 0$. Then $V = (0)$ and we choose an element $r \in R$ such that $rm \neq 0$; the existence of such an r is guaranteed by the irreducibility of M.

Now suppose dim $V > 0$ and let $V = V_0 \oplus C_R(M)w$, $w \neq 0$, $w \notin V_0$. Then dim $V_0 = \dim V - 1$ and we assume that the statement holds for V_0, that is, we assume that for any $m \in M$, $m \notin V_0$, there is an $r \in R$ such that $rV_0 = 0$ and $rm \neq 0$.

Let $A(V_0)$ be the annihilator of V_0 in R. Then if $A(V_0)m = (0)$ for $m \in M$, we must have $m \in V_0$. $A(V_0)$ is a left ideal of R and so $A(V_0)w$ is a submodule of M. Since $w \notin V_0$, $A(V_0)w \neq (0)$, so we have $A(V_0)w = M$.

Suppose the desired result does not hold. Then there is an $m \in M$, $m \notin V$, such that $rm = 0$ whenever $rV = 0$. Define $T: M \to M$ as follows: for $x \in M$ with $x = aw$, $a \in A(V_0)$, set $Tx = am$. If $x = a_1w$, $a_1 \in A(V_0)$, then $(a - a_1)w = 0$ and since $(a - a_1)V_0 = (0)$, we have $(a - a_1)V = (0)$. Thus $(a - a_1)m = 0$, that is, $am = a_1m$, so T is well defined. Clearly $T \in E(M)$. If $x = aw$, $a \in A(V_0)$, and $r \in R$, then $rx = r(aw) = (ra)w$. Thus

$$T(rx) = (ra)m = r(am) = r(Tx).$$

Therefore $T \in C_R(M)$.

Hence if $a \in A(V_0)$, we have

$$am = T(aw) = a(Tw) \qquad \text{so that} \qquad a(m - Tw) = 0.$$

Thus $m - Tw \in V_0$ and so $m \in V_0 \oplus C_R(M)w = V$, a contradiction.

Let R be a ring of linear transformations on a vector space V over a division ring D. R is *k-fold transitive* if, given $i \leq k$ and any $v_1, \ldots, v_i \in V$ linearly independent over D, and any $w_1, \ldots, w_i \in V$, there is an $r \in R$ such that $rv_1 = w_1, \ldots, rv_i = w_i$.

In this terminology the Jacobson density theorem says that under the hypotheses of that theorem, R is n-fold transitive for any finite n less than or equal to the dimension of M over $C_R(M)$. We have the following strong converse of the density theorem.

> **Theorem 19.** *Let R be a twofold transitive ring of linear transformations on a nontrivial vector space V over a division ring D. Then V is an irreducible R-module, R is dense on V, and $D = C_R(V)$.*

Proof. Let $v \in V$, $v \neq 0$. Since R is one-fold transitive, given any $w \in V$, there is an element $r \in R$ such that $rv = w$. But this implies that V is an irreducible R-module. We consider elements of D as linear transformations of

V by identifying an element with the left translation by that element. Since $d(rv) = r(dv)$ for all $v \in V$, $r \in R$, $d \in D$, $D \subset C_R(V)$.

Suppose we have $f \in C_R(V)$, $f \notin D$. Let $v \in V$, $v \neq 0$. Suppose v and fv are not linearly independent, i.e., suppose we can find d_1, $d_2 \in D$, not both zero, such that $d_1 v + d_2(fv) = 0$. If $d_1 = 0$, then $d_2(fv) = 0$ and $d_2 \neq 0$. Hence $fv = 0$ and since $f \neq 0$ and V is irreducible, $v = 0$, a contradiction. Thus $d_1 \neq 0$ and similarly $d_2 \neq 0$.

Let $d = -d_1^{-1}d_2$ so that $v = d(fv)$. Therefore $(1 - fd)v = 0$. If $(1 - fd) \in D$, then $f \in D$, so $(1 - fd) \notin D$ and hence $1 - fd \neq 0$. So as before $v = 0$, a contradiction.

Since v and fv are thus linearly independent, there is an $r \in R$ such that $rv = 0$ and $r(fv) = v$. However, since $f \in C_R(V)$, we have

$$v = r(fv) = f(rv) = 0,$$

a contradiction. Therefore, we cannot have $f \in C_R(V) \setminus D$, that is, $C_R(V) = D$. The density of R on V follows from the density theorem.

We are now ready to characterize primitivity as Theorem 15, Chapter 2, characterized simplicity.

Theorem 20. *Let R be a primitive ring. Then for some division ring D, either $R \simeq D_n$ for some finite n or, given any positive integer m, there is a subring S_m of R and a surjective ring homomorphism $S_m \rightarrow D_m$.*

Proof. By the density theorem, R is a dense ring of linear transformations on a vector space V over a division ring D. If $\dim V = n$, then by the density of R on V, we must have $R \simeq D_n$.

Suppose $\dim V$ is not finite. Then given any positive integer m, we can find m linearly independent elements $v_1, \ldots, v_m \in V$. Let V_m be the subspace generated by $v_1, \ldots, v_m$. Let $S_m = \{x \in R \mid xV_m \subset V_m\}$. Thus S_m is precisely the set of all elements of R which induce linear transformations of V_m. By the density of R on V, every linear transformation is induced in this way. Therefore, we have a surjective homomorphism $S_m \rightarrow D_m$.

In Chapter 5 we shall discuss a different generalization of the classical radical which uses a stronger condition on rings than primitivity, that of *primeness.* We recall that a ring R is prime if whenever A, B are ideals of R and $AB = (0)$, then either $A = (0)$ or $B = (0)$. This is equivalent to each of the following:

1) The left annihilator of a nonzero left ideal is the zero ideal.

2) The right annihilator of a nonzero right ideal is the zero ideal.

3) Whenever $aRb = (0)$, a, $b \in R$, then either $a = 0$ or $b = 0$.

Theorem 21. *A primitive ring is a prime ring.*

Proof. Let P be a nonzero left ideal of R and suppose $bP = (0)$. Let M be a faithful, irreducible R-module. Then $PM \neq (0)$, and so $PM = M$. But then $bM = (bP)M = (0)$. Thus $b = 0$.

We conclude this section with a related property of primitive rings.

Theorem 22. *The center Z of a primitive ring R is an integral domain.*

Proof. Let $a, b \in Z$, $a \neq 0$, and $ab = 0$. Then $(0) = abR = aRb$. Therefore $b = 0$.

6. STRUCTURE THEOREMS

Let $\{R_\alpha\}_{\alpha \in A}$ be a family of rings. We denote by $\prod R_\alpha$ the set of all A-tuples $\{x_\alpha\}$, where $x_\alpha \in R_\alpha$. We define pointwise addition and multiplication which make $\prod R_\alpha$ into a ring, called the *strong direct sum* (or direct product) of $\{R_\alpha\}_{\alpha \in A}$. (See Chapter 3, Section 2, for the analogous construction for modules.)

For each $\beta \in A$ we define $\pi_\beta : \prod R_\alpha \to R_\beta$ by $\pi_\beta(\{x_\alpha\}) = x_\beta$. Each π_β is surjective and is called the *βth-projection*.

A ring R is a *subdirect sum* of a family of rings $\{R_\alpha\}_{\alpha \in A}$ if there is an injective homomorphism

$$f : R \to \prod R_\alpha$$

such that for each $\beta \in A$

$$\pi_\beta f : R \to R_\beta$$

is a surjective homomorphism.

Lemma. Let R be a ring and let $\{R_\alpha\}_{\alpha \in A}$ be a family of rings. Then R is a subdirect sum of $\{R_\alpha\}_{\alpha \in A}$ if and only if for each $\beta \in A$ there is a surjective homomorphism

$$g_\beta : R \to R_\beta$$

such that

$$\bigcap_{\alpha \in A} \text{kernel } g_\alpha = (0).$$

Proof. Sufficiency. We define $f : R \to \prod R_\alpha$ by

$$f(r) = \{g_\beta(r)\}.$$

Then for each β, $\pi_\beta f(r) = g_\beta(r)$ and so $\pi_\beta f$ is surjective, since g_β is. Let $r \in \text{kernel } f$. Then $g_\alpha(r) = 0$ for all α, that is, $r \in \bigcap_{\alpha \in A} \text{kernel } g_\alpha$. Hence $r = 0$ and so f is injective.

Necessity. We let f and π_β be as in the definition of subdirect sum. Setting $g_\beta = \pi_\beta f$, we get that each g_β is surjective.

Let $r \in \cap \text{kernel } g_\alpha$. Suppose $r \neq 0$. Then we have $f(r) \neq 0$ and so for some β, $\pi_\beta f(r) = g_\beta(r) \neq 0$. But then $r \notin \text{kernel } g_\beta$ and hence $r \notin \bigcap_{\alpha \in A} \text{kernel } g_\alpha$, a contradiction. Thus $\bigcap_{\alpha \in A} \text{kernel } g_\alpha = (0)$.

Corollary. Let R be a ring and let $\{P_\alpha\}_{\alpha \in A}$ be a family of ideals of R. If $\bigcap_{\alpha \in A} P_\alpha = (0)$, then R is a subdirect sum of the family of rings $\{R/P_\alpha\}_{\alpha \in A}$.

Theorem 23. *A ring R is semisimple if and only if it is a subdirect sum of primitive rings.*

Proof. The necessity follows from the corollary above and the corollary preceding Theorem 15.

To show the sufficiency we suppose that R is a subdirect sum of a family $\{R_\alpha\}_{\alpha \in A}$ of primitive rings. Let $g_\beta : R \to R_\beta$ be the surjective homomorphism of the lemma. For each β, $R/\text{kernel } g_\beta \simeq R_\beta$ and R_β is primitive. Hence kernel g_β is a primitive ideal of R. Thus $J(R) \subset \text{kernel } g_\beta$ for each β, and hence $J(R) \subset \bigcap_{\alpha \in A} \text{kernel } g_\alpha = (0)$.

We have previously observed (corollary to Theorem 8) that the Jacobson and Wedderburn radicals coincide in Artinian rings. We also have:

Theorem 24. *If a ring R is left (right) Artinian, then the following statements are equivalent:*

1) *R is primitive.*

2) *R is simple.*

3) *R is isomorphic to the full ring of linear transformations of a finite-dimensional vector space over a division ring D, that is, $R \simeq D_n$ for some positive integer n.*

Proof

(1) $\Rightarrow$ (3). Let M be a faithful, irreducible R-module. By the Jacobson density theorem, (3) will follow if we can show that M is finite dimensional over $C_R(M)$.

Suppose that it is not. Then there is an infinite sequence $x_1, x_2, \ldots$ of elements of M such that for any k, $x_1, \ldots, x_k$ are linearly independent over $C_R(M)$. Let

$$I_k = \{r \in R \mid rx_1 = \cdots = rx_k = 0\}.$$

I_k is a left ideal of R and we have a descending sequence

$$I_1 \supset I_2 \supset \cdots.$$

But then there is an n such that $I_n = I_{n+1}$. This means that

$$rx_1 = \cdots = rx_{n+1} = 0$$

whenever $rx_1 = \cdots = rx_n = 0$. But by the density theorem there is an $r \in R$ such that $rx_1 = \cdots = rx_n = 0$ and $rx_{n+1} \neq 0$, a contradiction. Hence (3) follows.

(3) $\Rightarrow$ (2). Theorem 15, Chapter 2.

(2) $\Rightarrow$ (1). Suppose $J(R) \neq (0)$ and R is simple. Then $J(R) = R$, but since $J(R)$ is, by Theorem 8, nilpotent, $J(R)^2 \neq R$. Thus $R^2 = J(R)^2 = (0)$, a contradiction of the simplicity of R. Hence $J(R) = (0)$ and so R has a primitive ideal $P \neq R$. But R is simple so $P = (0)$ and $R \simeq R/P$ is primitive.

PROBLEMS

1. Show that any integral domain can be the center of a primitive ring.

2. Show that if R is a ring with identity such that the nonunits of R form an ideal N, then N is the Jacobson radical of R.

3. Give an example of a ring without minimal condition and with nonzero Jacobson radical.

4. Give an example of a (Jacobson) radical ring and of a (Jacobson) semisimple ring (without minimal condition and other than Z).

5. If R_S is the full ring of quotients of a ring R, what is $J(R_S)$ in terms of $J(R)$?

6. Give an example of a primitive ring and of a subdirect sum of primitive rings.

7. Show that an ideal I of a ring R is regular if and only if $I = \{m\}_l$, where m is a generator of a cyclic R-module M. Show that if M is irreducible, $\{m\}_l$ is maximal.

8. Show that a prime ring with a minimal left ideal is primitive.

9. Prove the equivalence of the definitions of prime ring given before Theorem 21.

CHAPTER 5

Other Radicals and Radical Properties

In this chapter we discuss other generalizations of the classical radical. As listed by Amitsur, the main properties that it is desirable for a radical to satisfy are:

1) The radical exists in every ring.
2) If N is the radical of R, the radical of R/N is the zero ideal of R/N.
3) The radical of an ideal is the intersection of the ideal and the radical of the whole ring.
4) The radical also contains certain one-sided ideals.
5) The radical of a matrix ring over a ring R is the matrix ring over the radical of R.

We shall examine various of these properties in connection with the radicals we discuss in this chapter. We have already observed that the classical radical satisfies all but (1) and that the Jacobson radical satisfies all of these requirements. The other radicals we shall introduce were defined for the purpose of securing property (1), or at least extending the existence of a radical to a larger class of rings than those with minimal or maximal conditions, while retaining the other properties.

The generalizations of Chapters 6 and 7 extend the radical to algebraic systems other than rings, with, in some cases, an accompanying loss of the other characteristics.

1. RADICAL IDEALS

Baer has defined the notion of radical ideal as follows: A subset P of a ring R is a *radical ideal* if

1) P is an ideal.
2) P is a nil ideal.
3) R/P has no nonzero nilpotent right ideals.

The sum of all ideals in R satisfying (1) and (2) is the *upper radical* of R and is denoted by $U(R) = U$. The intersection of all those ideals in R satisfying (1) and (3) is the *lower radical* of R, $L(R) = L$.

Theorem 1. *The upper and lower radicals of R are radical ideals in R.*

Proof. It is clear that U and L are ideals in R. U, being the sum of nil ideals, is itself nil. Let I be the unique ideal such that $U \subset I$ and $I/U = N(R/U)$, where $N(R/U)$ is the sum of the nilpotent ideals of R/U. Then there exists a positive integer n such that $x^n \in U$ for all $x \in I$. But then I is a nil ideal and $I \subset U$. Hence $I = U$ and $N(R/U) = (0)$. Thus U satisfies (1), (2), and (3).

Turning our attention to L, we note that L is nil since $L \subset U$. We let I/L be a nilpotent right ideal in R/L, where $L \subset I \subset R$. Then there is an integer t such that $I^t \subset L$. Suppose that J is any ideal in R satisfying (3). Then $L \subset J$ and $((I + J)/J)^t = (0)$ since $(I + J)^t \subset I^t + J^t \subset L + J = J$. From (3), $(I + J)/J = (0)$ and $I \subset J$. Hence $I \subset L$, that is, $I/L = (0)$. Hence L is a radical ideal in R.

We note that as a consequence of the definition, all radical ideals lie between L and U; the converse is not true.

There is also a constructive procedure for arriving at L:

i) $Q(0) = (0)$.

ii) Suppose that the ideal $Q(u)$ has been defined for u less than v.

Case 1. If $v = w + 1$ is not a limit ordinal, then $Q(v)$ is the uniquely determined ideal in R which contains $Q(w)$ and which satisfies $Q(v)/Q(w) = N(R/Q(w))$, where again N is used to denote the sum of the nilpotent ideals; clearly $Q(v)$ is an ideal in R.

Case 2. If v is a limit ordinal, then we denote by $Q(v)$ the union of all the ideals $Q(u)$ for u less than v. Then $Q(v)$ is an ideal in R.

iii) Since the $Q(v)$ form an ascending chain of ideals in R, there exists a smallest ordinal z such that $Q(z) = Q(z + 1)$. We set $Q(z) = Q$.

Clearly Q is an ideal in R and R/Q has no nonzero nilpotent right ideals. Hence from the definition of L, $L \subset Q$.

Now suppose that an ideal T satisfies (3). It is clear that $Q(0) \subset T$ and thus we assume $Q(u) \subset T$ for u less than v. Then also $Q(v) \subset T$, and thus by transfinite induction $Q \subset T$. But then $Q \subset L$. Thus Q is the lower radical of R.

If $U(R) = L(R)$, we denote this ideal by $B(R)$ and call it the *Baer radical* of the ring R. This radical is not necessarily nilpotent and since there are rings where $U \neq L$, see, for example, Baer [1], this radical is not defined for all rings.

We also have an additional characterization of the upper radical.

Theorem 2. *If T is a radical ideal in a ring R and if every nonzero ideal in R/T contains a minimal right ideal, then T is the upper radical of R.*

Proof. Suppose J is a nil ideal in R, $J \not\subset T$. Then there exists an ideal V, $T \subset V \subset T + J$, such that V/T is a minimal right ideal in R/T. But $V/T \subset (T + J)/T$ and J is a nilideal, so V/T is a nilideal. V/T, being minimal, is either nilpotent or idempotent. Since T is a radical ideal, V/T is idempotent. But then V/T has a nonzero idempotent element, contradicting the fact that it is nil. Hence T contains every nilideal in R and must contain U, the sum of all the nilideals of R. On the other hand, since T is a radical ideal, it is contained in U.

Baer also defines an *antiradical* $M(R)$ as the sum of all the minimal right ideals of a ring R; $M(R) = (0)$ if there are no minimal right ideals in R. The terminology is due to the fact that the radical ideals and the antiradical annihilate each other.

We define an ascending chain of ideals by transfinite induction:

i) $M_1 = M(R)$.

ii) M_{v+1} is the uniquely determined ideal in R such that $M_v \subset M_{v+1}$ and $M(R/M_v) = M_{v+1}/M_v$.

iii) If v is a limit ordinal, M_v is the union of all ideals M_u for u less than v.

iv) There exists a smallest ordinal $m = m(R)$ such that $M_m = M_{m+1}$.

Theorem 3. $R = M_m$ (*for m a finite or infinite ordinal*) *if and only if every quotient ring of R satisfies the following condition:*

(∗) *Every nonzero right ideal contains a minimal right ideal.*

Proof. Sufficiency. If the condition is satisfied by every quotient ring of R and if $M_v \subsetneqq R$, then R/M_v contains a minimal right ideal so that $M_v \subsetneqq M_{v+1}$. But $M_m = M_{m+1}$ for some ordinal m.

Necessity. If $R = M_m$ for some ordinal m and if T is an ideal different from R, it is possible to construct a well-ordered ascending chain of right ideals $J(v)$ with the following properties:

i) $J(0) = (0)$.

ii) $J(v) \subsetneqq J(v + 1)$ and there does not exist a right ideal J satisfying

$$J(v) \subsetneqq J \subsetneqq J(v + 1).$$

iii) If v is a limit ordinal, then $J(v)$ is the union of all the right ideals $J(u)$ for u less than v.

iv) $J(w) = R$ for some finite or infinite ordinal w.

If J is some right ideal in R such that $T \subsetneqq J$, we want to show that J/T contains a minimal right ideal of R/T. There exists a smallest ordinal z such that $T \subsetneqq J \cap J(z)$, since $T \subsetneqq J \cap J(w) = J$. Obviously from (iii), z is not a limit ordinal. Moreover, $(J \cap J(z))/T$ is a minimal right ideal of R/T, as was to be shown.

Corollary. If $R = M_m$ for some ordinal m, then the radical $B(R)$ of R exists.

Proof. If $R = M_m$, then it follows from Theorem 3 that $(*)$ is satisfied by R/L. Hence from the fact that U and L are radical ideals and from Theorem 2, $U = L = B(R)$.

We note that $R = M_m$ implies that R is right Artinian, and in fact if R is right or left Artinian, the Baer radical exists and coincides with the classical radical.

2. THE LEVITZKI RADICAL

We shall define another property of ideals and again take as our radical the maximum ideal with this property. The approach of this section is the generalization of the classical theory which is most closely connected to the original— one might say that this is the "obvious" generalization.

Levitzki called an ideal *semi-nilpotent* if each ring generated by a finite set of elements belonging to the ideal is nilpotent. An ideal which is not semi-nilpotent is called *semiregular*. Nilpotent ideals are semi-nilpotent, of course, and semi-nilpotent ideals are nil.

Theorem 4. *The sum I of two semi-nilpotent left ideals I_1 and I_2 is a semi-nilpotent left ideal.*

Proof. Suppose I is semiregular, i.e., I contains a finite set of elements $r_1, \ldots, r_n$ such that the ring I' generated by these elements is not nilpotent. Write

$$r_i = r_{1i} + r_{2i} \qquad \text{where} \qquad r_{ji} \in I_j.$$

The ring I'' generated by the r_{ji} is not nilpotent since I' is contained in it.

Define a set $s_1, \ldots, s_m$ as follows:

1) each s_i is either an r_{1i} or an r_{2i},

2) the ring generated by a proper subset of the s_i is nilpotent.

Since each I_i is semi-nilpotent, m is at least two. Now let T be the ring generated by all the s_i and U the ring generated by the r_i with i greater than one; U is nilpotent while T is not. Let r be such that $s_1^r = 0$ and p be such that $U^p = (0)$. We denote by $w_1, \ldots, w_s$ the finite set of all elements of the form

$$s_{i_1} \cdots s_{i_t} s_1^d, \qquad 0 < d < r, \quad 0 < t < p, \quad i_j \neq 1 \quad \text{for} \quad j = 1, \ldots, t.$$

Since T is not nilpotent, it follows that for each positive integer q, elements $v_1, \ldots, v_q$ can be found so that each v_i is a certain s_k and the product $v_1 \cdots v_q$ is different from zero.

From the definitions of r and p it follows that if $q > r$ and $q > p$, then the set $\{v_1, \ldots, v_q\}$ necessarily contains s_1 as well as elements different from s_1.

Hence by choosing an arbitrary integer y and fixing q so that q is greater than $(r + p)(y + 2)$, we have

$$v_1 \cdots v_q = fg_1 \cdots g_y h, \qquad \text{where} \qquad f, h \in T, \quad g_i \in \{w_1, \ldots, w_s\}.$$

Since $g_1 \cdots g_y \neq 0$, it follows that the ring generated by the w_i is not nilpotent. Since s_1 is either in I_1 or I_2, all the w_i are either in I_1 or in I_2, contradicting the assumption that I_1 and I_2 are both semi-nilpotent.

Thus I is semi-nilpotent.

Theorem 5. *The sum L of all semi-nilpotent left ideals of a ring R is a semi-nilpotent ideal which contains also all semi-nilpotent right ideals of R.*

Proof. It follows from the preceding theorem that the sum of a finite number of semi-nilpotent left ideals is a semi-nilpotent left ideal. If $\{r_1, \ldots, r_n\}$ is any finite set in L, then for each r_i, a finite number of semi-nilpotent left ideals $I_1^i, \ldots, I_{t_i}^i$ can be found such that r_i is in their sum, $i = 1, \ldots, n$. Hence the sum I of all the I_k^t, which is a semi-nilpotent left ideal, contains all the r_i, which implies that the ring generated by the r_i is nilpotent. Since this is true for each finite set of r_i, L is a semi-nilpotent left ideal.

To prove that L is a right ideal and hence a semi-nilpotent ideal, we show that if $a \in L$, $s \in R$ and T is the subring generated by as, then $T \subset L$. Suppose T is semiregular, i.e., elements $r_1, \ldots, r_n$ can be found in T so that the ring they generate is not nilpotent. Each r_i has the form $r_i = s_i as$, where the s_i is either an integer or an element of R. For an arbitrary positive integer x we can find an element different from zero which has the form $s_{i_1} as \cdots s_{i_x} as$. Hence it follows that the ring generated by $ss_1 a, \ldots, ss_n a$ is not nilpotent, which is a contradiction, since $ss_i a \in L$. The rest of the theorem follows from the fact, which can be proved analogously to the case of left ideals, that the sum of all semi-nilpotent right ideals is a semi-nilpotent ideal.

The sum of all semi-nilpotent ideals of a ring R is called the *Levitzki radical* of R, denoted by $L(R)$ when it is necessary to distinguish the ring. By the above theorem, $L(R)$ contains all one-sided semi-nilpotent ideals of R.

We exhibit another of the radical properties which the Levitzki radical has:

Theorem 6. *If L is the Levitzki radical of R, then the radical of R/L is the zero ideal.*

Proof. We show that if I, $L \subset I$, is a semiregular left ideal in R, then I/L is semiregular in R/L. Suppose the elements $r_1, \ldots, r_n \in I$ generate the non-nilpotent ring T. If I/L is semi-nilpotent, then the ring $\bar{T} = (T + L)/L$ is nilpotent, i.e., for some d we have $\bar{T}^d = (0)$ or $T^d \subset L$. We denote by $u_1, \ldots, u_m$ the finite set of all products of the form $r_{i_1} \cdots r_{i_d}$, and let U be the subring generated by the u_i. T^d is non-nilpotent for each d, and since $T^{sd+1} \subset U^s T$, we have $U^s \neq (0)$ for each s. On the other hand, by the definition of U, we have $U \subset T^d$; hence $U \subset L$, contradicting the fact that L is semi-nilpotent. Hence I/L is semiregular.

It is clear that in the presence of a maximal or minimal condition, the Levitzki radical coincides with the Wedderburn radical (and with the Jacobson).

Levitzki has also considered a *generalized radical*, defined to be the sum of all nil ideals of a ring (Baer's upper radical).

3. BROWN-McCOY RADICALS

The third variation which we discuss in this chapter is the radical defined originally for a general ring by McCoy, applying the methods Krull had used for commutative rings.

M is an *m-system* (generalized multiplicative system) of a ring R if $c, d \in M$ imply that there exists an $x \in R$ such that $cxd \in M$. Then the (McCoy) *radical* of an ideal I of a ring R is the set of all elements $r \in R$ such that every m-system which contains r contains an element of I. The *radical $M(R)$ of a ring R* is the radical of the zero ideal.

It is clear that $M(R)$ is always nil and that it contains every nilpotent ideal of R. We also shall develop a characterization in terms of minimal prime ideals.

We recall that a prime ideal P in R is said to be a minimal prime ideal belonging to an ideal I of R if $I \subset P$ and there does not exist a prime ideal P' in R such that $I \subset P' \subsetneqq P$.

We now connect this concept with that of an m-system.

Lemma 1. Let I be an ideal in R and M an m-system which does not intersect I. Then M is contained in an m-system M' which is maximal in the class of m-systems which do not intersect I.

Proof. Immediate consequence of Zorn's lemma.

Lemma 2. Let M be an m-system in R and I an ideal which does not intersect M. Then I is contained in an ideal P^* which is maximal in the class of ideals which do not intersect M. The ideal P^* is necessarily a prime ideal.

Proof. The existence of P^* follows from Zorn's lemma. Let $AB \subset P^*$, A and B ideals, and suppose $A \nsubseteq P^*$, $B \nsubseteq P^*$. Then the maximality of P^* implies that $P^* + A$ contains an element $m_1 \in M$ and $P^* + B$ contains an element $m_2 \in M$ so that for some $a \in A$, $b \in B$, $p_1, p_2 \in P^*$:

$$m_1 = p_1 + a,$$
$$m_2 = p_2 + b.$$

Then there exists an $x \in R$ such that $m_1 x m_2 \in M$; moreover, $m_1 x m_2 \notin P^*$. But then $axb \notin P^*$. However, $axb \in AB \subset P^*$, which is a contradiction. Hence P^* is prime.

Lemma 3. A set P of elements of a ring R is a minimal prime ideal belonging to an ideal I if and only if the complement of P is maximal in the class of m-systems which do not intersect I.

Proof. Let P be a set of elements of R with the property that $R \setminus P = M$ is a maximal m-system which does not intersect I. If P^* is the prime ideal whose existence is shown in the preceding lemma, then the complement of P^* is an m-system which contains M and which does not intersect I. The maximal property of M implies that the complement of P^* is the complement of P and hence $P = P^*$. Thus P is a prime ideal containing I. Clearly there does not exist a prime ideal P' such that $I \subset P' \subsetneq P$ since this would imply that the complement of P' is an m-system which does not intersect I and which properly contains M. Hence P is a minimal prime ideal belonging to I.

Conversely, if P is a minimal prime ideal belonging to I, the complement M of P is an m-system which does not intersect I, and Lemma 1 shows the existence of a maximal m-system M' which contains M and does not intersect I. From above, $R \setminus M' = P'$ is a minimal prime ideal belonging to I. Since $M \subset M'$, it follows that $P' \subset P$ and thus $I \subset P' \subset P$, from which it follows that $P' = P$ and $M = M'$. Thus the complement of P is a maximal m-system which does not intersect I.

Compare the following theorem with Theorem 9, Chapter 1.

Theorem 7. *The McCoy radical of an ideal I is the intersection of all minimal prime ideals belonging to I.*

Proof. If $M(I)$ is the radical of I, $M(I)$ is contained in the same prime ideals as I. Thus $M(I)$ is contained in the intersection of all the minimal prime ideals belonging to I. Now let $a \in R \setminus M(I)$. There exists an m-system M which contains a but does not intersect I. By Lemma 1, M is contained in a maximal m-system M' which does not intersect I. By Lemma 3, the complement of M' is a minimal prime ideal belonging to I and clearly the complement of M' does not contain a. Hence a cannot be in the intersection of all the minimal prime ideals belonging to I and the theorem is proved.

Corollary. The McCoy radical of a ring R is the intersection of all the minimal prime ideals of R.

We now check to see what properties our most recently introduced radical has.

Theorem 8. *If M is the McCoy radical of R, R/M has zero McCoy radical.*

Proof. Let $\bar{a} = a + M$ be an element of the radical of R/M. Then $\bar{a}$ is contained in all prime ideals of R/M. If $\bar{a} \neq 0$, $a \notin M$ and hence a is not contained in some prime ideal P in R. Since $M \subset P$, we have R/P is isomorphic to $(R/M)/(P/M)$, from which it follows that P/M is a prime ideal in R/M. Furthermore, P/M does not contain $\bar{a}$ since a is not in P. This contradiction shows that we must have $\bar{a} = 0$.

Theorem 9. *If I is an ideal of a ring, then the McCoy radical of the ring I is $I \cap M(R)$.*

Proof. Let $M(I)$ be the radical of I. Then clearly $M(I)$ is contained in $I \cap M(R)$. On the other hand, if $b \in I \cap M(R)$, then every m-system in R containing b contains 0. In particular, every m-system in I containing b contains 0. Thus $b \in M(I)$ and $I \cap M(R) \subset M(I)$.

To get a characterization of the McCoy radical of a matrix ring in terms of the radical of the base ring, we rely on the results of Problems 6 and 7 of Chapter 2 and the following lemma:

Lemma. *If R is a ring with identity, then R_n is a prime ring if and only if R is a prime ring.*

Proof. We let E_{ij} denote the matrix with the identity in the (i,j) position and zeros elsewhere. If R is not a prime ring, there exist nonzero elements $a, b \in R$ such that $aRb = (0)$. This implies that $(aE_{11})R_n(bE_{11}) = (0)$ with aE_{11} and bE_{11} nonzero elements of R_n. Thus R_n is not a prime ring.

Conversely, we suppose that R_n is not a prime ring and hence that there exist nonzero matrices (a_{ij}), $(b_{ij}) \in R_n$ such that $(a_{ij})R_n(b_{ij}) = (0)$. Let us assume that $a_{pq} \neq 0$, $b_{rs} \neq 0$. Now, for every x in R we must have

$$\left[\sum_{i,j} a_{ij}E_{ij}\right][E_{qr}x]\left[\sum_{k,l} b_{kl}E_{kl}\right] = \sum_{i,l} a_{iq}xb_{rl}E_{il} = 0.$$

In particular, the coefficient of E_{ps} must be zero, that is, $a_{pq}xb_{rs} = 0$. Since this holds for every $x \in R$, we have $a_{pq}Rb_{rs} = (0)$ and R is not a prime ring.

We note that an ideal I of an arbitrary ring R is prime if and only if R/I is a prime ring.

Theorem 10. *If $M(R)$ is the McCoy radical of a ring R, then the full matrix ring R_n has radical $M(R)_n$.*

Proof. First suppose R has an identity. Then there is a one-one correspondence between the ideals I in R and the ideals I_n in R_n. Moreover, $(R/I)_n$ is isomorphic to R_n/I_n. Hence by the lemma I_n is a prime ideal in R_n if and only if I is a prime ideal in R. Thus if $M(R)$ is the radical of R and P_i are the prime ideals in R, we have $M(R_n) = \cap(P_i)_n = (\cap P_i)_n = M(R)_n$.

If R does not have an identity, we embed R in a ring R' with identity such that R is an ideal of R'. Then the radical of R is $M(R') \cap R$. Then the radical of R'_n is $M(R')_n$ and since R_n is an ideal in R'_n the radical of R_n is

$$M(R')_n \cap R_n = (M(R') \cap R)_n = M(R)_n.$$

So far we have neglected the question of generalization of the structure theorems, i.e., once a radical has been defined for a general ring, can one give a characterization of rings with zero radical which generalizes the structure theorem for rings with minimal condition—as one can for the Jacobson radical? For the McCoy radical we have:

Theorem 11. *A ring R is isomorphic to the subdirect sum of prime rings if and only if $M(R) = (0)$.*

Proof. As we have observed, if P is a prime ideal in a ring R, R/P is a prime ring, and conversely. Since the radical of R is the intersection of all the prime ideals in R, the theorem follows.

We note that the Wedderburn and Jacobson radicals have convenient characterizations as the sum of all ideals of a ring which have a certain property. The McCoy radical lacks this feature, although it is a nil ideal which contains every nilpotent ideal. Some mathematicians, in fact, prefer to reserve the term "radical" for an entity defined by a summation process and to call those distinguished ideals with intersection characterizations (such as the McCoy radical, see Theorem 7) "residuals." Of course, the Jacobson radical is a residual as well as a radical.

Brown and McCoy have defined a whole series of radicals. Suppose F is a mapping of a ring R into the set of ideals of R such that if $a \to a'$ defines a homomorphism of R onto a ring R' and $F(a)'$ is the image of $F(a)$, then $F(a') = F(a)'$. Then a is *F-regular* if and only if $a \in F(a)$ and an ideal I is *F-regular* if and only if $a \in F(a)$ for all $a \in I$. The *F-radical* of R, $N_F(R)$, is the set of all elements $b \in R$ which generate *F-regular* ideals (b) in R.

A ring R is *subdirectly irreducible* if in every isomorphic representation of R as a subdirect sum of rings R_i, $i \in I$, the natural projection of R onto R_i is an isomorphism for some i. Equivalently, R is subdirectly irreducible if and only if the intersection of its nonzero ideals is not the zero ideal.

> **Theorem 12.** $N_F(R)$ is the intersection of all ideals I in R such that R/I is subdirectly irreducible and has zero F-radical.

Proof. We show first that the intersection is contained in $N_F(R)$. If $b \notin N_F(R)$, then for some $a \in (b)$, $a \notin F(a)$. By Zorn's lemma, there is an ideal I containing $F(a)$, but not containing a, such that every ideal in R that contains I as a proper subset does contain a. If $\bar{a} = a + I$, it follows that every nonzero ideal in R/I contains $\bar{a} \neq 0$, so that R/I is subdirectly irreducible. But since $F(\bar{a}) = \overline{F(a)} = 0$, $\bar{a} \notin F(\bar{a})$. Thus every nonzero ideal in R/I contains an element which is not *F-regular*, so that R/I has zero *F-radical*. Since $a \notin I$, it follows that $b \notin I$, and b is not in the intersection.

Conversely, $N_F(R)$ is in the intersection. For, if $b \in N_F(R)$ and I is any ideal such that R/I is subdirectly irreducible and has zero *F-radical*, then $\bar{b} = b + I$ is in the *F-radical* of R/I, since *F-regularity* is preserved under homomorphism. Since R/I has zero *F-radical*, $\bar{b} = 0$, and $b \in I$. Thus b is in the intersection.

Corollary. The *F-radical* of R is the sum of all *F-regular* ideals in R.

Proof. This result follows from the fact that $N_F(R)$ consists of the elements of R which generate *F-regular* ideals. Since $N_F(R)$ is an ideal, it is clearly an *F-regular* ideal which contains every *F-regular* ideal of R.

Theorem 13. *A ring R has zero F-radical if and only if it is isomorphic to the subdirect sum of subdirectly irreducible rings of zero F-radical.*

Proof. If R has zero F-radical, then by Theorem 11, $R = R/\cap I_i$, where R/I_i is subdirectly irreducible and has zero F-radical. But from the lemma to Theorem 23, Chapter 4, $R/\cap I_i$ is isomorphic to the subdirect sum of all such R/I_i.

On the other hand, let R be isomorphic to the subdirect sum of subdirectly irreducible rings R_i of zero F-radical. Then each R_i is isomorphic to R/I_i, I_i an ideal of R. Then $N_F(R)$ is contained in the intersection of the I_i, which is (0).

Theorem 14. *A subdirectly irreducible ring R has zero F-radical if and only if its minimal ideal contains an element $a \neq 0$ such that $F(a) = (0)$.*

Proof. Let J be the minimal ideal of R, that is, the intersection of all the nonzero ideals of R. If there exists $a \in J$, $a \neq 0$, such that $F(a) = (0)$, then J is not F-regular. But J is contained in every nonzero ideal of R, so by the corollary to Theorem 1, $N_F(R) = (0)$. Conversely, if $N_F(R) = (0)$, then no nonzero ideals are F-regular, so there is an $a \neq 0$ in J such that $a \notin F(a)$. But if $F(a) \neq (0)$, $J \subset F(a)$, so we must have $F(a) = (0)$.

It turns out that the F-radical is really too general; it does not always reduce to the classical radical in the presence of a minimal condition. However, we do have the following result:

Theorem 15. *The ring $R/N_F(R)$ has zero F-radical.*

Proof. We let $\bar{b}$ denote an element of the F-radical of $R/N_F(R)$, and let I be any ideal in R such that R/I is subdirectly irreducible and has zero F-radical. Since R/I is isomorphic to $(R/N_F)/(I/N_F)$, it follows from the fact that $N_F(R)$ is the intersection of all ideals I in R such that R/I is subdirectly irreducible and has zero F-radical that $\bar{b} \in I/N_F$. Hence b is in I; in fact b is in the intersection of all such I, namely N_F. Thus $\bar{b} = 0$.

Now we consider a special case of a mapping F as described above. We define a mapping G by $G(a) = $ the ideal generated by elements of the form

$$xa + x + \sum y_i a z_i - \sum y_i z_i,$$

where x, y_i, z_i vary over R and the sums are finite. The *G-radical* of a ring R, $N_G(R)$, is then the F-radical for the case when F is the specific mapping G. It is sometimes known as the *Brown-McCoy radical*.

We now want to establish structure theorems for this radical analogous to those for the Wedderburn, Jacobson, and McCoy radicals. We note that if a ring R has more than one nonzero element and an identity 1, then $1 \notin G(1) = (0)$ so that its G-radical cannot be all of R.

The proof of the following remark is contained in the proof of Theorem 10, Chapter 2.

Remark. If e is a right identity of a simple ring R, then e is the (two-sided) identity for R.

    Theorem 16. *A subdirectly irreducible ring has zero G-radical if and only if it is a simple ring with identity.*

Proof. If the ring has only 0 and 1 as elements, the result is clear. If a sub-directly irreducible simple ring R has more than one nonzero element and an identity, then 1 is in its minimal ideal, namely R itself, but $G(1) = (0)$. Hence by Theorem 1, R has zero radical.

    Conversely, if R is subdirectly irreducible and has more than one nonzero element, then if R has zero radical, by Theorem 13 its minimal ideal contains an element $a \neq 0$ such that $G(a) = (0)$. Hence $ax = -x$ for all $x \in R$ and R is contained in the minimal ideal. Thus R is simple and has a right identity $-a$. By the remark preceding this theorem, this is an identity.

    This theorem and Theorem 15 enable us to characterize the radical.

    Theorem 17. *The G-radical of a ring R is the intersection of all ideals M in R such that R/M is a simple ring with identity.*

    Also we obtain at once from Theorems 13 and 16:

    Theorem 18. *A ring R has zero G-radical if and only if it is isomorphic to a subdirect sum of simple rings with identity.*

    As we have remarked, the F-radical may not necessarily coincide with the classical radical when the ring has a minimal condition; however, for the special case of the G-radical, Theorem 18 reduces to the Wedderburn structure theorem.

    Theorem 19. *If a ring R is Artinian and has zero G-radical, then R is isomorphic to the direct sum of a finite number of simple rings with identity.*

Proof. There exist ideals $\mathcal{M} = \{I_i\}_{i \in I}$ such that $\cap I_i = (0)$ and R/I_i is simple for each i. Since R has the minimal condition, among the finite subsets of $\mathcal{M}$, there is a minimal one whose intersection is (0), say $\cap I_i = (0)$, $i = 1, \ldots, n$, and no subset of $\mathcal{M}$ of less than n ideals has intersection zero. Then it is clear that R is isomorphic to the subdirect sum of the R/I_i, $i = 1, \ldots, n$, under an isomorphism given by

$$a \to (a_1, \ldots, a_n) \qquad \text{where} \qquad a_i = a + I_i.$$

Now we let

$$a \in \bigcap_{\substack{i=1 \\ i \neq j}}^{n} I_i \setminus I_j.$$

Then $a \to (0, \ldots, a_j, \ldots, 0)$. But R/I_j is simple, so $(a_j) = R/I_j$. Hence every element of the form $(0, \ldots, r_j, \ldots, 0)$, $r_j \in R/I_j$, is the image of an element of R under the given isomorphism. Hence R is isomorphic to the direct sum of the R/I_i, $i = 1, \ldots, n$.

While discussing coincidence of radicals, we might remark that a certain resemblance of the mapping G to the condition of quasi-regularity is clear. If $a \in R$ is left quasi-regular, then a is an element of the left regular ideal $\{xa + x \mid x \in R\}$. Moreover, if $b \in J(R)$, every element $a \in bR \subset J(R)$ must be left quasi-regular by Theorem 3, Chapter 4. Hence, since $G(a)$ is the ideal generated by the left ideal $\{xa + x\}$, $a \in G(a)$. Thus $J(R) \subset N_G(R)$.

Theorem 20. *If R is a right Artinian ring, then $N_G(R) = J(R)$.*

Proof. It suffices to prove that $N_G(R) \subset J(R)$. $R/J(R)$ is right Artinian and Jacobson semisimple. Thus $R/J(R)$ is isomorphic to the direct sum of a finite number of simple rings, each of which has an identity. Thus by Theorem 18, $N_G(R/J(R)) = (0)$. Hence if $a \in N_G(R)$, then $\bar{a} = a + J(R)$ is in the G-radical of $R/J(R)$ so $\bar{a} = 0$, that is, $a \in J(R)$.

We complete our consideration of the G-radical by showing that it has radical property 5.

First we prove some lemmas.

Lemma 1. Let I be an ideal in R_n and a the element in the (i, j) position of a matrix A in I. If x and y are elements of R, then I contains a matrix with xay in the (p, q) position and zeros elsewhere.

Proof. Let X_{ij} denote the matrix with x in the (i, j) position and zeros elsewhere. Then $X_{pi} A Y_{jq}$ is the required matrix in I.

Lemma 2. R is a simple ring with identity if and only if R_n is a simple ring with identity.

Proof. Suppose R is simple with identity and I is a nonzero ideal in R_n, $a \neq 0$ an element of some matrix in I. Then the ideal (a) must be R. Hence if $r \in R$, there is a matrix in I with r in any given position and zeros elsewhere, by Lemma 1. But by adding matrices of this type we get $R_n = I$. It is obvious that R_n must have an identity. Conversely, the one-one mapping $I \rightarrow I_n$ of the ideals of R into a subset of the ideals of R_n gives that R_n is not simple if R is not simple, and it is known (see Problem 6, Chapter 2) that R_n has no identity if R does not.

Lemma 3. If R/I is a simple ring with identity, then R_n/I_n is a simple ring with identity. Conversely, if I is an ideal in R_n such that R_n/I is a simple ring with identity, then the set J of all elements which are entries in the matrices of I is an ideal in R, $I = J_n$ and R/J is a simple ring with identity.

Proof. The first statement follows from Lemma 2 and the fact that R_n/I_n is isomorphic to $(R/I)_n$.

For the converse, let J^* be the set of elements of R which appear in the $(1, 1)$ position in matrices of I. J^* is an ideal in R and $J^* \subset J$. We show the reverse inclusion.

Since R_n/I has an identity, R_n contains a matrix $U = (u_{ij})$ such that

$$UXU - X \in I \qquad \text{for all} \quad X \in R_n.$$

In particular if X is a matrix with an arbitrary element $r \in R$ in the $(1, 1)$ position and zeros elsewhere, we see that

$$(*) \qquad\qquad u_{11}ru_{11} - r \in J^* \qquad \text{for all} \quad r \in R.$$

Now let $a \in J$; there is a matrix in I containing a in some position, so by Lemma 1 there is a matrix in I containing $u_{11}au_{11}$ in the $(1, 1)$ position. Hence $u_{11}au_{11} \in J^*$ and by $(*)$, $a \in J^*$. Thus $J \subset J^*$ and $J = J^*$.

It is evident that $I \subset J_n$, so we need only show that $J_n \subset I$. If $a \in J$, then $UA_{hk}U$ is the sum of matrices of the type considered in Lemma 1; hence $UA_{hk}U \in I$. But then $A_{hk} \in I$. But any matrix of J_n can be expressed as a sum of matrices of the form A_{hk}. Thus $J_n \subset I$ and $J_n = I$.

Finally, $(R/J)_n \simeq R_n/J_n = R_n/I$, which is a simple ring with identity so that by Lemma 2, R/J is a simple ring with identity.

We are now ready to prove:

Theorem 21. $N_G(R_n) = (N_G(R))_n$.

Proof. From Lemma 3 and the fact that the set of ideals of R can be mapped in a one-one way into the set of ideals of R_n, it is clear that the ideals J in R for which R/J is a simple ring with identity correspond one-one with the ideals I in R_n for which R_n/I is a simple ring with identity. Furthermore, the inter-sections of corresponding ideals must also correspond. Hence by Theorem 17, the G-radicals correspond to give the desired result.

To close this section we mention briefly two other special cases of the F-radical and the resulting structure theorems. We define mappings as follows:

$$G^*(a) = G(a^2) = \text{the ideal generated by elements of the form}$$
$$xa^2 + x + \sum r_i a^2 s_i + \sum r_i s_i,$$

and

$$H(a) = \text{the ideal generated by elements of the form}$$
$$\sum r_i a s_i - \sum r_i s_i,$$

where x, r_i, and s_i are in R and the sums are finite.

We can then use the radicals which these mappings determine to charac-terize the structure of various rings as follows:

Theorem 22. *A ring R has zero G^*-radical if and only if it is isomorphic to the subdirect sum of simple rings, each with identity 1 and an element whose square is -1.*

Proof. $G^*(a) = 0$ if and only if $-a^2$ is a right identity for R. Moreover, a subdirectly irreducible ring has zero G^*-radical if and only if it is a simple ring with identity. Then the result follows from Theorems 13 and 14 and the fact that the G^*-radical is a special case of the F-radical.

Theorem 23. *A ring R has zero H-radical if and only if it is isomorphic to a subdirect sum of rings each of which is either a simple ring with identity or a subdirectly irreducible zero ring.*

Proof. It is clear that $H(a) = (0)$ if and only if

$$(*) \qquad\qquad xay - xy = 0 \qquad \text{for all} \quad x, y \in R.$$

Thus a subdirectly irreducible ring R has zero H-radical if and only if its minimal ideal J contains a nonzero element a for which $(*)$ holds. We consider two cases.

We suppose first that the subdirectly irreducible ring R has no right or left annihilator except zero, that is, $zR = (0)$ implies $z = 0$, and $Rz = 0$ implies $z = 0$. From $(*)$ we see that $(xa - x)R = 0$ and $R(ax - x) = 0$ for every x in R. Hence $ax = xa = x$, and a is the identity of R. But $a \in J$, so R is a simple ring with identity.

Suppose on the other hand that R has a nonzero element c such that $cR = 0$ or $Rc = 0$. Without loss of generality we assume that $cR = 0$. It follows that (c) consists of all elements of the form $nc + rc$, where n is an integer and $r \in R$. But $a \in (c)$ since $J \subset (c)$; hence $aR = (0)$. From $(*)$ we have that $xy = 0$ for all $x, y \in R$, that is, $R^2 = (0)$.

Conversely, in either case, it is clear that a subdirectly irreducible ring has zero H-radical.

4. AMITSUR'S PROPERTIES

Amitsur generalized the lower radical defined by Baer as follows:

Let P be a property of rings invariant under homomorphism. We call an ideal a *P-ideal* if it possesses the property P. We define a sequence where $U_n = U_n(R)$ is the nth P-radical of R:

1) $U_0 = (0)$.

2) U_n, for n a limit ordinal, is the union of all U_v for v less than n.

3) U_n, for n not a limit ordinal, is the union of all ideals A such that A/U_{n-1} is a P-ideal in R/U_{n-1}.

$U(R, P)$, the *upper P-radical* of R, is the limit of this sequence, i.e., the minimal ideal U_n such that $U_n = U_{n+1}$.

A ring R is *P-semisimple* if it does not contain nonzero P-ideals. A $\bar{P}$-*ideal* is an ideal I in a ring R such that R/I is P-semisimple.

A *P-radical* ideal in R is an ideal in a ring R which is both a P-ideal and a $\bar{P}$-ideal in R.

A property P of ideals is called an *HI-property* if:

A) the zero ideal is a P-ideal,

B) every homomorphism maps P-ideals onto P-ideals.

The following theorem is a consequence of more general results on complete lattices which will be given in Chapter 6 (Theorems 19 and 20); we include now only its statement.

Theorem 24. *If P is an HI-property, then the intersection of any set of $\bar{P}$-ideals of a ring R is a $\bar{P}$-ideal; the intersection of all $\bar{P}$-ideals of R, which is the minimal $\bar{P}$-ideal, is the upper P-radical $U(R)$ of R. Furthermore, if a P-radical ideal N of R exists, then $N = U(R)$ and N is uniquely determined as the maximal P-ideal of R.*

In the latter case N is called the *P-radical* of R.

If a property P of ideals satisfies (A), (B), and the following:

C) for every ideal I in a ring R which is not a P-ideal, there exists an ideal $J \subset I$ such that there are no nonzero P-ideals of R/J contained in I/J,

it is called an *RI-property*.

We state another theorem which is a special case of results to be given in the next chapter (Theorem 22):

Theorem 25. *Let P be an HI-property. Then the P-radical exists in every ring if and only if P is an RI-property.*

It is possible to specialize the discussion of properties of ideals to properties of rings. Then under certain further restrictions it is possible to obtain radical properties 3, 4, and 5 for these P-radicals.

We recall that an element a of a ring R is von Neumann regular if there exists a relative inverse $u \in R$ such that $aua = a$. If every element of an ideal is von Neumann regular, the ideal is said to be a *von Neumann regular ideal*. Then von Neumann regularity is an *HI*-property, while quasi-regularity is an *RI*-property.

We call I an *M-ideal* if every m-system of I contains zero. Then M is an *HI*-property, and the prime ideals of a ring R are M-ideals. Moreover, M is an *RI*-property and the M-radical is the intersection of all the prime ideals, i.e., the McCoy radical.

The F-regularity of Brown and McCoy is also an *HI*-property and yields, in the notation of this section, an upper F-radical, which is the Brown and McCoy F-radical.

5. RESULTS OF NAGATA

Nagata has used an approach which might be said to be roughly to the methods of McCoy as that of Amitsur is to those of Baer. He introduced the general concept of a *C*-radical, of which the McCoy and Jacobson radicals, along with other radicals newly defined by him, are special cases; however, most of his results are proved only for special cases.

Let *C* be a condition for rings; a ring satisfying *C* is called a *C-ring*. An ideal *P* of a ring *R* such that *R/P* is a *C*-ring is called a *C-ideal*. A ring which is isomorphic to a subdirect sum of *C*-rings is called a *semi-C-ring*. An ideal which is an intersection of *C*-ideals is called a *semi-C-ideal*. The intersection of all *C*-ideals of a ring *R* is called the *C-radical* of *R*.

We remark that a *C*-radical is thus a "residual."

Examples. A Jacobson semisimple ring would in this terminology be designated semiprimitive. Also, the McCoy radical is a semiprime ideal which is the prime radical of a ring.

We mention briefly two other radicals.

A ring *R* is *e-primitive* if every nonzero ideal in *R* contains a nonzero idempotent element. We define *e*-primitive ideal and semi-*e*-primitive ring and ideal analogously to above. We call the intersection of all *e*-primitive ideals simply the *e-radical*.

Theorem 26. *If an e-primitive ring (ideal) is a subdirect sum (an intersection) of e-primitive rings (ideals), it coincides with one of them. Therefore, an e-primitive ring (ideal) is primitive.*

Proof. The first assertion is clear and the second follows from the fact that the Jacobson radical contains no nonzero idempotent element.

Corollary. A semi-*e*-primitive ring is a semiprimitive ring.

An element *a* of a ring *R* is *semi-idempotent* if the ideal generated by $a^2 - a$ in *R* does not contain *a*. An ideal is *quasi-nilpotent* if it contains no semi-idempotent elements.

Theorem 27. *An element a of a ring R is semi-idempotent if and only if there exists an e-primitive ideal P such that $a^2 - a \in P$, $a \notin P$.*

Proof. The "if" is clear. On the other hand, if *a* is semi-idempotent, then $a + (a^2 - a)$ is an idempotent element of $R/(a^2 - a)$, which shows the existence of the desired *P*.

It follows that the *e*-radical is a quasi-nilpotent ideal. We observe that the *e*-radical is an *F*-radical if we define

$$F(a) = (a^2 - a),$$

and hence from the corollary to Theorem 12 we get that the *e*-radical is the sum of the quasi-nilpotent ideals of the ring *R*.

The *N-radical* of a ring *R* is the intersection of all prime ideals *P* of *R* such that *R/P* is simple. The *N-quasi-radical* of *R* is the intersection of all ideals *I* such that *R/I* is simple.

The reason for the "quasi" terminology is that this notion fails to coincide with the classical radical in the presence of a minimal condition.

Remark. If R is commutative, then the N-radical is just the Jacobson radical.

6. RELATIONS AMONG THE RADICALS

As noted, most of our radicals coincide with the classical radical and hence with each other in the presence of a minimal condition. We shall also show some relations among them in more general cases. The results listed are not exhaustive.

We have shown that the Jacobson and Brown-McCoy radicals coincide in Artinian rings. It is also clear that they coincide in commutative rings. However, in general the two radicals do not coincide, since a primitive ring need not be a simple ring with identity. Thus the two concepts are distinct generalizations of the classical radical. Similarly, since the concepts of prime ring and of primitive ring do not in general coincide (any integral domain is a prime ring, whereas an integral domain is primitive if and only if it is a field), the McCoy and Jacobson radicals do not in general coincide.

Next we look at the Jacobson and Baer radicals.

Theorem 28. *If I is an ideal in a ring R such that $I \subset J(R)$ and every nonzero left ideal in R/I contains a minimal left ideal and R/I has no nonzero nilpotent left ideals, then $I = J(R)$.*

Proof. Suppose $I \neq J(R)$. Then there exists J such that $I \subsetneqq J \subset J(R)$ and J/I is a minimal left ideal in R/I. J/I is not nilpotent, so $J/I = (J/I)^2$. Thus there exists a nonzero idempotent $\bar{e} = e + I$ in J/I. But since $e \in J(R)$, we have that $-e$ is quasi-regular and there exists $f \in R$ such that $-e + f - ef = 0$. But

$$e + I = e^2 + I = e(f - ef) + I = (ef - e^2 f) + I = (ef - ef) + I = I,$$

that is, $e \in I$, a contradiction. Thus $J(R) = I$.

Corollary. If every nonzero left ideal in R/U, where U is the upper Baer radical of R, contains a minimal left ideal, then $J(R) = U$.

We note that the generalized radical of Levitzki is nil, being the sum of nil ideals, and is a radical ideal in the sense of Baer. It is in fact the upper Baer radical of the ring.

There is also a relation between the lower radical of Baer and the McCoy radical.

An infinite sequence of elements of a ring R,

$$b_0, b_1, \ldots,$$

is an *m-sequence* if for each nonnegative integer n there exists an element $c_n \in R$ such that $b_{n+1} = b_n c_n b_n$. An *m*-sequence *vanishes* if some term of the sequence is zero. Since each term of an m-sequence is a left factor as well as a right factor of all subsequent terms, we have the following:

Lemma 1. If some term of an m-sequence is contained in a left (right) ideal I, then all subsequent terms are also contained in I.

Lemma 2. The elements of an m-sequence form an m-system.

Proof. Consider an m-sequence $\{b_i\}$. We have to show that for any pair of terms b_i, b_k of the sequence there exists a term b_j and an element c_{ik} of R such that $B_j = b_i c_{ik} b_k$. From the definition, this holds for any b_j with j greater than i and greater than k.

An element a of a ring R and an infinite sequence $\{b_i\}$ are *associated* with each other if $b_0 = a$, and for some infinite sequence $\{c_i\}$ we have $b_{n+1} = b_n c_n b_n$, $n = 0, 1, \ldots$. As a consequence of the above definitions, we have:

Lemma 3. Each infinite sequence which is associated with some element of a ring R is an m-sequence, and each m-sequence is associated with its initial element.

Theorem 29. *An element $a \in R$ belongs to the lower radical of R if and only if each sequence which is associated with a is a vanishing m-sequence.*

Proof. We use the constructive characterization of the lower radical $L(R)$. Suppose that $a \in L(R)$ and consider a sequence associated with a, so that we have $a_0 = a$. By Lemma 1, it follows that all terms of the sequence are elements of $L(R)$. Hence each element of the sequence is contained in some $Q(v)$. Thus for each non-negative integer i there exists a smallest ordinal v_i such that $a_i \in Q(v_i)$. If for some i the ordinal v_i were a limit ordinal, a_i would be in $Q(w)$ for some $w < v_i$, contradicting the minimality of v_i. Hence none of the ordinals v_i is a limit ordinal. Denote by k a non-negative integer so that v_k is the minimum of the v_i, $i = 0, 1, \ldots$. Either $v_k = 1$ or $v_k = w + 1$, $w \geq 1$. Suppose the latter. By the definition of $Q(w + 1)$ it follows that for some positive integer m, the smallest left ideal $\widetilde{Ra_k}$ containing a_k satisfies

$$(*) \qquad\qquad (\widetilde{Ra_k})^m \subset Q(w).$$

Now we have $a_{k+1} = a_k d_k a_k$ in $(\widetilde{Ra_k})^2$, and for an arbitrary positive integer it follows that $a_{k+p} \in (\widetilde{Ra_k})^{2^p}$. Hence by choosing p so that $2^p > m$, we obtain

$$(**) \qquad\qquad a_{k+p} \in (\widetilde{Ra_k})^{2^p} \subset (\widetilde{Ra_k})^m \subset Q(w).$$

By $(**)$ we have that $v_{k+p} \leq w < v_k$, which contradicts the minimality of v_k. Thus $v_k = 1$ and $(\widetilde{Ra_k})^m = (0)$, $a_{k+p} = 0$, so that each sequence associated with a is a vanishing m-sequence.

On the other hand, we want to show that any element $a \notin L(R)$ is associated with a nonvanishing m-sequence. Let $a_0 = a$. Since $L(R)$ is a radical ideal, it follows that $(\widetilde{Ra_0})(\widetilde{Ra_0}) \nsubseteq L(R)$. Hence for some $b_0 \in R$ we have $a_0 b_0 a_0 \notin L(R)$. We let $a_1 = a_0 b_0 a_0$ be the next term of the required sequence. Continuing in this way, we obtain a nonvanishing m-sequence associated with a.

Theorem 30. *The McCoy radical of a ring R coincides with the lower Baer radical of R.*

Proof. Suppose that for some element $a \in R$ we have $a \in M(R)$ and $a \notin L(R)$. By the preceding theorem there exists a nonvanishing m-sequence which is associated with a. By Lemmas 2 and 3 we know that the elements of such a sequence form an m-system. Since this system contains a and does not contain 0, we cannot have $a \in M(R)$. Hence $M(R) \subset L(R)$.

Suppose now that there exists an element a such that $a \in L(R)$ and $a \notin M(R)$. By the definition of $M(R)$ there exists an m-system S which contains a and does not contain 0. Hence for some $b_0 \in R$ we have $0 \neq ab_0 a \in S$. We let $a = a_0$ and $a_0 b_0 a_0 = a_1$. Continuing this process, we obtain a nonvanishing m-sequence which is associated with a. But then by Theorem 29, $a \notin L(R)$. Hence $L(R) \subset M(R)$.

7. MORE ABOUT RADICAL PROPERTIES

To present a somewhat more systematic approach to the type of results in the last section, Divinsky has adapted a definition given by Kurosch for groups to rings: A property S of rings is a *radical property* if:

A) Every homomorphic image of an S-ring is an S-ring.

B) Every ring R contains an S-ideal (i.e., an ideal which has property S as a ring) which contains every other S-ideal of R; this ideal is the *S-radical* of R.

C) R/I is S-semisimple, i.e., the S-radical of R/I is the zero ideal.

If R is a ring with property S, then it is an *S-radical ring*.

If S and T are two radical properties, we say that $S \leq T$ if every S-radical is also a T-radical. If the rings are associative, as ours are, this is equivalent to requiring that every S-radical be contained in the corresponding T-radical.

We note that the property N of being nil is a radical property, giving the classical radical for rings with a minimal condition. On the other hand, nilpotency is not a radical property, for the sum of nilpotent ideals need not be nilpotent. Since his purpose was to generalize the classical radical, Divinsky sought radical properties Q which coincide with the property N in the sense that for all rings R with a minimal condition, the Q-radical of R equals the N-radical of R.

Given any class of rings $\mathscr{P}$, the *lower radical property* determined by $\mathscr{P}$ is defined as follows:

A ring R is of first degree over $\mathscr{P}$ if it is a homomorphic image of some ring in $\mathscr{P}$ or if $R = (0)$. A ring R is of degree n greater than one over $\mathscr{P}$ if every nonzero homomorphic image of R contains a nonzero ideal which is a ring of degree $n - 1$ over $\mathscr{P}$. If n is a limit ordinal, a ring is of degree n over $\mathscr{P}$ if it is of some degree m less than n over $\mathscr{P}$. A ring is called *L-radical* if it is of some degree over $\mathscr{P}$. This yields a radical property L for which all rings in $\mathscr{P}$ are radical, and this property is equal to or less than any other radical property for which all rings in $\mathscr{P}$ are radical.

Given a set of rings $\mathscr{S}$ such that:

D) Every nonzero ideal of a ring R in $\mathscr{S}$ can be homomorphically mapped onto some nonzero ring of $\mathscr{S}$,

the *upper radical property* is defined as follows:

Consider the class $\overline{\mathscr{S}}$ of all rings R such that every nonzero ideal of R can be homomorphically mapped onto some nonzero ring of $\mathscr{S}$. A ring is *U-radical* if it cannot be homomorphically mapped onto a nonzero ring of $\overline{\mathscr{S}}$. This yields a radical property U for which all rings in $\mathscr{S}$ are semisimple; U is equal to or greater than any other radical property for which all rings in $\mathscr{S}$ are semisimple.

We adopt the following notation:

$Z =$ the lower radical property determined by all the zero rings which have no nonzero proper ideals,

$D =$ the lower radical property determined by all the nilpotent rings which are nil radicals of left Artinian rings,

$B =$ the lower radical property determined by all the nilpotent rings,

$N =$ the lower radical property determined by all the nil rings,

$M =$ the upper radical property determined by all finite-dimensional matrix rings over division rings (since this class consists only of simple rings, every element of it clearly has property D).

It is clear that $Z \le D \le B \le N \le M$.

If the property Q coincides with the property N on left Artinian rings, then all rings determining Z are Q-radical. Therefore $Z \le Q$. All finite-dimensional matrix rings over division rings are Artinian and thus are nil semisimple and therefore Q-semisimple. Hence $Q \le M$. Moreover, every nilpotent ring is N-radical, and if it is a nil radical of a left Artinian ring it is also Q-radical. Thus $D \le Q \le M$.

> **Theorem 31.** *A general radical property Q coincides with the classical radical N on left Artinian rings if and only if $D \le Q \le M$.*

Proof. Half of the theorem has been demonstrated above. To prove the other half it suffices to show that D and M coincide with N on Artinian rings.

Let R be a left Artinian ring. Let N be its N-radical and M its M-radical, $N \le M$. Then R/N is the direct sum of a finite number of rings D_i, where each D_i is a matrix ring over a division ring. M/N is an ideal of R/N and so it is the finite direct sum of the D_i's which it contains. Thus M can be mapped homomorphically through M/N onto one of these D_i, which is M-semisimple. However, M is M-radical and so is every homomorphic image of M. The only ring which is both radical and semisimple is (0). Thus $M/N = (0)$, that is, $M = N$.

Let D be the D-radical of a left Artinian ring. Its N-radical N is nilpotent and is the nil radical of a left Artinian ring, and therefore N is the D-radical, $N = D$, concluding the proof.

Every N-radical left Artinian ring R is also Z-radical. For if R is nilpotent, let $R^m = (0) \neq R^{m-1}$. By the minimal condition R^{m-1} contains a minimal ideal I of R. If J is any ideal of I, it is also an ideal of R, since $RJ = (0)$. Thus I is a zero ring with no nonzero proper ideals and I is contained in R. Similarly, every homomorphic image of R contains a zero ring with no nonzero proper ideals and therefore R is of degree two over the zero rings with no nonzero proper ideals. Thus R is Z-radical.

However, it is not the case that the N-radical and the Z-radical of a ring always coincide. In fact we shall show that $Z < D$.

To see this we let $A = \{ax + be \mid a, b$ rational numbers, $x^2 = 0, e^2 = e, ex = xe = x\}$. A is a commutative Artinian ring which is a two-dimensional vector space over the rationals. Its only nonzero proper ideal is $N = \{ax\}$. N is the N-radical, and thus also the D-radical, since A is Artinian, of A. The Z-radical of A must be contained in N; we show that N is Z-semisimple.

Suppose that N contains some nonzero Z-ideals, each of which is of some degree over the class of rings determining Z. Let v be the minimal ordinal such that N has an ideal I of degree v. It is clear that v is not a limit ordinal and since I is of degree v, every nonzero homomorphic image of I, and in particular I itself, must contain a nonzero ideal, say J, of degree $v - 1$. But $N^2 = (0)$ so $JN = (0)$ and J is an ideal of N. But then N contains an ideal of degree $v - 1$ over the class of zero rings with no nonzero proper ideals, contradicting the minimality of v, unless $v = 1$. Thus N contains an ideal of degree one. But any homomorphic image of a zero ring with no nonzero proper ideals is a zero ring with no nonzero proper ideals, so that the only rings of degree one are the zero rings with no nonzero proper ideals themselves. However, any nonzero ideal of N is merely an additive subgroup; hence it contains the infinite cyclic group generated by any nonzero element, a nonzero proper ideal.

Thus N has no nonzero Z-ideals and is Z-semisimple.

It is also the case that in general $M \neq N$, for the set of all rational numbers of the form $2m/(2n + 1)$, n, m integers, is a Jacobson radical ring which is M-radical, but N-semisimple.

We claim that the B-radical is the lower Baer radical. Let R be the integers with the usual addition and zero product, i.e., the product of any two integers is 0. Then let B' be the radical property determined by R. If all nilpotent rings are radical, then R is radical, that is, $B' \leq B$. On the other hand, every nilpotent ring contains an ideal which is a zero ring with cyclic additive group and thus is a homomorphic image of R. Thus every nilpotent ring is of degree two over R and thus if R is radical, so are all nilpotent rings, that is, $B \leq B'$. Then since clearly the B'-radical is the same as the lower Baer radical, we have established our claim.

The above result gives us that $B \neq N$, for N is the upper Baer radical, which is not in general equal to the lower Baer radical.

These results together with the following theorem give us

$$Z < D < B < N < M.$$

Theorem 32. $D < B$.

Proof. Let R be the integers with zero product as above. We show that R is D-semisimple.

Suppose R contains some D-ideals. Every nonzero ideal of R is isomorphic to R and thus if R has a nonzero D-ideal, it must be D-radical itself. Let v be the minimum ordinal such that R is of degree v over the class of all nilpotent rings which are nil radicals of left Artinian rings. Then clearly v is not a limit ordinal. Every nonzero homomorphic image of R then contains a nonzero ideal of degree $v - 1$ and in particular R contains such an ideal. Therefore R is itself of degree $v - 1$, which contradicts the minimality of v, unless $v = 1$. Thus R is a homomorphic image of a nil radical of a left Artinian ring.

Let R' be a left Artinian ring, A its nil radical, and I an ideal of A such that A/I is isomorphic to R. Then $A^2 \subset I$. We consider the ring R'/A^2. It is also left Artinian and its nil radical is A/A^2, which can be homomorphically mapped onto R, for

$$(A/A^2)/(I/A^2) \simeq A/I \simeq R.$$

Thus we assume without loss of generality that $A^2 = (0)$.

Every element of A is of the form $mx + h$, where m is an integer, $h \in I$, and x is a representative of the generator of the infinite cyclic additive group A/I. Note that $mx \in I$ implies that $m = 0$.

We now consider the sequence of left ideals of R':

$$R' \supset R'x \supset R'(2x) \supset R'(2^2x) \supset \cdots \supset R'(2^nx) \supset \cdots.$$

None of these can be zero, for if $R'(2^nx) = (0)$, then

$$(2^nx) \supsetneqq (2^{n+1}x) \supsetneqq \cdots \supsetneqq (2^{n+r}x) \supsetneqq \cdots,$$

where $(2^{n+r}x)$ is the additive group generated by $2^{n+r}x$, is an infinite descending chain of nonzero left ideals of R', contradicting the fact that R' is left Artinian.

Also because R' is left Artinian there exists n such that $R'(2^nx) = R'(2^{n+1}x)$. Thus for every element $f \in R'$ there exists an element $g \in R'$ such that $f(2^nx) = g(2^{n+1}x)$.

We note that $R' \neq A$, for if it were, A would be left Artinian and so would A/I, which is isomorphic to R, which is not left Artinian. Hence R'/I is a nonzero semisimple ring, so by Theorem 10, Chapter 2, R' contains an idempotent e which is an identity modulo A, that is, for all $a \in R'$, $a = ae + (a - ae)$, where $a - ae \in A$. Thus $ax = aex$ since $A^2 = (0)$. Then $a(x - ex) = 0$ for all $a \in R'$ and $R'(x - ex) = (0)$. If $ex = x + h$, there exists an element $b \in R'$ such that $e(2^n x) = b(2^{n+1} x)$. However, $bx \in A$, and therefore $bx = mx + h'$, where m is an integer. Then

$$e(2^n x) = 2^n x + 2^n h = b(2^{n+1} x) = 2^{n+1} mx + 2^{n+1} h'.$$

Therefore

$$x(2^n - m(2^{n+1})) = 2^{n+1} h' - 2^n h,$$

which is in I. Thus $2^n - m(2^{n+1}) = 0$, which is impossible.

On the other hand, if $ex \neq x + h$, then $ex = qx + h$, where $q \neq 1$ and $x - ex \neq 0$. Then

$$(x - ex) \supset (2(x - ex)) \supset (2^2(x - ex)) \supset \cdots \supset (2^n(x - ex)) \supset \cdots$$

is a descending chain of left ideals of R', where $(2^n(x - ex))$ is the additive group generated by $2^n(x - ex)$. Each is nonzero, for if $2^n(x - ex) = (0)$, then $2^n(x - qx - h) = 2^n(1 - q)x - 2^n h = 0$. Thus $2^n(1 - q)x \in I$, which is impossible unless $q = 1$.

This is a properly descending chain, for if $(2^n(x - ex)) = (2^{n+1}(x - ex))$, there exists an integer k such that

$$2^n(x - ex) = k(2^{n+1}(x - ex)).$$

Therefore, $2^n(x - qx - h) = k(2^{n+1}(x - qx - h))$ and

$$x(2^n(1 - q) - k(2^{n+1}(1 - q))) = h(2^n - k(2^{n+1})) \in I.$$

Therefore $2^n(1 - q)(1 - 2k) = 0$, which is impossible for k an integer.

Thus in either case we have a contradiction. Therefore R is D-semisimple.

CHAPTER 6

Generalizations to Other Systems

We now look at the other approach to generalizing the radical; namely, we extend various notions of radicals to systems other than rings. The purpose is obvious: since radicals lead to theorems telling us a great deal about the structure of rings, it is hoped that similar knowledge can be gained by studying radicals in other algebraic entities.

1. ALGEBRAS

The Wedderburn structure theorem was first proved for finite-dimensional algebras over a field of characteristic zero, so originally the problem was to extend the theory of radicals to rings. Then the concept of algebra was generalized to include algebras over rings, so that rings became a special case of algebras, namely Z-algebras. Thus in the subsequent theory of radicals the question which arises is whether the results can be generalized to arbitrary algebras. In the first section we consider only associative algebras over commutative rings with identity and study mainly the case of the Jacobson radical.

First we must define what we mean by an algebra module. Let A be an algebra over a commutative ring K with identity and M an abelian group written additively. Then M is an *(algebra) A-module* if and only if it is a K-module and a (ring) A-module such that

$$\alpha(am) = (\alpha a)m = a(\alpha m)$$

for all $\alpha \in K$, $a \in A$, $m \in M$.

Then the definitions for ring modules may be carried over to algebra modules, e.g., M is irreducible if and only if $AM \neq (0)$ and M has only itself and (0) as submodules. A check of the results on primitivity, the radical, and semisimplicity shows that they can also be carried over to algebras.

However, the interesting question is whether the radical defined in terms of algebra modules coincides with that defined for the algebra as a ring. In order to make the comparison, we look at the internal structure of the algebra.

Theorem 1. *If A is a K-algebra, K a commutative ring with identity, then the set of regular maximal left algebra ideals coincides with the set of regular maximal left ideals of A as a ring.*

Proof. Let I be a regular maximal left (ring) ideal in A and let e be such that $A(1 - e) \subset I$. For each $\alpha \in K$, αI is clearly a left ideal in A. Suppose that for some α, $\alpha I \not\subset I$. Then since I is maximal, we have $I + \alpha I = A$. Thus

$$e = a_1 + \alpha a_2, \qquad a_1, a_2 \in I.$$

Then

$$e^2 = a_1 e + \alpha a_2 e = a_1 e + a_2 \alpha e,$$

so that $e^2 \in I$. But $e - e^2 \in I$, so $e \in I$ and $I = A$, contradicting the maximality of I. Thus $\alpha I \subset I$ for all $\alpha \in K$ and I is a regular maximal left algebra ideal.

On the other hand, suppose that I is a regular maximal left algebra ideal of A. Then I is a proper regular left ideal of A and by Lemma 2 of Theorem 1, Chapter 4, can be embedded in a regular maximal left ideal I'. But I' is, by the first part of the proof, a left algebra ideal. Thus $I = I'$.

Using this result we can show:

Theorem 2. *If A is a K-algebra, K a commutative ring with identity, then every irreducible algebra A-module is an irreducible (ring) module. Moreover, every irreducible (ring) A-module can be regarded in precisely one way as an irreducible algebra module.*

Proof. As in the case of ring modules, an algebra module M is irreducible if and only if $M \neq (0)$, M is cyclic, and $Rm = (0)$ implies that $m = 0$. Thus the first assertion of the theorem is clear.

We now let M be an irreducible (ring) A-module. To define a multiplication on M by elements of K, we observe that if $0 \neq m \in M$, then $m = am$ for some $a \in A$. Thus we define

$$\alpha(am) = (\alpha a)m, \qquad m \in M, \quad a \in A, \quad \alpha \in K.$$

To show that the operation is well defined, it suffices to show that $bm = 0$ implies that $\alpha(bm) = (\alpha b)m = 0$. We have $b \in \{m\}_l$, which is a maximal regular left (ring) ideal of A because M is irreducible. But by Theorem 1, $\{m\}_l$ is a maximal regular left algebra ideal. Thus $(\alpha b)m = 0$.

It remains to show that

$$(*) \qquad\qquad \alpha(am) = (\alpha a)m = a(\alpha m).$$

But

$$(\alpha a)m = (\alpha a)(bm) = \alpha(ab)m = a(\alpha b)m = (a\alpha)(bm) = a(\alpha m), \qquad b \in A.$$

Thus M is an irreducible algebra module with the algebra operation uniquely determined by $(*)$.

We can now obtain the result that we want.

Theorem 3. *If A is a K-algebra, where K is a commutative ring with identity, then the radical of A as an algebra is the same as the radical of A as a ring.*

Proof. I is a primitive algebra ideal if and only if I is the annihilator of an irreducible algebra module. But by Theorem 2, I is the annihilator of an irreducible (ring) module and hence is a primitive ideal of A. Thus that the radical must be the same follows from the definition of the radical in terms of annihilators.

We remark that it is also possible to develop the radical theory for algebras in terms of the quasi-regular characterization; in fact, Perlis did the original quasi-regularity work for algebras.

The next problem which arises is the applicability of structure theorems to algebras. A check of the proofs of Chapter 4 will show that the theory does carry over.

A special kind of algebra which is of interest because of its analytic properties is a normed algebra. An (associative) algebra A over the real or complex numbers is a *normed algebra* provided that there is associated with each $x \in A$ a real number $\|x\|$, called the *norm* of x, with the following properties:

1) $\|x\| \geq 0$, and $\|x\| = 0$ if and only if $x = 0$ (the additive identity of A).

2) $\|x + y\| \leq \|x\| + \|y\|$.

3) $\|\alpha x\| = |\alpha|\,\|x\|$, α a real or complex number.

4) $\|xy\| \leq \|x\|\,\|y\|$.

5) If A has an identity 1, then $\|1\| = 1$.

Although we shall not be interested in the topological properties, we remark that if A is complete with respect to the norm, it is a Banach space and A is called a *Banach algebra*. Every normed algebra can be completed to become a Banach algebra.

One can define the (Jacobson) radical of a normed algebra in any one of the equivalent ways used for rings. It is possible to give an additional characterization. An element x of a normed algebra A is *topologically nilpotent* if

$$\lim_{n \to \infty} \|x^n\|^{1/n} = 0.$$

An ideal of a normed algebra is a *topologically nil ideal* if each of its elements is topologically nilpotent. Then it can be shown, using the notion of the spectrum of an element, that the radical of a normed algebra is a topologically nil ideal which is the sum of all topologically nil one-sided ideals. One has an analogue of the usual structure theorem:

A semisimple Banach algebra is (continuously) isomorphic to the normed subdirect sum of primitive Banach algebras.

For other applications, the Brown-McCoy radical is more useful. A Banach algebra with zero Brown-McCoy radical is usually said to be *strongly semisimple*. Such an algebra is (continuously) isomorphic to the normed subdirect sum of simple Banach algebras with identity. The proofs of these structure theorems are principally adaptations of those of the analogous theorems of Chapters 4 and 5 to provide for the norm.

In the case of a commutative Banach algebra, there is this additional structure theorem due to Gelfand: A semisimple commutative Banach algebra with identity is isomorphic to an algebra of continuous functions on a compact Hausdorff space.

2. GROUP ALGEBRAS

We recall from Chapter 3 that one interesting class of algebras is that of group algebras. It turns out that members of a large class of group algebras are in fact (Jacobson) semisimple.

Our first result is the following:

Theorem 4. *If G is a finite group and K is a field of characteristic zero, then the group algebra $K(G)$ is semisimple.*

Proof. This is a direct result of Theorem 3, Chapter 3, and the following theorem:

Theorem 5 (Maschke's Theorem). *If G is a finite group and K a field such that char $K \nmid o(G)$, then every left $K(G)$-(algebra) module is completely reducible.*

Proof. Let $(0) \neq M$ be a $K(G)$-(algebra) module, $(0) \neq N$ a submodule of M. Then M and N are K-modules and hence vector spaces. Thus there exists a vector space V such that

$$M = N \oplus V.$$

For $m \in M$ we let

$$m = n + v, \qquad n \in N, \quad v \in V$$

and define $f: M \to N$ by

$$f(m) = n.$$

Then f is a K-module homomorphism characterized by the properties:

1) $f(m) = m$ for $m \in N$,
2) $f(M) \subset N$.

In fact, if $g: M \to M$ is any K-module homomorphism satisfying (1) and (2), g determines a decomposition of M as

$$M = g(M) + (1 - g)M,$$

where $(1 - g)M = \{m - g(m) \mid m \in M\}$. If g is an algebra homomorphism, i.e., a $K(G)$-module homomorphism as well as a K-module homomorphism, then it is easy to see that $g(M)$ and $(1 - g)M$ are $K(G)$-(algebra) submodules. Thus the problem reduces to producing a projection $M \to N$ which is an algebra homomorphism.

We note that for g to be a $K(G)$-module homomorphism, it suffices to show that

$$g(xm) = xg(m) \quad \text{for} \quad x \in G, \quad m \in M.$$

We define $f': M \to M$ by

$$f' = \frac{1}{o(G)} \sum_{x \in G} xfx^{-1}.$$

Then for $y \in G$,

$$yf'y^{-1} = \frac{1}{o(G)} \sum_{x \in G} yxfx^{-1}y^{-1}$$

$$= \frac{1}{o(G)} \sum_{x \in G} (yx)f(xy)^{-1} = f'.$$

Thus $yf'(m) = f'(ym)$, $m \in M$, as desired. Also it is clear that f' satisfies (1) and (2) above.

Theorem 4 can be generalized in two directions: by removing the finiteness condition on the group G or by replacing the field of characteristic zero by a field of arbitrary characteristic or by an arbitrary commutative ring. We shall give examples of both types of results.

Theorem 6. *Over a field of characteristic p the group algebra of a finite group has a nontrivial radical if and only if the order of the group is divisible by p.*

Proof. If the characteristic of the field does not divide the order of the group, the proof is essentially as for Theorem 4.

On the other hand, if p divides the order of a group G, we let

$$s = \sum_{g_i \in G} g_i.$$

Then $sg_i = s$, for each i, and hence if

$$\alpha = \sum_{g_i \in G} k_i g_i$$

is any element of $K(G)$, then

$$s\alpha = \alpha s = \left(\sum k_i\right)s,$$

so that the scalar multiples of s form an ideal of $K(G)$ which we shall denote by I. However, $s^2 = s(\sum 1) = 0$ since $\sum 1$ is the order of G, which is equivalent to zero modulo p. Thus I is a nonzero nilpotent ideal of $K(G)$ and $K(G)$ is not semisimple.

Theorem 7. If G is a free abelian group and K a commutative ring without nonzero nilpotent elements, then K(G) is (Jacobson) semisimple.

Proof. We first suppose that $G = Z$. Then for $\alpha \in K(G)$, we have

$$\alpha = \sum_{i=r}^{s} k_i g^i, \qquad k_i \in K, \quad g \text{ the generator of } G.$$

The subring T of elements of the form $\sum_{i=0}^{s} k_i g^i$ is isomorphic to $K[x]$, the polynomial ring in one variable over K.

We let J be the radical of $K(G)$, $\alpha = \sum_{i=r}^{s} k_i g^i \in J$, and suppose $\alpha \neq 0$. We let

$$\beta = \sum_{i=1}^{t} k_i' g^i, \qquad t = s + 1 - r, \quad k_i' = k_{i+1-r}.$$

Then $\beta \in T \cap J$ and $\beta \neq 0$. Moreover, $T\beta \subset T \cap J$ is an ideal in T and $\gamma \in T\beta$ implies that

$$\gamma = \sum_{i=1}^{m} k_i'' g^i.$$

Let δ be the quasi-inverse of γ. Then if

$$\delta = \sum_{i=r}^{s} h_i g^i \qquad (r \leq 0),$$

we compare the terms of minimal degree of γ, δ, and $\delta\gamma$ in

$$\gamma + \delta - \delta\gamma = 0$$

to see that $h_r = 0$. Then $\delta \in T$ so that $T\beta$ is a quasi-regular ideal in T.

But T is a polynomial ring over a ring with no nonzero nilpotent elements, so by Theorem 13, Chapter 4, T is semisimple, contradicting the quasi-regularity of the nonzero ideal $T\beta$.

Hence $\alpha \in J$ implies that $\alpha = 0$ and $K(G)$ is semisimple.

We now suppose that G is free abelian of finite rank n and proceed by induction. Assuming that $K(G')$ is semisimple when G' is free abelian of rank $n - 1$, we write $G = G' \oplus Z$ so that $K(G) = [K(G')](Z)$. But then by the above argument, $K(G)$, being the group algebra over a semisimple (and hence having no nonzero nilpotent elements) ring of an infinite cyclic group, is semisimple.

Finally we let G be any free abelian group, J the radical of $K(G)$, and $\alpha \in J$. Letting X be the basis of G, we note that since only a finite number of the basis elements appear with nonzero coefficients in the expression for α, $\alpha \in K(G')$, where G' is a free abelian group with basis Y, a finite subset of X. Now $K(G')\alpha \subset J \cap K(G')$ is an ideal in $K(G')$ containing α, and

$$K(G) = [K(G')](G''),$$

where G'' is the free abelian group with $X \setminus Y$ as basis.

If $\gamma \in K(G')\alpha$ and δ is the quasi-inverse of γ,

$$\delta = \sum k_i g_i, \qquad k_i \in K(G'), \quad g_i \in G'',$$

then, letting g_1 be the identity, from

$$\gamma + \sum k_i g_i - \gamma \sum k_i g_i = 0$$

we obtain

$$\gamma + k_1 - \gamma k_1 = 0.$$

Thus γ has a quasi-inverse in $K(G')$. But then $K(G')\alpha$ is a quasi-regular ideal of $K(G')$. $K(G')$ is semisimple since G' has finite rank, and so $\alpha = 0$. Hence $J = 0$ and $K(G)$ is semisimple.

The above theorem can also be extended to the case of a nonabelian group which is locally finite over its center if K is taken to be a semisimple commutative algebra over the rational numbers.

The problem of the structure of group algebras has also been considered extensively in analysis. It is clear that the formal sum used in the definition of group algebra is simply a function from the group to the ring with the coefficient k_g in

$$\sum_{g \in G} k_g g,$$

giving the value of the function at the element $g \in G$. It is this notion which is used in defining the group algebra of a locally compact group to be the set of all complex-valued functions on the group which are integrable with respect to Haar measure, with convolution as the product. Then it is possible to show that the group algebra is Jacobson semisimple. If the locally compact group is either abelian or compact, then the group algebra thus defined is also Brown-McCoy semisimple. However, the proof of these and similar results depends upon topological and analytical results beyond the scope of this book.

3. NEAR-RINGS

A *near-ring* is a set N together with two operations, $+$ and $\cdot$, satisfying the axioms for a ring with the exception of commutativity of addition and the left distributive law (alternatively, the right distributive law). A *left ideal* of a near-ring N is an additive subgroup closed under left multiplication by arbitrary elements of N.

Example. The set of polynomials over a ring with the operations of addition and composition is a near-ring.

Suppose G is an additive group with elements of a near-ring N as left operators. Then G is a *left N-group* if

$$n'(ng) = (n'n)g \qquad \text{for all} \quad n, n' \in N, \quad g \in G.$$

If G is an additive subgroup of N which is also a left N-group, then it is called a *left N-module*. We observe that if N is a ring a left N-module is the same as a left ideal. In general if

$$(*) \qquad\qquad ne = e, \qquad \text{for } e \text{ the identity of } G, \quad \text{and all } n \in N,$$

the set of left ideals of the near-ring N is contained in the set of left modules of N. We limit our discussion to near-rings which satisfy $(*)$.

A near-ring N is said to be *semisimple* if N has no nonzero nilpotent left modules and has the minimal condition for left modules. The following results are proved in the same manner as for rings:

Theorem 8. *Every nonzero left module of a semisimple near-ring contains a nonzero idempotent element.*

Theorem 9. *Every minimal nonzero left module M of a near-ring N contains an idempotent e such that $Ne = Me = M$.*

Theorem 10. *If M is a left module of a semisimple near-ring, then M is the finite direct sum of minimal nonzero left N-modules.*

It would be nice if semisimplicity for near-rings could be tied in with a radical. We now turn our attention to this problem.

If M is a minimal left module of a near-ring N, we define

$$A_l(M) = \{r \in N \mid rM = 0\}.$$

Then $A_l(M)$ is an ideal of N. Let

$$\mathscr{M} = \{M \mid M \text{ a minimal left module of } N\}$$

and define

$$S = \bigcap_{M \in \mathscr{M}} A_l(M).$$

S is clearly an ideal of N.

Theorem 11. *Let N be a near-ring with the minimal condition on left modules. N is semisimple if and only if $S = (0)$.*

Proof. Suppose $S = (0)$. We must show that N has no nonzero nilpotent left modules. Let Q be a nilpotent left module of N and assume Q is minimal. If $Q^2 = (0)$, since $S = (0)$, there exists a minimal left module of N, say P, such that $PQ \neq (0)$. Hence there is a $p \in P$ such that $pQ = P$. Then $PQ = pQ^2 = (0)$, a contradiction. Thus N has no nonzero nilpotent left modules and is semisimple.

On the other hand, suppose N is semisimple. S is an ideal, so it is a left module. Hence S contains a minimal left module of N, say M. But $S \subset A_l(M)$ so that $M^2 = (0)$. Thus $S = (0)$.

Theorem 12. *If N is a near-ring with left minimal condition, then N/S is semisimple.*

Proof. It is clear that N/S has the minimal condition on left modules. Let $\bar{M}$ be a minimal nilpotent left module of N/S and let M be the preimage of $\bar{M}$ in N. Then M is a left module of N and $M^2 \subset S$. Suppose $M \not\subset S$. Then there exists a minimal left module M' of N such that $MM' \neq (0)$. Hence M' contains an element m such that $Mm = M'$. But $MM' = M(Mm) \subset Sm = (0)$ so $M \subset S$. Therefore $\bar{M} = (0)$ and N/S is semisimple.

It would appear that the intersection of the annihilators of the minimal left modules is our desired radical. However, this turns out to be not quite what we want. We now let N be a near-ring with left minimal condition as above and define

$\mathscr{P} = \{P \mid P$ an ideal of N, P has no nonzero idempotent elements, P contains at least one nonzero element which annihilates all idempotents of N from the left$\}$.

Let

$$T = \sum_{P \in \mathscr{P}} P,$$

where the sum is the weak direct sum and the empty sum is taken to be the zero ideal. Letting

$$\bar{S} = \bigcap_{\substack{\bar{M} \text{ a minimal} \\ \text{left module of } N/T}} A_l(\bar{M}),$$

we define $\sigma: N \to (N/T)/\bar{S}$ in the canonical manner and let $R =$ kernel σ. We call R the *radical* of the near-ring N. The proof of the following theorem is clear from the definition.

Theorem 13. *If N is a near-ring with left minimal condition, N/R is semisimple; N is semisimple if and only if $R = (0)$.*

We note that this radical coincides with the classical radical if N is a ring.

4. GROUPS

We follow a method analogous to the use of radical properties for rings in Chapter 5. We consider a class of groups which have a property θ, calling these θ-groups. If a group has a characteristic θ-subgroup containing all normal θ-subgroups of the group, then we shall call that θ-subgroup the θ-*radical* of the group. A group with no nontrivial θ-subgroups is called θ-*semisimple*. We shall require that the properties we consider satisfy the following:

1) A subgroup of a θ-group is a θ-group.

2) A homomorphic image of a θ-group is a θ-group.

3) θ is a local property.

4) Every group has a θ-radical.

We shall denote the θ-radical of a group G by $\theta(G)$.

Examples. Local finiteness, periodicity, and local nilpotence of a group are properties satisfying (1) through (4).

We note that the analogues of most of the "radical properties" listed at the beginning of Chapter 5 are satisfied by the θ-radical. Property (3)—in group form—may be easily obtained:

Lemma. If H is a normal subgroup of a group G, then $\theta(H)$ is a normal subgroup of $\theta(G)$ and $\theta(H) = \theta(G) \cap H$.

Proof. Since $\theta(H)$ is a characteristic subgroup of H it is a normal θ-subgroup of G, so $\theta(H) \subset \theta(G) \cap H$. On the other hand $\theta(G) \cap H$ is a θ-subgroup which is normal in H so that $\theta(G) \cap H \subset \theta(H)$.

We can also define an analogue of the Baer lower radical. For an arbitrary group G we construct an increasing sequence of characteristic subgroups

$$(e) = \theta_0(G) \subset \theta_1(G) \subset \cdots \subset \theta_\alpha(G) \subset \theta_{\alpha+1}(G) \subset \cdots$$

by the following rule:

1) If α is a limit ordinal, then $\theta_\alpha(G) = \bigcup_{\beta < \alpha} \theta_\beta(G)$.

2) $\theta_{\alpha+1}(G)/\theta(G) = \theta(G/\theta_\alpha(G))$.

We call this sequence the θ-*radical series* for G. If γ is the first ordinal for which $\theta_\gamma(G) = \theta_{\gamma+1}(G)$, then $\theta_\gamma(G)$ is the *upper θ-radical* of G, denoted by $\bar{\theta}(G)$. It is clear that $G/\bar{\theta}(G)$ is semisimple. If $\bar{\theta}(G) = G$, then the group is θ-*radical*.

We want to show that the upper radical has the properties we would expect of it. First we need another definition. We recall that a series of groups

$$(e) = G_0 \subset G_1 \subset \cdots \subset G_\alpha \subset \cdots \subset G_{\alpha+1} \subset \cdots \subset G_\gamma = G$$

is a normal series for G if G_α is a normal subgroup of $G_{\alpha+1}$. Any subseries from G_α to G_β, $\alpha < \beta$, is then said to *join* G_α and G_β. Two subgroups H, K of a group G, $H \subset K$, are *normally linked* if there is an ascending normal series joining H and K.

Theorem 14. *If K and H, $H \subset K$, are normally linked subgroups of a group G, then $\theta(H) \subset \theta(K)$ and $\theta(H) = \theta(K) \cap H$.*

Proof. Let

$$H = H_0 \subset \cdots \subset H_\alpha \subset H_{\alpha+1} \subset \cdots \subset H_\alpha = K$$

be a normal series joining H to K. By induction on the length of this series, we show that if $\alpha \leq \beta$, then $\theta(H_\alpha) \subset \theta(H_\beta)$.

The statement is clear for $\alpha = \beta = 0$. Suppose it has been proved for all α and β, $\alpha \leq \beta$, less than γ. We prove it for $\beta = \gamma$.

If γ is not a limit ordinal, by the lemma we have $\theta(H_{\gamma-1}) \subset \theta(H_\gamma)$. If $\alpha \leq \gamma$, then $\alpha \leq \gamma - 1$ and by the induction hypothesis $\theta(H_\alpha) \subset \theta(H_{\gamma-1}) \subset \theta(H_\gamma)$. Since $\theta(K) \cap H$ is a normal subgroup of H, we have $\theta(K) \cap H \subset \theta(H)$ and clearly $\theta(H) \subset H \cap \theta(K)$.

An ascending normal (invariant) series whose factor groups are all θ-groups is called an *ascending normal (invariant) θ-series*.

Theorem 15. *If a group G has an ascending normal θ-series, then G is θ-radical. In particular, the existence of an ascending normal θ-series implies that of an ascending invariant series.*

Proof. Let

$$(e) = H_0 \subset H_1 \subset \cdots \subset H_\gamma = G$$

be an ascending normal θ-series. Since H_1 is normally linked with G, $\theta(H_1) = H_1 \cap \theta(G)$ so that $\theta_1(G) \neq (e)$.

Suppose that for all $\alpha < \beta$ we have constructed the characteristic subgroups $\theta_\alpha(G)$. For β a limit ordinal we let

$$\theta_\beta(G) = \bigcup_{\alpha < \beta} \theta_\alpha(G).$$

If β is not a limit ordinal, we consider $G/\theta_{\beta-1}(G)$. This group has a normal series whose terms are the images of the terms of the series for G under the canonical projection η. Since images of θ-groups are θ-groups, $G/\theta_{\beta-1}(G)$ thus has a nontrivial θ-radical. Thus we let $\theta_\beta(G) = \eta^{-1}(\theta(G/\theta_{\beta-1}(G)))$.

Corollary 1. The product of two θ-radical normal subgroups of an arbitrary group is a θ-radical normal subgroup.

Corollary 2. The extension of a θ-radical group by a θ-radical group is again a θ-radical group.

Corollary 3. Subgroups and homomorphic images of a θ-radical group are also θ-radical.

For the proof of each of these corollaries we construct the appropriate ascending normal θ-series.

These lead to the proof of the main results characterizing the upper radical in a manner similar to that we developed for rings.

Theorem 16. *The upper θ-radical of an arbitrary group G is a θ-radical characteristic subgroup containing all θ-radical normal subgroups of G.*

Proof. If $\bar{\theta}(G)$ were contained in a larger θ-radical normal subgroup, $G/\bar{\theta}(G)$ would not be semisimple, as it must be from its construction. On the other hand, if R is a θ-radical normal subgroup, it is contained in $\bar{\theta}(G)$, for by Corollary 1 its product with $\bar{\theta}(G)$ is radical.

Theorem 17. *The upper θ-radical of an arbitrary group G is the intersection of all normal subgroups of G whose factor groups are θ-semisimple.*

Proof. We know that $G/\bar{\theta}(G)$ is semisimple so it suffices to prove that if G/H is semisimple, then $\bar{\theta}(G) \subset H$. Suppose this is not the case. Then $\bar{\theta}(G)H$

strictly contains H and

$$\bar{\theta}(G)H/H \simeq \bar{\theta}(G)/(H \cap \bar{\theta}(G)).$$

But then G/H is not semisimple, a contradiction.

Example. Plotkin has shown that every group has a locally nilpotent characteristic subgroup containing all locally nilpotent normal subgroups of that group. It is clear that such a maximum locally nilpotent normal subgroup is a radical with respect to the property of local nilpotence; it is frequently called the *Hirsch-Plotkin* radical. For finite groups this radical coincides with the Fitting subgroup, the subgroup of a group generated by all its nilpotent normal subgroups. The upper radical which corresponds to the property of local nilpotence is the intersection of those normal subgroups whose factor groups have trivial Hirsch-Plotkin radical.

5. RADICALS IN LATTICES

Various radicals have been defined in special structures, for example, automorphism groups of groups, group pairs, by analogy with the cases of rings and groups. A check of the references in the bibliography will provide the details of such constructions. We shall, however, conclude this chapter with the definition of radicals in more general settings which include rings (both associative and nonassociative) as special cases. We recall that in a lattice any pair, and hence any finite subset, of elements has an lub and a glb. A lattice is *complete* if any arbitrary collection of elements of the lattice has an lub and a glb. Every complete lattice L has a zero element 0_L and an identity I_L with the properties that for all $a \in L$, $0_L \leq a$ and $a \leq I_L$. A *sublattice* L of a lattice M is a subset of the elements of M which themselves form a lattice.

Amitsur is primarily responsible for the results on radicals of lattices. His starting point was radicals in rings, but instead of looking at ring properties invariant under ring homomorphisms, he considered binary relations between ideals as elements of the complete lattice of ideals of a ring. Thus the formulation can be given in the general setting of a complete lattice.

A binary relation r defined in a complete lattice M is called an *H-relation* in M if r satisfies the following:

1) If arb for $a, b \in M$, then $a \geq b$.

2) ara for every $a \in M$.

3) If arb and $c \geq b$, then $\text{lub}\{a, c\}rc$.

When arb and $a, b \in L$, a sublattice of M, a is an *r-element over b* in L. $a \in L$ is an *r*-element in L if $ar0_L$. L is *r-semisimple* in M if L does not possess nonzero *r*-elements.

Suppose $a \leq b$, $a, b \in L$. If $[a, b] = \{x \in L \mid a \leq x \leq b\}$ is *r*-semisimple, we write $a\bar{r}b$ in L. An element b is said to be an *r̄-element over a* in L if $a\bar{r}b$ in L. If $a\bar{r}I_L$, a is said to be an *r̄-element in L*. An element $x \in L$ is called an *r-radical* in L if x is both an *r*-element in L and an *r̄*-element in L.

Example. If M is the lattice of ideals of a ring R and r is the relation defined by

$$IrJ \text{ if and only if } I^n \subset J \subset I \text{ for some integer } n,$$

then r is an H-relation. Moreover, the q-elements are the radical ideals of Baer and the r-radical is the nilpotent radical of R, if it exists. In fact, this whole extension of the theory of radicals to lattices is based on Baer's notions as discussed in Chapter 5.

In general, we say that if I, J are ideals of a ring R, $J \subset I$ and I/J has a property P of rings, then I is *P-related* to J, written IrJ; a *P-radical* $P(R)$ of a ring R is a maximal ideal of R such that $P(R)$ possesses a given property P and such that $R/P(R)$ has no nonzero ideals possessing the property. An ideal is a *P-ideal* if and only if it is a *P-ring*, that is, it has property P of rings.

In what follows, we consider a set $\mathscr{L}$ of complete sublattices of a complete lattice M such that $L \in \mathscr{L}$ implies that every L-interval $[a, b] = \{x \in L \mid a \leq x \leq b\}$ is in $\mathscr{L}$ and assume that r is an H-relation in M.

We define inductively

$$u_0(L, r) = 0_L,$$

$$u_1(L, r) = \text{lub}\{p \mid pr0_L \text{ in } L\},$$

$$u_\alpha(L, r) = \text{lub}\{u_\beta(L, r), \beta < \alpha\} \qquad \text{for } \alpha \text{ a limit ordinal}$$

$$= \text{lub}\{p \mid pru_{\alpha-1}(L, r) \text{ in } L\} \qquad \text{for } \alpha \text{ not a limit ordinal.}$$

We shall use u_α for $u_\alpha(L, r)$ when no confusion is possible.

We prove some lemmas giving us information about radicals.

Lemma 1. There is an ordinal γ such that $u_\gamma(L, r) = u_\tau(L, r)$ for every ordinal $\tau \geq \gamma$ and $u_\alpha(L, r) < u_\beta(L, r)$ for $\alpha < \beta \leq \gamma$ (if $\gamma > 1$)

Proof. Since the chain $\{u_\alpha\}$ is a subset of L, there exists a minimal γ such that $u_\gamma = u_{\gamma+1}$. The rest of the lemma follows immediately by the definition of the u_α and by the minimality of γ.

The element $u_\alpha(L, r)$ is called the αth *r-radical* of L, and u_γ, the element of the preceding lemma, is called the *upper r-radical* of L (in M). This element will be denoted by $u(L, r)$.

We now generalize the results of Baer by examining the relation between the upper r-radical of L and the $\bar{r}$-elements of L. It is apparent that if $a\bar{r}b$ in L, then $a\bar{r}b$ in every sublattice of L which contains both a and b.

Lemma 2. Let $p, q \in [a, b]$ in L be such that $q\bar{r}b$ and pra; then $q \geq p$.

Proof. It follows by (3) in the definition of H-relation that $\text{lub}\{p, q\}rq$ in L. Since $q\bar{r}b$ and $b \geq \text{lub}\{p, q\} \geq q$, $\text{lub}\{p, q\} = q$. Thus $q \geq p$.

In particular if $a = I_L$ and $b = 0_L$, we have:

Corollary. Each $\bar{r}$-element in L is greater than or equal to every r-element of L.

From the corollary we obtain:

Theorem 18. *Every sublattice L possesses at most one r-radical.*

Proof. If r_1 and r_2 are two r-radicals of L, then since $r_1 \bar{r} I$ and $r_2 r 0$, $r_1 \geq r_2$. Similarly $r_2 \geq r_1$.

Thus if L possesses an r-radical, we refer to it as *the* r-radical of L and denote it by $r(L, r)$.

But $r(L, r)$ is an $\bar{r}$-element, so we have:

Corollary. If $r(L, r)$ exists in L, then $r(L, r)$ is the maximum r-element of L.

Lemma. Let Q be a set of $\bar{r}$-elements in L; then $t = \mathrm{glb}\{q \mid q \in Q\}$ is also an $\bar{r}$-element in L.

Proof. Let $p \in L$ be such that prt. Since $q \geq t, q \in Q$, it follows by Lemma 2 above that $q \geq p$. But this holds for every $q \in Q$; hence $t \geq p$. This proves that t is an $\bar{r}$-element.

Since I_L is an $\bar{r}$-element in L, the set of all $\bar{r}$-elements in L is not empty. We have:

Corollary. The glb of all $\bar{r}$-elements of L is the minimal $\bar{r}$-element in L.

We can now obtain the following characterization of the upper radical:

Theorem 19. *The upper r-radical $u(L, r)$ is the minimal $\bar{r}$-element of L.*

Proof. Since by Lemma 1 to Theorem 18, $u(L, r) = u_\gamma = u_{\gamma+1}$, we have by the definition of $u_{\gamma+1}$ that $u(L, r)$ is an $\bar{r}$-element in L. Hence if $m = \mathrm{glb}\{q \mid q$ is an $\bar{r}$-element in $L\}$, $m \leq u(L, r)$. To prove that $u(L, r) \leq m$, it suffices to show that $m \geq u_\alpha(L, r)$ for every ordinal α. But by the preceding corollary, m is an $\bar{r}$-element in L. This gives us that $m \geq u_1(L, r)$. Now we suppose that $m \geq u_\beta(L, r)$ for every ordinal $\beta < \alpha$. For a limit ordinal α it is clear that $m \geq u_\alpha$. If α is not a limit ordinal, then since $m \geq u_{\alpha-1}$, it follows by Lemma 2 to Theorem 18 that $m \geq p$ for every p which is an r-element over $u_{\alpha-1}$. This implies that $m \geq u_\alpha$, which completes the proof.

This leads to a necessary and sufficient condition for the existence of a radical.

Theorem 20. *A necessary and sufficient condition that $r(L, r)$ exist is that $u(L, r)$ be an r-element. In this case $r(L, r) = u(L, r)$.*

Proof. From Theorem 19 we have that $u(L, r)$ is an $\bar{r}$-element. Hence if $u(L, r)$ is an r-element, $u(L, r)$ is the r-radical. Conversely, we suppose that $r(L, r)$ exists. Since $r(L, r)\bar{r} I_L$, it follows from Theorem 19 that $r(L, r) \geq u(L, r)$. But since $r(L, r)$ is an r-element,

$$u(L, r) \geq u_1(L, r) \geq r(L, r).$$

Thus $r(L, r) = u(L, r)$, and $u(L, r)$ is an r-element in L.

We also have the expected relation between the upper r-radicals of two lattices.

Theorem 21. *If $L' \subset L$ and $0_L = 0_{L'}$, then $u(L, r) \geq u(L', r)$.*

We show that for all α, $u(L, r) \geq u_\alpha(L', r)$. If $pr0$ in L', then $pr0$ in L; hence $u(L, r) \geq u_1(L', r)$. We proceed by induction. If α is a limit ordinal, then $u(L, r) \geq u_\alpha(L', r)$ if $u(L, r) \geq u_\beta(L', r)$ for every $\beta < \alpha$. If α is not a limit ordinal, we have that if $pru_{\alpha-1}(L', r)$, then the same relation holds in L. Hence from $u(L, r) \geq u_{\alpha-1}(L', r)$ we get that $u(L, r) \geq p$. But then $u(L, r) \geq u_\alpha(L', r)$.

We seek further conditions for the existence of the r-radical of a lattice. It is clear that if $u([0, a], r) < a$, then $[u([0, a], r), a]$ is a nonzero semisimple interval of a lattice L containing a. If $[x, a]$ is a nonzero semisimple interval in L, then $u([0, a], r) \leq x < a$. Consequently we have the following lemmas.

Lemma 1. $u([0, a], r) = a$ if and only if none of the nonzero L-intervals $[x, a]$ is semisimple.

Lemma 2. $u(L, r) \geq u([0, a], r)$ for all $a \in L$.

Lemma 3. $\bar{r}$ is a transitive relation in L.

Proof. Suppose $a\bar{r}b$ and $b\bar{r}c$. If $c \geq p \geq a$ and pra, then $\text{lub}\{p, b\}rb$. But $c \geq \text{lub}\{p, b\} \geq b$, and so $\text{lub}\{p, b\} = b$. But then $b \geq p \geq a$, so that $a\bar{r}b$ implies that $p = a$. Hence $a\bar{r}c$ in L.

Now we have:

Theorem 22. *The r-radical exists in every sublattice L of M if and only if r satisfies*

4) *For every $a, b \in L$, $a < b$, such that b is not an r-element over a, there is an element $c \in L$ such that $c\bar{r}b$ in L.*

Proof. Let r be an H-relation which satisfies (4). If $u(L, r)$ is not an r-element, then there is $u(L, r) > c \geq 0_L$ such that $c\bar{r}u(L, r)$. By Theorem 19, $u(L, r)\bar{r}I_L$; hence by Lemma 3, $c\bar{r}I_L$. Hence by Theorem 19 we cannot have $u(L, r) > c$. Thus $u(L, r)$ is an r-element and we have from Theorem 20, $u(L, r) = r(L, r)$, so $r(L, r)$ exists.

On the other hand, let r be an H-relation for which the r-radical exists in every sublattice $L \in \mathscr{L}$. Let $b > a$ and b be not an r-element over a in L. The L-interval $[a, b]$ is a lattice for which the r-radical r must exist. But $b > r \geq a$ and $r\bar{r}b$ in L, so (4) is satisfied.

An H-relation which satisfies (4) is called an *R-relation*.

Example. If M is the lattice of ideals of a ring R and $A, B \in M$, $A \supset B$, we define

$$ArB \text{ if and only if } A/B \text{ is quasi-regular.}$$

Then r is an H-relation and the r-radical is the Jacobson radical.

It would be nice to be able to establish for lattices generalizations of some of the results for radicals of rings. Very little can be done in such a general setting; however, it is possible to prove an analogue of the result relating the radical of a ring to the radicals of its ideals. We need a slightly more general concept to handle this situation.

A set M is a *complete pseudo-lattice* if there is defined in M a binary relation $\leq$ such that:

1) there is $0 \in M$ such that $0 \leq x$ for all $x \in M$,

2) every M-interval $[a, b] = \{x \in M \mid a \leq x \leq b\}$ is a complete lattice with respect to $\leq$.

By an H-relation r in a complete pseudo-lattice M we mean a relation r defined in M which is an H-relation in every M-interval in M and satisfies:

3′) If lub$\{a, b\}$, glb$\{a, b\}$ are defined in M, then $a\bar{r}$ lub$\{a, b\}$ implies that glb$\{a, b\}\bar{r}b$ in M.

We observe that if M is a complete lattice, condition (3) in the definition of an H-relation implies (3′). As before we denote the r-radical (if it exists) of the M-interval $[n, m]$ by $r(n, m)$.

We then have:

Theorem 23. *Let $[n, m]$ be an interval of a complete pseudo-lattice M, r an H-relation. If $r(n, m)$ exists, then $r(q, m)$ exists for every $q \in [n, m]$, and $r(q, m) = \text{glb}\{q, r(n, m)\}$ if and only if r satisfies:*

1) *if arb, then crb for every $c \in [b, a]$.*

2) *if $a\bar{r}b$, then $a\bar{r}c$ for every $c \in [a, b]$.*

Proof. Suppose r satisfies (1) and (2), and $r(n, m)$ exists. Since $r(n, m) \geq$ glb$\{r(n, m), q\} \geq n$ and $r(n, m)rn$, (1) gives us that glb$\{r(n, m), q\}rn$. We now have $m \geq$ lub$\{r(n, m), q\} \geq r(n, m)$ and $r\bar{r}m$ so that (2) yields $r\bar{r}$ lub$\{r(n, m), q\}$. This implies that glb$\{r(n, m), q\}\bar{r}q$, by (3′) in the definition of H-relation. Thus we have that glb$\{r(n, m), q\}$ is the r-radical of $[q, m]$.

Since (1) and (2) are special cases of the statement of the theorem, the converse is immediate.

To illustrate how the results for lattices specialize to rings we restate Theorem 23 for the case of rings.

A property P of rings is called an *R-property* if:

1) The trivial ring is a P-ring.

2) Homomorphic images of P-rings are P-rings.

3) Every non-P-ring is homomorphic to a nonzero ring which has no nonzero P-ideals. (Compare with RI-properties of ideals in Section 4, Chapter 5.)

We observe that an R-property defines an R-relation in the complete pseudo-lattice of subrings of a given ring, where for subrings A, B of the ring we write $B \leq A$ if B is an ideal in the subring A. For a ring A, we denote the radical defined by an R-relation by $r(A)$. Now we have:

Theorem 23′. *Let P be an R-property. Then $r(I) = I \cap r(R)$ for every ideal I of a ring R if and only if P satisfies:*

4) *All ideals of a P-ring are P-rings.*

5) *All ideals of a P-semisimple ring are P-semisimple rings.*

Some of the results of Chapter 5 may be obtained simultaneously for several kinds of radicals, e.g., Brown-McCoy, Jacobson, Baer, by using the lattice approach. Amitsur also applied these results to a special type of category; categories and radicals in them are discussed in Chapters 8 and 9.

6. ABSTRACT ALGEBRAS

We shall discuss radicals for a class of algebraic entities which includes groups and loops as well as not-necessarily-associative rings. The notions of structure which we introduce here represent an early attempt to do what we shall use a categorical setting for in Chapters 8 and 9, namely achieve sufficient generality to encompass the familiar systems without sacrificing the machinery needed to derive interesting results.

An *abstract algebra* is a nonempty set of elements A together with a number of operations f_α, where each f_α is a function assigning, for some finite $n(\alpha)$, to each $n(\alpha)$-tuple of elements of A a value $f_\alpha(x_1, \ldots, x_{n(\alpha)}) \in A$. The number of operations may be finite or infinite, but each operation is finitary. Then a *subalgebra* is a subset of A closed under each operation and a *homomorphism* is a function which preserves all operations.

We list here for reference the definitions of some "pregroup" systems. A *groupoid* is a nonempty set G together with a binary operation $\circ$ such that if $a, b \in G$, there is a unique $c \in G$ such that $a \circ b = c$. A *semigroup* is a groupoid with an associative operation, that is, $(a \circ b) \circ c = a \circ (b \circ c)$ for all $a, b, c \in G$. A *quasi-group* is a groupoid G such that if any two of a, b, c are given as elements of G, the equation $a \circ b = c$ uniquely determines the third as an element of G. A *loop* is a quasi-group with a two-sided identity, i.e., there exists an element $e \in G$ such that $a \circ e = a = e \circ a$ for all $a \in G$. A *loop algebra* is an abstract algebra A such that one of the operations f_α is a binary operation making A into a loop. In particular, nonassociative rings and semigroups are loop algebras.

Let A and B be two subsets of a loop algebra S. We let

$$AB = \{ab \mid a \in A, b \in B\},$$

where juxtaposition indicates the loop operation of S. In particular, we let $A' = AA$. We define a *loop algebra homomorphism* to be a map which preserves the loop operation and an *ideal* to be a subset of S which is the kernel of such a homomorphism. A *prime ideal* of S is an ideal P of S such that if $AB \subset P$, A, B ideals of S, then either $A \subset P$ or $B \subset P$.

A loop algebra S is a *B-algebra* if $S' = (0)$. Then it is easy to show that B defines an H-relation in the lattice of subalgebras of a loop algebra S, where the binary relation of the lattice is given as in the case of rings. We denote the upper B-radical derived from this relation by $B(S)$. Then we can show that:

Theorem 24. $B(S)$ *is the intersection of all the prime ideals of S.*

Proof. We note that the prime ideals are $\bar{B}$-ideals, so from Theorem 19 we have that the intersection X of all the prime ideals of S contains $B(S)$. We need to show that for every $a \notin B(S)$ there is a prime ideal P in S which does not contain a. Let A_1 be the minimal ideal in S containing $a_1 \notin B(S)$ and $B(S)$. Then $A_1' \subset B(S)$. Now let $a_2 \in A_1'$ be such that $a_2 \notin B(S)$. Thus we obtain a sequence of elements $a_1, a_2, \ldots$ such that $a_i \notin B(S)$ and $a_{i+1} \in A_1'$, where A_i is the minimal ideal of S containing $B(S)$ and a_i. Applying Zorn's lemma we get that there is a maximal ideal P containing $B(S)$ but none of the a_i. Since a_1 was arbitrary, we need only show that P is prime.

If $P_1 P_2 \subset P$ and $P \subsetneq P_i$, $i = 1, 2$, then by the maximality of P there exist $a_j \in P_1$ and $a_k \in P_2$, for some j, k. But then some $a_l \in P_1 \cap P_2$. Thus we have $a_{l+1} \in A_l' \subset P_1 P_2 \subset P$, which is a contradiction.

We observe that if the loop algebra is a ring, this is the McCoy radical. Although a few more results generalizing the work of Brown and McCoy can be obtained in a similar fashion, no interesting structure theorems have been derived in this general setting.

PROBLEMS

1. Prove Theorems 1, 2, 3, 7, and 10 of Chapter 4 for algebras over a commutative ring with identity.
2. Find the radical of the group algebra over Z_2 of each of the following groups:
   a) $Z_2 \oplus Z_2$,
   b) S_3,
   c) the group of symmetries of a square.
3. Find the radical of the group algebra of the additive group of the rational numbers over
   (a) Z_2,   (b) Z.
4. What are the left ideals of the example of a near-ring given in Section 3?
5. Show that for finite groups the upper radical with respect to the property of local nilpotence is the maximum solvable normal subgroup of a group.

6. Show that a finite group is radical if and only if it is solvable.

7. Show that a relation r in a complete lattice is an R-relation if and only if r satisfies the following two conditions:

   i) If arb and brc, then arc.

   ii) If $a_1 \leq a_2 \leq \cdots$ is an ascending chain of r-elements over b, then lub $\{a_i\}$ is also an r-element over b.

8. Give an m-sequence characterization for the radical of a loop algebra based on that for the radical of a ring given in Chapter 5.

CHAPTER 7

Lie and Jordan Algebras

In this chapter we derive a structure theorem for nonassociative algebras; its main applications are to Jordan and Lie algebras. These algebras are intrinsically interesting algebraically, but their primary importance derives from their wide application to the study not only of other branches of mathematics, such as differential geometry, but to such fields as physics and genetics. Our discussion will be limited to some basic definitions and properties and the necessary preliminaries for the radical-based structure theory.

1. DEFINITIONS AND EXAMPLES

The algebras which we have discussed in Chapter 3 have an associative product. However, more generally, we can define a *nonassociative algebra* as a module A over a commutative ring K with identity with a multiplication satisfying the distributive laws and such that

$$(ma)(nb) = (mn)(ab) \quad \text{for all} \quad a, b \in A, \quad m, n \in K.$$

A *subalgebra* is simply a submodule closed under the algebra multiplication (note that we do not require an identity as in the associative case), while an *ideal* is a submodule closed under multiplication by arbitrary elements of the algebra. A *nonassociative algebra homomorphism* is a module homomorphism which preserves the algebra product.

Unfortunately the concept of nonassociative algebra is so general that very little can be said about nonassociative algebras which do not satisfy additional identities. Thus we shall look briefly at three special types of algebras: alternative, Lie, and Jordan. We shall confine our discussion to nonassociative algebras over a field (usually of characteristic not two). Each of these classes is defined by a set of identities and hence is closed with respect to taking subalgebras, homomorphic images, and direct sums. Conversely, any class of nonassociative algebras closed under these operations can be defined by a set of identities.

We define an operation

$$(a, b, c) = (ab)c - a(bc),$$

133

called the *associator*, where a, b, $c \in A$, a nonassociative algebra over a field K, juxtaposition indicating the algebra product. If a nonassociative algebra A satisfies the identity

$$(a, b, b) = 0 = (b, b, a) \qquad \text{for all} \quad a, b \in A,$$

A is an *alternative algebra*. An interesting property of alternative algebras is that any subsystem generated by two elements has associative multiplication.

Examples. Associative algebras are, of course, alternative. An example of an alternative algebra which is not associative is the Cayley numbers. The Cayley numbers are an eight-dimensional vector space over the real numbers. To define the product it is sufficient to define multiplication on a basis. Let $\{1, e_0, \ldots, e_6\}$ be a basis. Then we define

$$1e_i = e_i 1 = e_i, \qquad i \in Z_7,$$
$$e_i e_j + e_j e_i = 0 \qquad \text{for } i \neq j,$$
$$e_i^2 = -1, \qquad i \in Z_7,$$

and for $i \in Z_7$, $e_i e_{i+1} = e_{i+3}$, $e_{i+3} e_i = e_{i+1}$, and $e_{i+1} e_{i+3} = e_i$.

A nonassociative algebra A is a *Jordan algebra* if

$$ab = ba$$

and

$$(a^2, b, a) = 0 \qquad \text{for all} \quad a, b \in A.$$

This type of algebra first arose in connection with the study of quantum mechanics.

Suppose A is an associative algebra over a field (of characteristic not two). In terms of the associative multiplication, written $a \circ b$, we define a new operation

$$ab = \tfrac{1}{2}(a \circ b + b \circ a).$$

Clearly this operation is commutative. Also

$$4a^2(ba) = a^2 \circ (b \circ a + a \circ b) + (b \circ a + a \circ b) \circ a^2$$
$$= a^2 \circ b \circ a + a^3 \circ b + b \circ a^3 + a \circ b \circ a^2,$$

while

$$4(a^2 b)a = (a^2 \circ b + b \circ a^2) \circ a + a \circ (a^2 \circ b + b \circ a^2)$$
$$= a^2 \circ b \circ a + b \circ a^3 + a^3 \circ b + a \circ b \circ a^2.$$

So since the field is not of characteristic 2, $(a^2 b)a = a^2(ba)$. Thus if we denote by A^+ the set of elements of A with the vector space structure of A but with this new multiplication, then A^+ is a Jordan algebra. Hence a Jordan algebra can arise in a natural way from an associative algebra. Of course, if an associative algebra is commutative, A^+ is just the same algebra as A. If a Jordan algebra J is isomorphic to a subalgebra of A^+ (where A^+ is derived from an associative A as above), then J is a *special Jordan algebra*.

Example. Let V be a vector space over a field K (char $K \neq 2$) and $\langle \, , \, \rangle$ a symmetric bilinear form defined on V. Let $A = K \oplus V$ and define a multiplication on A by

$$(a1 + v)(b1 + w) = (ab + \langle v, w \rangle)1 + aw + bv, \qquad v, w \in V, \quad a, b \in K.$$

Then A is a Jordan algebra; indeed it is a special Jordan algebra although the verification of that fact is nontrivial.

There exist Jordan algebras which are not special; these are called *exceptional Jordan algebras*.

Example. We return to the Cayley numbers. *Real* Cayley numbers are scalar multiples of 1, while *imaginary* Cayley numbers are those vectors in the orthogonal complement of the real Cayley numbers. We then define conjugation as for complex numbers: the real part remains fixed and the imaginary part goes into its additive inverse. We then define an $n \times n$ Hermitian matrix over the Cayley numbers to be an $n \times n$ matrix (a_{ij}) such that a_{ji} is the conjugate of a_{ij}, that is, the transpose is the conjugate of the matrix. Then the vector space of 3×3 Hermitian matrices over the Cayley numbers, with multiplication of matrices defined in the obvious manner, is an exceptional Jordan algebra.

Again we let A be an associative algebra (over a field of characteristic not two) with multiplication written $a \circ b$; we define a new operation, called the *commutator* or *Lie bracket*:

$$[a, b] = a \circ b - b \circ a.$$

Then A with its vector space structure and with the associative multiplication replaced by the bracket operation is a nonassociative algebra which satisfies the identities

$$[a, a] = 0, \qquad \text{or equivalently} \qquad [a, b] = -[b, a] \quad \text{(anticommutativity)},$$

and

$$[[a, b], c] + [[b, c], a] + [[c, a], b] = 0 \quad \text{(Jacobi identity)}.$$

Any nonassociative algebra satisfying these identities is called a *Lie algebra*. The Poincaré-Birkhoff-Witt theorem states that every Lie algebra is isomorphic to a subalgebra of some algebra constructed as above from an associative algebra.

Example. The vector cross product of vectors in Euclidean space satisfies the identities

$$X \times X = 0$$

and

$$(X \times Y) \times Z + (Y \times Z) \times X + (Z \times X) \times Y = 0.$$

Since the set of vectors in Euclidean n-space is a vector space over the real numbers, when equipped with the cross product, it is a Lie algebra.

If L is a Lie algebra obtained from a commutative algebra, that is,

$$[x, y] = xy - yx = 0 \qquad \text{for all} \quad x, y \in L,$$

then L is said to be *abelian*.

2. ALBERT'S RADICAL

We first remark that some of the characterizations of radicals of rings which we gave in Chapter 5, notably that of Brown and McCoy, do not depend upon associativity and hence may be applied directly to nonassociative rings. We shall concern ourselves with the definition of radicals for nonassociative, i.e., not necessarily associative, algebras over a field of characteristic zero; many of the results hold in a more general setting, but the proofs are much more complicated.

Albert called a nonassociative algebra *semisimple* if it is the direct sum of a finite number of *simple* nonassociative algebras, i.e., nonassociative algebras A such that $AA \neq (0)$, where AA is the subalgebra spanned by the set $\{aa' \mid a, a' \in A\}$, with juxtaposition indicating the nonassociative product in A, and such that the only ideals of A are (0) and A itself. Then if A is homomorphic to a semisimple algebra, its *radical*, $N_A(A)$, is the intersection of the family B_i of ideals of A for which A/B_i is semisimple. In order to prove a simple structure theorem, we shall need a lemma:

> **Lemma.** If B is an ideal of a nonassociative algebra A such that A/B is isomorphic to the direct sum of nonzero simple nonassociative algebras C_i, $i = 1, \ldots, n$, then there exist ideals B_i of A, $i = 1, \ldots, n$, such that each A/B_i is a nonzero simple nonassociative algebra and B is the intersection of the B_i.

Proof. We let M_i be the kernel of the canonical map from A/B onto C_i. Then M_i is an ideal of A/B and $(A/B)/M_i \simeq C_i$. Each M_i determines an ideal B_i of A such that $B \subset B_i$ and $M_i = B_i/B$. Hence A/B_i is isomorphic to

$$(A/B)/(B_i/B) = (A/B)/M_i,$$

which is isomorphic to C_i so that A/B_i is a nonzero simple nonassociative algebra. To see that the intersection of the B_i is B, we note that the intersection of the M_i is (0).

As a direct consequence we obtain:

> **Theorem 1.** *If A is a nonassociative algebra with identity, the radical $N_A(A)$ is the intersection of all ideals B_i of A for which A/B_i is a simple nonassociative algebra with identity.*

It is also possible to extend this definition of radical to groups with operators. If G is a group with a class E of endomorphisms including all inner automorphisms, then an *ideal* of G is a subgroup S of G such that $s \in S$ and $e \in E$ imply that $es \in S$. The radical of G is then the intersection of the maximal ideals of G such that G/S is simple (in the sense above).

3. NILPOTENCY AND SOLVABILITY

Albert's radical is, in a sense, a consequence of structure theorems rather than a means of obtaining them. We turn to the traditional approach, that of looking at properties of ideals. In order to define a "classical" radical for a nonassociative algebra, we need an extended definition of nilpotency. We shall use the following: A nonassociative algebra A is *nilpotent* if there exists an integer n such that all possible products of n elements in A are equal to zero. That is, we define a sequence

$$A^{(0)} = A, \qquad A^1 = AA, \qquad \text{and} \qquad A^{i+1} = A^i A,$$

where, as in Section 2, AA is the subalgebra spanned by the set of products of elements of A, and if there exists an integer n such that $A^n = (0)$, A is nilpotent. Each A^i is an ideal of A and an ideal is *nilpotent* if it is nilpotent as an algebra.

It is possible, as in the associative case, to show that the sum of a finite number of nilpotent ideals is nilpotent. Moreover, any finite-dimensional nonassociative algebra has a maximum nilpotent ideal called the *nil radical*. However, the construction of this radical does not lead to a satisfactory structure theory for all nonassociative algebras; among other difficulties is that if I is a nilpotent ideal of a nonassociative algebra A and A/I is also nilpotent, one cannot conclude, as one can for associative algebras, that A is itself nilpotent. Hence we introduce a new notion. The *derived series* of a nonassociative algebra A is defined by

$$A^{(0)} = A, \qquad A^{(1)} = A' = AA, \qquad \text{and} \qquad A^{(i+1)} = A^{(i)} A^{(i)}.$$

An algebra A is *solvable* if $A^{(n)} = (0)$ for some positive integer n. We note that each term of the derived series is an ideal of A. Moreover, an ideal is *solvable* if it is solvable as an algebra.

As usual, if the only ideals of A are (0) and A and if $A' \neq (0)$, A is *simple*.

Examples. The Lie subalgebra S of the algebra of $n \times n$ matrices over a field K consisting of strictly upper triangular matrices, with the Lie algebra product defined by $[x, y] = xy - yx$, $x, y \in S$, where xy denotes ordinary matrix multiplication, is nilpotent. The subalgebra of the matrix algebra which consists of all upper triangular matrices is solvable.

Remark 1. For associative and some nonassociative algebras, for example, Jordan algebras, the notions of solvability and nilpotency are identical, and in general nilpotency implies solvability. Also, if every element of a finite-dimensional Jordan algebra A is nilpotent, that is, for $a \in A$ there is a positive integer n_a such that $a^{n_a} = 0$, where a^{n_a} is the Jordan product of a with itself, then A is nilpotent. For arbitrary nonassociative algebras this is not the case. For example, if L is a Lie algebra, $x^2 = 0$ for all $x \in L$, but not all Lie algebras are nilpotent.

Remark 2. We recall that a derived series for a group G is defined by

$$G^{(0)} = G, \qquad G^{(1)} = G' = [G, G], \qquad \text{and} \qquad G^{(i+1)} = (G^{(i)})',$$

where the derived subgroup G' of G is the subgroup generated by all elements of the form $aba^{-1}b^{-1}$, a, $b \in G$. Then G is solvable if $G^{(n)} = (e)$ for some positive integer n.

A basic result in the theory of Lie algebras—indeed the reason for their importance—is the correspondence between Lie groups, which are essentially groups which are differentiable manifolds, and Lie algebras. The Lie algebra of a Lie group is simply the tangent space at the identity with an appropriately defined nonassociative product. Subalgebras of the Lie algebra of a Lie group are in one-one correspondence with Lie subgroups and this correspondence preserves solvability. For a detailed exposition see, e.g., Chevalley, *Theory of Lie Groups*, Princeton University Press, 1946.

We now use the notion of solvability of algebras to develop a structure theory.

> **Lemma.** Every subalgebra and every homomorphic image of a solvable nonassociative algebra A is solvable. If A contains a solvable ideal I such that A/I is solvable, then A is solvable.

Proof. The first two statements are clear. If I is an ideal such that A/I is solvable, then $A^{(k)} \subset I$ for some positive integer k. But I is solvable, so $I^{(j)} = (0)$ for some positive integer j. Thus we have $A^{(k+j)} \subset I^{(j)} = (0)$ and A is solvable.

> **Theorem 2.** *The sum of any two solvable ideals is a solvable ideal.*

Proof. Let I and J be solvable ideals. Then, as in the associative case, $I \cap J$ is an ideal of I, and we have

$$(I + J)/J \simeq I/(I \cap J).$$

The algebra on the right is the homomorphic image of a solvable algebra and hence solvable. Since J is solvable, we apply the lemma to get that $I + J$ is solvable.

By virtue of Theorem 2, every finite-dimensional nonassociative algebra has a maximum solvable ideal, which we shall call its (solvable) *radical*. Moreover, if R is the solvable radical of a nonassociative algebra, then from the above, A/R has zero radical. A nonassociative algebra with zero (solvable) radical will be called *semisimple*.

4. A STRUCTURE THEOREM FOR NONASSOCIATIVE ALGEBRAS

In order to develop a structure theorem we need to look at the vector space structure of a nonassociative algebra.

We call a symmetric bilinear form $\langle \, , \, \rangle$ defined on a nonassociative algebra A an *associative form* if

$$\langle x, yz \rangle = \langle xy, z \rangle$$

holds for all $x, y, z \in A$. It is clear that if I is an ideal of A, then

$$I^{\perp} = \{x \in A \mid \langle x, y \rangle = 0 \text{ for all } y \in I\}$$

is also an ideal of A.

Theorem 3. *Let A be a finite-dimensional nonassociative algebra such that:*

1) A has a nondegenerate associative form $\langle \, , \, \rangle$,

2) A contains no nonzero nilpotent ideal.

Then A is uniquely expressible as a direct sum

$$A = A_1 \oplus \cdots \oplus A_n$$

of ideals A_i which are simple nonassociative algebras.

Proof. We induct on the dimension of A. Assuming that the result holds for algebras satisfying (1) and (2) and of dimension less than $\dim A$, we let A_1 be a minimal ideal of A (if $A_1 = A$, the result is clear). $A_1^{\perp}$ is an ideal of A. $A_1 \cap A_1^{\perp}$, being an ideal of A_1, is either A_1 or (0). If $A_1 \cap A_1^{\perp} = A_1$, we let $x, y \in A_1$ and $z \in A$. Then $\langle xy, z \rangle = \langle x, yz \rangle = 0$. But the form is nondegenerate, so $xy = 0$. Since x and y are arbitrary elements of A_1, $A_1^2 = (0)$, contradicting condition (2).

Thus $A_1 \cap A_1^{\perp} = (0)$, and by ordinary linear algebra $A = A_1 \oplus A_1^{\perp}$. Now $\langle \, , \, \rangle$ induces a nondegenerate associative form on $A_1^{\perp}$, and any ideal I of $A_1^{\perp}$ is an ideal of A since $A_1 A_1^{\perp} = (0)$. Hence A_1 satisfies the hypotheses of the theorem, and by the induction assumption

$$A_1^{\perp} = A_2 \oplus \cdots \oplus A_n,$$

where the A_i are ideals of $A_1^{\perp}$, and hence of A, which are simple algebras. A_1, being minimal, is also simple, which proves the theorem.

5. JORDAN ALGEBRAS

It is relatively easy to define an appropriate symmetric bilinear form for Jordan algebras. We follow the methods of Paige.

If A is a nonassociative algebra over a field K of characteristic zero, then for $x \in A$ we have linear transformations of A (as a vector space):

$$R_x : a \rightarrow ax,$$

$$L_x : a \rightarrow xa,$$

called the *right* and *left multiplications* of A. We observe that

1) $R_x(ab) = (ab)x = a(bx) = R_{bx}a$, that is, $R_x b = R_{bx}$,

2) $R_{x+y}a = a(x + y) = ax + ay = R_x a + R_y a = (R_x + R_y)a$, that is,

$$R_{x+y} = R_x + R_y,$$

and similarly for L_x.

Now if A is a Jordan algebra, since $ab = ba$, we have $L_a b = R_a b$ or $L_a = R_a$. From the identity $(a^2 b)a = a^2(ba)$ in the definition of Jordan algebra, we obtain

$$R_a R_{a^2} b = R_a L_{a^2} b = L_{a^2} R_a b = R_{a^2} R_a b.$$

We write this as

3) $[R_a, R_{a^2}] = 0$,   where $[\,,\,]$ is the commutator bracket.

We may linearize (3) by replacing a by $x + y + z, x + y, x + z, y + z,$ $x, y,$ and z in turn to get

$$[R_{x+y+z}, R_{(x+y+z)^2}] - [R_{x+y}, R_{(x+y)^2}] - [R_{x+z}, R_{(x+z)^2}] - [R_{y+z}, R_{(y+z)^2}]$$

$$+ [R_x, R_{x^2}] + [R_y, R_{y^2}] + [R_z, R_{z^2}] = 0.$$

Then we use (1) and (2) to get

4) $[R_x, R_{yz}] + [R_y, R_{zx}] + [R_z, R_{xy}] = 0.$

Now operating on an element b of a Jordan algebra A by (4), we get

5) $(bx)(yz) + (by)(zx) + (bz)(xy) = (b(yz))x + (b(zx))y + (b(xy))z,$ for arbitrary $b, x, y, z \in A$.

If we treat (5) as multiplications on x, we get

$$R_{yz} R_b x + R_{by} R_z x + R_{zb} R_y x = R_{b(yz)} x + R_y R_b R_z x + R_z R_b R_y x$$

or

6) $R_{yz} R_x + R_{zx} R_y + R_{xy} R_z = R_{x(yz)} + R_y R_x R_z + R_z R_x R_y.$

Interchanging x and y in (6) and subtracting the result from (6) yields

7) $R_{x(yz)} - R_{(xy)z} = R_y R_z R_x + R_x R_z R_y - R_y R_x R_z - R_z R_x R_y$

or

8) $R_{x(yz)} - R_{(xy)z} = [[R_x, R_z], R_y].$

Restricting our attention to finite-dimensional Jordan algebras, we observe that a transformation R_x may be represented by a matrix (a_{ij}) relative to a basis of A. The trace of (a_{ij}), being the sum of the eigenvalues of R_x, is independent of the choice of basis and corresponding matrix representation. Hence we may use the notation trace R_x. We note that

$$\langle x, y \rangle = \text{trace } R_{xy}$$

defines an associative form on a Jordan algebra A. Hence to apply Theorem 3 to Jordan algebras we need only prove the following lemmas.

Lemma 1. If A is a nonzero semisimple Jordan algebra, A contains a nonzero idempotent e such that trace $R_e \neq 0$.

Proof. If every $x \in A$ were nilpotent, then A would be nilpotent and hence solvable (see Remark 1). Hence there is an element $x \in A$ which is not nilpotent. This element generates an associative subalgebra (Problem 1). By Theorem 8, Chapter 2, this subalgebra contains a nonzero idempotent element e. Setting $x = y = z = e$ in (6), we obtain

9) $2R_e^3 - 3R_e^2 + R_e = R_e(2R_e - 1)(R_e - 1) = 0$ for any idempotent $e \in A$.

Thus the eigenvalues of R_e must be 0, $\frac{1}{2}$, or 1. But since $R_e e = e$, it follows that if e is a nonzero idempotent, R_e must have 1 as one of its eigenvalues. But the trace is the sum of the eigenvalues, so trace $R_e \neq 0$.

Lemma 2. The associative form $\langle x, y \rangle =$ trace R_{xy} of a semisimple finite-dimensional Jordan algebra A is nondegenerate.

Proof. If $A^\perp$ contains an idempotent $e \neq 0$, then

$$\langle e, e \rangle = \text{trace } R_{ee} = \text{trace } R_e \neq 0,$$

by Lemma 1. But this is not possible because $e \in A^\perp \subset A$ and $\langle a, e \rangle = 0$ for all $a \in A$, $e \in A^\perp$. Hence every element of $A^\perp$ must be nilpotent and thus $A^\perp$ is a solvable ideal. Thus $A^\perp$ is contained in the radical of A, which is (0). Hence if $\langle a, x \rangle = 0$ for all $a \in A$, we must have $x = 0$. Thus trace R_{xy} is nondegenerate on A.

We now have:

Theorem 4. *Any finite-dimensional semisimple Jordan algebra A is uniquely expressible as a direct sum of a finite number of ideals which are simple Jordan algebras.*

6. LIE ALGEBRAS

The problem of applying Theorem 3 to other nonassociative algebras to get a structure theorem for semisimple algebras reduces to finding an appropriate nondegenerate form. We shall do this for the important case of Lie algebras.

Throughout the rest of this section we let L be a finite-dimensional Lie algebra over a field K of characteristic zero. If V is a finite-dimensional vector space over K, we denote $\text{Hom}_K(V, V)$ by $\text{End}(V)$, that is,

$$\text{End}(V) = \{f : V \to V \mid f \text{ is a linear transformation}\}.$$

$\text{End}(V)$ can be made into a Lie algebra by defining the product as

$$[f, g] = fg - gf,$$

where fg indicates the composition of f and g. We shall denote an associative product by juxtaposition and a Lie product by a bracket in what follows. A *representation* of a Lie algebra L is a Lie algebra homomorphism

$$\pi:L \to \text{End}(V),$$

where V is a finite-dimensional vector space. The *dimension* of a representation is the dimension of V. If dim $V = n$, $\text{End}(V)$ is isomorphic (as a Lie algebra) to the algebra of $n \times n$ matrices over the field K with the Lie product defined by the commutator operation. Hence we can consider any representation as a homomorphism into a matrix algebra; moreover, since the image of the Lie algebra L is a subalgebra, we can talk of subalgebras of a matrix algebra instead of representations if we choose.

Let ad $a:L \to L$ be the linear transformation given by

$$\text{ad } a(x) = [x, a].$$

Then the Lie algebra homomorphism $a \to \text{ad } a$ of L into $\text{End}(L)$ is called the *adjoint representation* of L, and is denoted by ad_L. Since L is a finite-dimensional vector space, ad a has a matrix representation with respect to any basis and $\text{tr}(\text{ad } a)$ is independent of the choice of basis. Thus we define a symmetric bilinear form

$$\langle a, b \rangle = \text{tr}(\text{ad } a)(\text{ad } b),$$

which we call the *Killing form* of L. It is easily verified that the Killing form is associative.

We need an additional notion. If π is a representation of a Lie algebra L over a field K, a *weight* of π is a linear transformation

$$\lambda:L \to K$$

such that there exists $0 \neq v \in L$ with the property that for any $x \in L$

$$\pi(x)v = \lambda(x)v.$$

The element v is said to be a *weight vector*.

Theorem 5. *If L is a Lie algebra over a field K, $\pi:L \to \text{End}(V)$ a representation and λ a weight of $\pi|M$, M an ideal of L, then λ vanishes on $[L, M]$, the space generated by $\{[l, m] \mid l \in L, m \in M\}$.*

Proof. Let $0 \neq v_0 \in V$ be a weight vector of λ. Then

$$\pi(m)v_0 = \lambda(m)v_0$$

for all $m \in M$.

We fix $x \in L$ and by induction we define a sequence of vectors $v_0, v_1, \ldots$ in V by

$$v_{i+1} = \pi(x)v_i.$$

We shall show that for all $m \in M$,

$$\pi(m)v_i = \lambda(m)v_i \qquad (\text{mod } v_0, \ldots, v_{i-1}),$$

where (mod $v_0, \ldots, v_{i-1}$) means plus a linear combination of these vectors. We induct on i. Certainly

$$\pi(m)v_0 = \lambda(m)v_0.$$

Moreover

$$\pi(m)v_{i+1} = \pi(m)\pi(x)v_i = \pi([m, x])v_i + \pi(x)\pi(m)v_i$$

$$= \lambda(m)v_i + \pi(x)\lambda(m)v_i \quad (\text{mod } v_0, \ldots, v_{i-1}, \pi(x)v_0, \ldots, \pi(x)v_{i-1})$$

$$= \lambda(m)\pi(x)v_i \quad (\text{mod } v_0, \ldots, v_i)$$

$$= \lambda(m)v_{i+1} \quad (\text{mod } v_0, \ldots, v_i).$$

Hence, by induction

$$\pi(m)v_i = \lambda(m)v_i \quad (\text{mod } v_0, \ldots, v_{i-1}).$$

Now we let W be the subspace of V spanned by $v_0, v_1, \ldots$. Then

$$\pi(m)W \subset W \quad \text{for all} \quad m \in M.$$

Moreover, on W each $\pi(m)$ is represented by the matrix

$$\begin{pmatrix} \lambda(m) & & & * \\ & \cdot & & \\ & & \cdot & \\ 0 & & & \lambda(m) \end{pmatrix}.$$

Thus $\mathrm{tr}_W\pi(m) = \lambda(m)\dim W$. Now

$$\pi(x)W \subset W,$$

and so

$$\lambda([x, m])\dim W = \mathrm{tr}_W\pi([x, m])$$

$$= \mathrm{tr}_W(\pi(x)\pi(m) - \pi(m)\pi(x))$$

$$= 0.$$

Since x is arbitrary and $\lambda([x, m]) = 0$, $\lambda([L, M]) = 0$.

A representation $\pi: L \to \mathrm{End}(V)$ is *reducible* if and only if there exists a subspace W, $(0) \neq W \subsetneq V$, such that

$$\pi(x)W \subset W \quad \text{for all} \quad x \in L.$$

Such a subspace is said to be *invariant* under π. If π is not reducible, it is said to be *irreducible*.

If $\pi: L \to \mathrm{End}(V)$ is a representation of a Lie algebra L, M is a subalgebra of L and λ is a weight of $\pi|M$, then we set

$$V_{M,\lambda} = \{v \in V \mid \pi(m)v = \lambda(m)v \text{ for all } m \in M\}.$$

We can now give the following corollary to Theorem 5.

Corollary. If M is an ideal of the Lie algebra L and λ is a weight of $\pi|M$, then $V_{M,\lambda}$ is invariant under π.

Proof. Let $v \in V_{M,\lambda}$. Then

$$
\begin{aligned}
\pi(m)\pi(x)v &= \pi([m, x])v + \pi(x)\pi(m)v \\
&= \lambda([m, x])v + \pi(x)\lambda(m)v \\
&= \lambda(m)\pi(x)v.
\end{aligned}
$$

Thus $\pi(x) \in V_{M,\lambda}$ and $\pi(x)V_{M,\lambda} \subset V_{M,\lambda}$.

If L is a finite-dimensional Lie algebra over a field K and M is a (vector) subspace, then $\dim L - \dim M$ is the *codimension* of M. If M is an ideal of a Lie algebra, its codimension is its codimension as a subspace.

Lemma. If L is a solvable Lie algebra, $L \neq (0)$, then there exists an ideal M of L of codimension 1.

Proof. Since L is solvable, $L' \neq L$. Hence there exists a subspace M of L of codimension 1 with $L' \subset M$. Then

$$[M, L] \subset [L, L] = L' \subset M,$$

and so M is an ideal of L.

We can now prove Lie's theorem.

Theorem 6 (Lie). *The only irreducible representations of a finite-dimensional solvable Lie algebra L over an algebraically closed field K of characteristic zero are of dimension 1 (i.e., any representation has a weight).*

Proof. We induct on the dimension of L. Suppose

$$\pi : L \to \text{End}(V)$$

is irreducible. We let $M \subset L$ be an ideal of codimension 1. Then by the induction hypothesis, $\pi|M$ has a weight λ. Then

$$\pi(x)V_{M,\lambda} \subset V_{M,\lambda}$$

for all $x \in L$. Since the representation is irreducible, $V_{M,\lambda} = V$.

Let $x \in L \setminus M$. Since V is a vector space over an algebraically closed field, $\pi(x)$ has an eigenvector v. Then Kv is invariant under $\pi(x)$ and all $\pi(m)$, $m \in M$. Since M has codimension 1 in L, Kv is invariant under $\pi(y)$ for all $y \in L$. The irreducibility of π implies that $V = Kv$.

Hence the theorem follows.

We can use this theorem to establish the existence of a common eigenvector for all of the linear transformations in the image of a representation. For if λ is a weight for the representation π of L, we have that

$$\pi(x)v = \lambda(x)v$$

for all $x \in L$, so that the weight vector v is a common eigenvector for all the $\pi(x)$. Thus we have the corollary:

Corollary. Let $\pi : L \to \mathrm{End}(V)$ be a representation of a solvable Lie algebra over an algebraically closed field K. Then there exists a basis $\{e_1, \ldots, e_n\}$ of V with respect to which each of the endomorphisms $\pi(x)$ can be represented by a matrix of the form

$$\begin{pmatrix} * & & & * \\ & \cdot & & \\ & & \cdot & \\ 0 & & & * \end{pmatrix}.$$

Proof. We let $e_1 \neq 0$ be a common eigenvector of all the $\pi(x)$, $x \in L$, and set $E_1 = e_1 K$. The representation π induces a representation π_1 on V/E_1. Hence if $\dim V/E_1 > 0$, there exists $e_2 \in V$ such that $e_2 + E_1$ is an eigenvector of all the $\pi_1(x)$, $x \in L$. Continuing in this manner, we find a basis $\{e_1, \ldots, e_n\}$ of V such that for each $x \in L$,

$$\pi(x)e_i = 0 \qquad \mathrm{mod}(e_1, \ldots, e_i),$$

from which the corollary follows.

We now direct our attention to nilpotency of Lie algebras, especially with regard to subalgebras of the Lie algebra of $n \times n$ matrices over a field of characteristic zero. A matrix z is *nilpotent* if $z^n = 0$ for some positive integer n, where z^n is the ordinary matrix product of z with itself n times. A linear transformation $A : V \to V$ is *nilpotent* if $A^n = 0$ for some positive integer n, where A^n indicates the n-fold composition of A with itself, i.e., if z is a matrix representation of A with respect to any basis of V, then z is nilpotent. A representation

$$\pi : L \to \mathrm{End}(V)$$

is *nilpotent* if and only if each $\pi(x)$ is. It is clear that if L is a nilpotent Lie algebra, then ad_L is a nilpotent representation of L. In the case of matrix algebras, we have the following result.

Theorem 7. Let L be a subalgebra of the Lie algebra $\mathscr{M}_n$ of $n \times n$ matrices over a field K of characteristic zero such that each element of L is nilpotent. Then ad_L is nilpotent.

Proof. For $z \in \mathscr{M}_n$ we define L_z and R_z to be left and right multiplication as usual. Then $\mathrm{ad}\, z = L_z - R_z$. Hence for $y \in \mathscr{M}_n$

$$(\mathrm{ad}\, z)^p(y) = (L_z - R_z)^p(y)$$

$$= \sum_{q=0}^{p} \binom{p}{q}(-1)^q L_z^{p-q} R_z^q(y)$$

$$= \sum_{q=0}^{p} \binom{p}{q}(-1)^q z^{p-q} y z^q.$$

If $z^n = 0$, then for $p > 2n$,

$$z^{p-q}yz^q = 0.$$

Hence if $z \in L$, ad z is nilpotent so ad_L is nilpotent.

We shall need a further result about nilpotent representations.

Theorem 8. *If $\pi: L \to End(V)$ is a nilpotent representation, then any weight of π is 0.*

Proof. Suppose $v \neq 0$ is such that

$$\pi(x)v = \lambda(x)v$$

for all $x \in L$. Then

$$0 = \pi(x)^n v = \lambda(x)^n v.$$

Hence $\lambda(x) = 0$ for all $x \in L$.

We use this to prove a partial converse of the remark preceding Theorem 7.

Theorem 9. *If L is a Lie algebra whose adjoint representation is nilpotent, then L is solvable.*

Proof. We induct on the dimension of L. In the one-dimensional case, L is abelian and hence solvable.

If $\dim L > 1$, we let M be a proper subalgebra of maximal dimension. Then ad_M is nilpotent, and so by the induction assumption M is solvable. Now $\mathrm{ad}_L(m)$ for $m \in M$ leaves M invariant, since M is a subalgebra. Therefore we have an induced representation

$$\pi: M \xrightarrow{\mathrm{ad}_L} End(L/M).$$

Since ad_L is nilpotent, so is π. Since M is solvable, π has a weight, which is zero since π is nilpotent. Thus there exists $x + M \in L/M$ such that

$$[m, x] = (\mathrm{ad}_L m)(x) = \pi(m)(x + M)$$
$$= 0 \quad (\mathrm{mod}\ M)$$

for all $m \in M$, so that $[m, x] \in M$ for all $m \in M$. Hence x and M span a subalgebra, which by the maximality of M is L itself. Thus $[M, L] \subset M$, so that M is a solvable ideal of codimension 1. Then L/M is of dimension 1 and thus solvable. Consequently L is solvable.

Our main theorems of this section require several lemmas.

Lemma 1. Let $x \in \mathscr{M}_n$, the Lie algebra of $n \times n$ matrices over an algebraically closed field K of characteristic zero. Then $x = s + n$ with $sn = ns$ and n nilpotent, s diagonalizable. Furthermore s and n are polynomials in x without constant term. Moreover, $\mathrm{ad}\ x = \mathrm{ad}\ s + \mathrm{ad}\ n$ is the corresponding decomposition for $\mathrm{ad}\ x$.

Proof. The first two statements are standard linear algebra. We let $v_1, \ldots, v_n$ be a basis of K^n of eigenvectors of s, that is, $sv_i = \lambda_i v_i$, $\lambda_i \in K$, $i = 1, \ldots, n$.

We define $E_{ij} \in \mathcal{M}_n$ by $E_{ij}v_k = \delta_{jk}v_i$, where $\delta_{jk} = 1$ if $j = k$ and 0 otherwise. Then

$$(\text{ad } s)E_{ij} = (\lambda_i - \lambda_j)E_{ij}.$$

Thus ad s is diagonalizable over K, ad n is nilpotent (see the proof of Theorem 7), and $(\text{ad } s)(\text{ad } n) = (\text{ad } n)(\text{ad } s)$.

Lemma 2 (Bourbaki). Let $\mathcal{M}_n$ be as in Lemma 1, A a subspace of $\mathcal{M}_n$, B a subspace of A, and let $T = \{t \in \mathcal{M}_n \,|\, (\text{ad } t)(A) \subset B\}$. If $z \in T$ is such that tr $zt = 0$ for all $t \in T$, then z is nilpotent.

Proof. We let $z = s + n$ as in Lemma 1. We show that $s = 0$. Let $\{v_1, \ldots, v_n\}$ be a basis for K^n such that $sv_i = \lambda_i v_i$, $\lambda_i \in K$, $i = 1, \ldots, n$. K, being of characteristic zero, contains an isomorphic copy of the rational numbers Q, so we assume that Q is itself a subfield of K. We let $V = \{v \in K \,|\, v = q_1\lambda_1 + \cdots + q_n\lambda_n, q_i \in Q\}$, that is, V is the rational subspace of K spanned by the λ_i. We show that $V = (0)$.

Let $f \in \text{Hom}_Q(V, Q)$ and let $t \in \mathcal{M}_n$ be defined by $tv_i = f(\lambda_i)v_i$, $i = 1, \ldots, n$. Then if $E_{ij}v_k = \delta_{jk}v_i$ (as above), we have

$$(\text{ad } s)E_{ij} = (\lambda_i - \lambda_j)E_{ij}$$

and

$$(\text{ad } t)E_{ij} = (f(\lambda_i) - f(\lambda_j))E_{ij}.$$

Now we let P be a polynomial over K such that for all i and j,

$$P(\lambda_i - \lambda_j) = f(\lambda_i) - f(\lambda_j);$$

then $P(\text{ad } s) = \text{ad } t$. Thus ad t is a polynomial in ad z, without constant term, since ad s is. Hence $(\text{ad } t)(A) \subset B$ and $t \in T$. Hence $0 = \text{tr } zt = \sum_i f(\lambda_i)\lambda_i$. But $f \in \text{Hom}_Q(V, Q)$, so that

$$0 = f(\text{tr } zt) = \sum_i f(\lambda_i)^2.$$

Thus $f(\lambda_i) = 0$, $i = 1, \ldots, n$, and since the λ_i are a basis of V over Q, $f = 0$. Hence $\text{Hom}_Q(V, Q) = (0)$ and it follows that $V = (0)$. Now we have that s has all zero eigenvalues and is diagonalizable; hence $s = 0$.

Theorem 10 (*Cartan's Criterion for Solvability*). *Let L be a Lie algebra over an algebraically closed field K of characteristic zero, $\langle \, , \rangle$ its Killing form. Then L is solvable if and only if $\langle x, y \rangle = 0$ for all $x \in L'$, $y \in L$.*

Proof. Suppose L is solvable. Then, by the corollary to Theorem 6, every element of $\text{ad}_L L$ can be represented by a matrix of the form

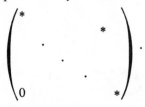

Moreover, if $[x, x'] \in L'$, then $\text{ad}_L[x, x'] = [\text{ad}_L x, \text{ad}_L x'] = \text{ad}_L x \, \text{ad}_L x' - \text{ad}_L x' \, \text{ad}_L x$. Since the diagonal entries of these products arise only from the products of the diagonal entries of $\text{ad}_L x$ and $\text{ad}_L x'$, the diagonal of $\text{ad}[x, x']$ contains only zeros. Hence for $x \in L'$, $y \in L$,

$$\langle x, y \rangle = \text{tr } \text{ad}_L x \, \text{ad}_L y = 0.$$

On the other hand, suppose that $\langle x, y \rangle = 0$ for all $x \in L'$, $y \in L$. Then if $h \in \text{ad}_L L'$, $t \in \text{ad}_L L$, $\text{tr } ht = 0$. We let

$$T = \{ t \in \mathcal{M}_n \mid \text{ad } t(\text{ad}_L L) \subset \text{ad}_L L' \}, \qquad n = \dim \text{ad}_L L.$$

If $t \in T$ and $u, v \in \text{ad}_L L$, then $\text{tr } t[u, v] = \text{tr}[t, u]v = 0$, since $[t, u] \in \text{ad}_L L'$ and $v \in \text{ad}_L L$. Hence if $h \in \text{ad}_L L'$, then $h \in T$ and $\text{tr } ht = 0$ for all $t \in T$, so that by Lemma 2, h is nilpotent. Thus $\text{ad}_L \mid L' = \text{ad}_{L'}$ is a nilpotent representation. Hence by Theorem 9, L' is solvable. But L/L' is abelian and thus solvable, so L is also solvable.

The Killing form is the associative form we shall use to apply Theorem 3 to Lie algebras. We now use the Cartan criterion for solvability to show that it is nondegenerate on a semisimple Lie algebra; then we shall have that a finite-dimensional semisimple Lie algebra is the direct sum of a finite number of simple Lie algebras.

Theorem 11 (Cartan's Criterion for Semisimplicity). *A finite-dimensional Lie algebra L over an algebraically closed field K of characteristic zero is semisimple if and only if its Killing form is nondegenerate.*

Proof. We let

$$L^\perp = \{ x \in L \mid \langle x, y \rangle = 0, y \in L \},$$

where $\langle \ , \ \rangle$ is the Killing form on L. Then for $x, y \in L^\perp$, $\langle x, y \rangle = 0$, so by the Cartan solvability criterion $L^\perp$ is solvable. Thus if L is semisimple, $L^\perp = (0)$ and $\langle \ , \ \rangle$ is nondegenerate.

Now suppose L is not semisimple. Then L has a nonzero solvable ideal S. For some positive integer k, $S^{(k)} = B \neq (0)$ is an abelian ideal of L. If we choose a basis for L such that the first vectors form a basis for B, then $\text{ad } x$, $x \in L$, is of the form

$$\begin{pmatrix} * & * \\ \hline 0 & * \end{pmatrix}, \ \cdot$$

and $\text{ad } b$, $b \in B$, is of the form

$$\begin{pmatrix} 0 & * \\ \hline 0 & 0 \end{pmatrix}.$$

But this implies that $\text{tr}(\text{ad } x)(\text{ad } b) = 0$ for $x \in L$, $b \in B$. Thus $B \subset L^\perp$ and the Killing form is degenerate.

Theorems 3 and 11 give us one half of the following:

Theorem 12. *A finite-dimensional Lie algebra L over an algebraically closed field K of characteristic zero is semisimple if and only if it is the direct sum of a finite number of simple Lie algebras.*

Proof. It remains only to show that the direct sum of simple Lie algebras has zero radical. Suppose $L = L_1 \oplus \cdots \oplus L_n$, where L_i is simple, $i = 1, \ldots, n$. Then clearly

$$\langle \, , \, \rangle_L = \langle \, , \, \rangle_{L_1} + \cdots + \langle \, , \, \rangle_{L_n},$$

where $\langle \, , \, \rangle$ denotes the Killing form. Thus we need only prove that if L is simple, $\langle \, , \, \rangle_L$ is nondegenerate.

Let $L^\perp = \{x \in L \mid \langle x, y \rangle = 0 \text{ for all } y \in L\}$, as above. Since $L^\perp$ is an ideal of L, $L^\perp = L$ or $L^\perp = (0)$. If $L^\perp = (0)$, $\langle \, , \, \rangle$ is nondegenerate. If $L^\perp = L$, then by Cartan's criterion L is solvable and $L' \neq L$. But this implies that $L' = (0)$, which is impossible since L is simple.

7. SIMPLE LIE AND JORDAN ALGEBRAS

The reason why Theorems 4 and 12 are so important is that, as in the case of associative algebras, a great deal is known about the structure of simple Jordan and Lie algebras. In fact, simple Jordan and Lie algebras over certain fields have been completely characterized. Since the classification is quite easy to state for Lie algebras over the complex numbers, although it is obtained by techniques beyond the scope of this book, we include it as an illustration of this type of results. Other cases are similar but much more complicated.

Simple Lie algebras over the complex numbers C are of one of the following types:

Classical: A_n, B_n, C_n, D_n

$A_n = \{A \mid A \text{ is an } (n+1) \times (n+1) \text{ complex matrix with trace } A = 0\}, n \geq 1$,

$B_n = \{A \mid A \text{ is a } (2n+1) \times (2n+1) \text{ complex matrix with } {}^t\!A = -A\}, n \geq 2$,
($^t\!A$ is the transpose of A, that is, the (i,j)th entry of $^t\!A$ is the (j,i)th entry of A).

$C_n = \{A \mid A \text{ is a } 2n \times 2n \text{ complex matrix and } JA = -{}^t\!AJ\}, n \geq 3$. If I denotes the $n \times n$ identity matrix, J is the $2n \times 2n$ matrix

$$\begin{pmatrix} 0 & I \\ -I & 0 \end{pmatrix}.$$

$D_n = \{A \mid A \text{ is a } 2n \times 2n \text{ complex matrix with } {}^t\!A = -A\}, n \geq 4$.

The multiplication in each of the classical Lie algebras is the Lie bracket defined in terms of the usual matrix product:

$$[A, A'] = AA' - A'A.$$

Exceptional: G_2, F_4, E_6, E_7, E_8

We note that exceptional here does not mean, as in the case of Jordan algebras, that the algebra cannot be obtained from an associative algebra by redefining the multiplication.

If A is a nonassociative algebra, a linear transformation $D{:}A \to A$ such that

$$D(x{*}y) = Dx{*}y + x{*}Dy, \qquad \text{for all} \quad x, y \in A,$$

where $*$ denotes the algebra multiplication, is called a *derivation*. It is easy to see that the derivations of an algebra A over a field F form a vector space over F with operations defined in the obvious way. We define the Lie product of derivations D and D' to be

$$[D, D'] = DD' - D'D,$$

where juxtaposition indicates composition. Then the set of derivations on A is a Lie algebra over F. Using this we have that one exceptional Lie algebra is

$G_2 = $ (derivation algebra of the Cayley numbers) $\otimes$ C

and another is

$F_4 = $ (derivation algebra of the exceptional Jordan algebra of 3×3 Hermitian Cayley number matrices) $\otimes$ C.

The remaining exceptional Lie algebras have more complicated descriptions, which we shall not give here.

The classification of simple Jordan algebras over the complex numbers may be described as follows: for each classical simple Lie algebra there exists a corresponding simple Jordan algebra; in addition there is one exceptional simple Jordan algebra, namely the algebra of 3×3 Hermitian Cayley numbers tensored with C.

For more discussion of simple Lie algebras see, for example, Helgason, *Differential Geometry and Symmetric Spaces*, Academic Press, New York, N.Y., 1962; for Jordan algebras see Braun and Koecher, *Jordan-Algebren*, Springer, Berlin 1966.

PROBLEMS

1. Show that any subalgebra of a Jordan algebra generated by a single element is associative.

2. Let C be a commutative associative algebra (with identity) over a field K, L a Lie algebra over K. Show that $C \otimes L$ is a Lie algebra over K. Show that this is not necessarily true if C is not commutative. Is the tensor product of Lie algebras in general a Lie algebra?

3. Show that a finite-dimensional nil Jordan algebra is nilpotent. (See Remark 1.)

4. Show that the radical of a Jordan algebra is the orthogonal space of the algebra relative to the symmetric bilinear form

$$\langle x, y \rangle = \text{trace } R_{xy}.$$

5. Show that the (solvable) radical of a Lie algebra L over a field of characteristic zero is the orthogonal space of L' relative to the Killing form.

6. If L is a Lie algebra over a field of characteristic zero, R its solvable radical, and N its nilpotent radical, show that $[L, R] \subset N$.

7. Prove that the Killing form defined on a Lie algebra is associative.

8. If L is the Lie algebra of $n \times n$ matrices over the complex numbers, determine the derived series and the nilpotent series.

9. (Engel's Theorem) If L is a finite-dimensional Lie algebra over a field of characteristic zero, show that if $\pi: L \to \mathrm{End}(V)$ is a nilpotent representation, then there exists a basis in V such that each $\pi(x)$, $x \in L$, is represented by a matrix of the form

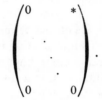

10. Prove that a finite-dimensional Lie algebra L is solvable if and only if there exists a chain
$$L = A_0 \supset A_1 \supset \cdots \supset A_n = (0),$$
where A_i is an ideal of codimension 1 in A_{i-1}.

CHAPTER 8

Category Theory

In order to establish a setting in which all the examples of the preceding chapters may be treated as special cases of a general theory, we introduce the language of *categories* and *functors*. The use of such terminology has increasingly invaded all areas of mathematics since its introduction in the early 1940's.

Although many intrinsically interesting results have been obtained in category theory, its greatest utility is as a unifying and clarifying device for seemingly diverse and complicated concepts. In fact, one reason why the notions were originally introduced was to define precisely what is (or should be) meant by the "natural" which occurs frequently when discussing transformations. Another purpose of category terminology is to provide a setting for homological algebra by abstracting those properties of modules which are needed for homological concepts. We shall cover only the basic notions of category theory, with emphasis on applications.

There are many ways of defining a category, but we shall adopt the approach which seems best suited to achieve the dual purposes of category theory—unification and simplification, that is, we look at various collections of mathematical objects and the ways of relating the objects to each other.

1. DEFINITION AND EXAMPLES

Let $\mathscr{C}$ be a class of *objects* $A, B, C, \ldots$ together with a family $\mathscr{M}$ of disjoint sets $\hom(A, B)$, one for each ordered pair A, B of objects. We write $f : A \to B$ for $f \in \hom(A, B)$ and call f a *morphism* of $\mathscr{C}$ with *domain* A and *range* B. We assume a rule assigning to each pair $f : A \to B$, $g : B \to C$ a unique morphism $gf = g \circ f : A \to C$ and note that this composition is defined precisely when range f = domain g. The union of $\mathscr{C}$ and $\mathscr{M}$, subject to the following axioms, is called a *category*:

C1) *Associativity.* If $f \in \hom(A, B)$, $g \in \hom(B, C)$, $h \in \hom(C, D)$, then $h(gf) = (hg)f$.

C2) *Identities.* For each object B, there exists a morphism $1_B : B \to B$ such that always $1_B f = f$, $g 1_B = g$ for $f : A \to B$ and $g : B \to C$.

If $\mathscr{C}$ is a set, the category is *small*.

In general, if the class of objects and the class of morphisms between them are known, the disjoint sets hom(A, B) are determined. Hence we identify a category by its objects and morphisms, and in fact we usually denote a category simply by its class of objects. Moreover, if confusion is likely, we write hom(A, B) $\in \mathscr{C}$ as $\mathrm{hom}_{\mathscr{C}}(A,B)$.

Examples

1. Let $\mathscr{S}$ be the class of all sets and hom(A, B) the set of all functions from A to B. Then $\mathscr{S}$ is the *category of sets*.

2. Let $\mathscr{G}$ be the class of all groups and hom(A, B) the set of all group homomorphisms from A to B. Then $\mathscr{G}$ is the *category of groups*.

3. If $\mathscr{T}$ is the class of all topological spaces and hom(A, B) the set of all continuous maps from A to B, then $\mathscr{T}$ is the *category of topological spaces*. A category with more structure is obtained by considering topological spaces with base points, i.e., the category whose objects are ordered pairs (A, x_A), where A is a topological space and $x_A \in A$. In this case we want as morphisms all continuous maps taking base points to base points.

Similarly, we can define the category of all differentiable manifolds and differentiable maps, the category of all vector bundles and vector bundle maps, the category of all rings and ring homomorphisms, etc. In other words we choose any mathematical objects and select as morphisms the kind of transformation of interest, checking only to be certain that the property of interest is preserved under an associative composition and that identities exist, e.g., the composition of group homomorphisms is closed and associative with the identity map as the identity for the category morphisms. Clearly we could make other choices for the morphisms; for example, we could use all functions between topological spaces as the morphisms in $\mathscr{T}$, but continuous functions are generally the only kind with which we are concerned in a topological context and hence we limit hom(A, B) accordingly.

We recall that a semigroup is a set together with an associative binary operation on the set; if there is an identity for the operation, then the semigroup is a *monoid*. If we ignore the problem of the existence of objects, and in fact categories are often defined in terms only of morphisms and a sometimes defined composition of them, then we see that a monoid is in fact a small category with a single identity, i.e., composition of morphisms is always defined. A *semigroupoid* is like a semigroup except that its operation is not everywhere defined; thus the morphisms of a category form a semigroupoid (and conversely).

For any set X, the set X^X of all functions $X \to X$ is a monoid and hence a category. Moreover, any group is a monoid and thus a category.

If $\mathscr{C}$ is any category and $\mathscr{C}' \subset \mathscr{C}$, we say that $\mathscr{C}'$ is a *subcategory* of $\mathscr{C}$ if

1) $\mathscr{C}'$ is a category,

2) $\mathrm{hom}_{\mathscr{C}'}(A, B) \subset \mathrm{hom}_{\mathscr{C}}(A, B)$ for all $A, B \in \mathscr{C}'$,

3) the composition of any two morphisms in $\mathscr{C}'$ is the same as their composition in $\mathscr{C}$,

4) each identity of $\mathscr{C}'$ is an identity of $\mathscr{C}$.

If, in addition, $\hom_{\mathscr{C}'}(A, B) = \hom_{\mathscr{C}}(A, B)$ for all $A, B \in \mathscr{C}'$, then $\mathscr{C}'$ is a *full subcategory* of $\mathscr{C}$.

For example, the category of all abelian groups and homomorphisms between them is a full subcategory of $\mathscr{G}$. However, the subcategory of $\mathscr{T}$ consisting of differentiable manifolds and differentiable maps is not full.

2. FUNCTORS

A (*covariant*) *functor* from a category $\mathscr{C}_1$ to a category $\mathscr{C}_2$ is an assignment

$$F:\mathscr{C}_1 \to \mathscr{C}_2$$

to each object of $\mathscr{C}_1$ precisely one object of $\mathscr{C}_2$ and to each morphism of $\mathscr{C}_1$ precisely one morphism of $\mathscr{C}_2$ (if $\mathscr{C}_1$ and $\mathscr{C}_2$ are small, F is a function) subject to the following:

F1) If 1_A is an identity morphism in $\mathscr{C}_1$, then $F(1_A)$ is an identity morphism in $\mathscr{C}_2$.

F2) If fg is defined in $\mathscr{C}_1$, then $F(f)F(g)$ is defined in $\mathscr{C}_2$ and $F(f)F(g) = F(fg)$. If f is a morphism of $\mathscr{C}_1$, $F(\text{domain } f) = \text{domain } F(f)$ and $F(\text{range } f) = \text{range } F(f)$.

If I from a category $\mathscr{C}$ to itself is given by $I(A) = A$ for each object $A \in \mathscr{C}$ and $I(f) = f$ for each morphism f of $\mathscr{C}$, then I is a functor, called the *identity functor* of $\mathscr{C}$.

Suppose $\mathscr{C}'$ is a subcategory of $\mathscr{C}$ and let $J:\mathscr{C}' \to \mathscr{C}$ be given by $J(A) = A$ for each object $A \in \mathscr{C}'$ and $J(f) = f$ for each morphism of $\mathscr{C}'$. Clearly J is a functor, called the *inclusion functor* of $\mathscr{C}'$ in $\mathscr{C}$.

Let F from $\mathscr{G}$ to $\mathscr{S}$ assign to each group its underlying set and to each group homomorphism the homomorphism itself (regarded as a set function). F is called a *forgetful functor*. Similar forgetful functors can be defined from $\mathscr{T}$ to $\mathscr{S}$, from the category of differentiable manifolds to $\mathscr{T}$, etc.

We can regard the assignment of the fundamental group to a topological space as a functor from the category of topological spaces with base points to the category of groups.

Let $F_A:\mathscr{G} \to \mathscr{G}$ be defined by

$$F_A(B) = A \oplus B \qquad \text{for all} \quad B \in \mathscr{G} \quad \text{and for} \quad f:B \to C,$$

a morphism of $\mathscr{G}$,

$$F_A(f) = (1_A, f),$$

where $(1_A, f)$ is given by $(1_A, f)(a, b) = (a, f(b))$. Then F is a functor. Similarly one can hold the second group fixed. A direct sum functor can obviously also be defined in many other categories.

In an analogous manner we can define a tensor product functor on appropriate categories.

A *contravariant functor* from a category $\mathscr{C}_1$ to a category $\mathscr{C}_2$ is an assignment $F: \mathscr{C}_1 \to \mathscr{C}_2$ subject to (F1) and the following:

F2*) If fg is defined in $\mathscr{C}_1$, then $F(g)F(f)$ is defined in $\mathscr{C}_2$ and $F(g)F(f) = F(fg)$. If f is a morphism of $\mathscr{C}_1$, $F(\text{domain } f) = \text{range } F(f)$ and $F(\text{range } f) = \text{domain } F(f)$.

If A and B are R-modules, we have defined $\text{Hom}(A, B)$. It is easy to see that if A or B is held fixed, it is a functor from the category of R-modules to that of abelian groups (to that of R-modules if R is commutative); it is contravariant in the first variable and covariant in the second. More generally, if $\mathscr{C}$ is any category, $A \in \mathscr{C}$, we can define a covariant functor $H^A: \mathscr{C} \to \mathscr{S}$ by $H^A(B) = \text{hom}(A, B)$ and if $f: B \to C$ then $H^A(f): \text{hom}(A, B) \to \text{hom}(A, C)$ is given by $H^A(f)(x) = fx$ for all $x \in \text{hom}(A, B)$. It is also possible to define a contravariant set-valued functor H_A by fixing the second object in $\text{hom}(-, A)$. Combining the two notions, one can define a "functor" of two variables: $H: \mathscr{C} \times \mathscr{C} \to \mathscr{S}$ given by

$$H(A_1, A_2) = \text{hom}(A_1, A_2),$$

for any pair of objects of $\mathscr{C}$, and $H(f_1, f_2): \text{hom}(A_1, A_2) \to \text{hom}(A'_1, A'_2)$ is the morphism

$$H(f_1, f_2)(x) = f_2 x f_1 \qquad \text{for} \quad x: A_1 \to A_2, \quad f_1: A'_1 \to A_1, \quad f_2: A_2 \to A'_2.$$

An assignment which is a functor in each of the variables separately is called a *bifunctor*.

A functor $F: \mathscr{C}_1 \to \mathscr{C}_2$ defines a collection of functions

$$\text{hom}(A, B) \to \text{hom}(F(A), F(B)),$$

or

$$\text{hom}(A, B) \to \text{hom}(F(B), F(A));$$

if each of these is one-one, F is a *faithful* functor and if each is onto, F is a *full* functor. If F is a faithful functor which is one-one on the objects of $\mathscr{C}_1$, then F is called an *embedding*. A full embedding which is covariant and which is also onto the objects of $\mathscr{C}_2$ is an *equivalence*.

Let * be a contravariant functor from a category $\mathscr{C}$ to a category $\mathscr{C}^*$ with a contravariant inverse (the existence of an inverse implies that * is one-one and onto on both objects and morphisms). To each $A \in \mathscr{C}$ there corresponds $A^* \in \mathscr{C}^*$, while to $f: A \to B$, a morphism of $\mathscr{C}$, there corresponds $f^*: B^* \to A^*$ in $\mathscr{C}^*$. We call $\mathscr{C}^*$ a *dual category* of $\mathscr{C}$, and * a *duality functor*.

Example. The functor which assigns to each abelian group its character group is a duality functor from the category of abelian groups to that of compact abelian Hausdorff topological groups.

The notion of duality is central to category theory. For each property of morphisms of a category we define a *dual property*: if P is a property of morphisms, $P*$ is the property defined by "f is $P*$" if and only if "$f*$ is P," where $*$ is a duality functor. Some properties are self-dual, e.g., the property of being an identity. Many examples of dual properties will occur later. For each theorem about a category, there is a corresponding dual statement in which each property of morphisms is replaced by its dual property and which is a theorem in the dual category; whether or not the statement holds in the original category depends upon the special properties of the category, as we shall see in Section 3. Duality may be roughly described as "reversal of arrows" because of the contravariance involved.

3. OBJECTS AND MORPHISMS

A morphism $e: A \rightarrow B$ of a category $\mathscr{C}$ is an *isomorphism* if there is a morphism $e': B \rightarrow A$ in $\mathscr{C}$ with $ee' = 1_B$ and $e'e = 1_A$. If this inverse e' exists, it is unique and is written as $e' = e^{-1}$. A group is thus a monoid in which every morphism is an isomorphism, i.e., inverses exist. The objects A and B are *isomorphic* in $\mathscr{C}$ if there exists an isomorphism in $\mathscr{C}$, $e: A \rightarrow B$. A morphism $k: B \rightarrow C$ of $\mathscr{C}$ is a *monomorphism* in $\mathscr{C}$ if it is left cancellable, i.e., if $f, g: A \rightarrow B$ morphisms of $\mathscr{C}$ with $kf = kg$ always implies that $f = g$. The dual property is, of course, right cancellability. A morphism $v: A \rightarrow B$ is an *epimorphism* if it is right cancellable. To express this in terms of duality, $f: A \rightarrow B$ is an epimorphism in $\mathscr{C}$ if and only if $f*: B* \rightarrow A*$ is a monomorphism in $\mathscr{C}*$. We note that even in a category where the morphisms are functions, monomorphisms are not necessarily one-one and epimorphisms are not necessarily onto.

Examples. We consider the category of pathwise connected topological spaces with base points and continuous maps (taking base points into base points). Then if A is a covering space over B, the covering map is continuous, but not in general one-one, for example, S^n over P^n. However, since if the compositions of any two morphisms into A with the covering map are equal, the morphisms are equal, the covering map is a monomorphism.

On the other hand, in the category of Hausdorff spaces and continuous maps, let Q be the rationals and R the reals. Then the injection $Q \rightarrow R$ is an epimorphism, for a map from R is completely determined by what it does on the rationals. Also, in the category of rings and ring homomorphisms, let Z be the integers; then $Z \rightarrow Q$ is an epimorphism but not onto. However, it is possible to show, using, e.g., free products with amalgamated subgroups, that the epimorphisms in the category of groups and group homomorphisms are precisely the onto homomorphisms, and in this category and that of rings, the monomorphisms are the one-one homomorphisms.

From the above we see that not every morphism which is both a mono-morphism and an epimorphism is an isomorphism. A category in which every morphism which is both a monomorphism and an epimorphism is an isomor-phism is called a *balanced* category. In general:

Theorem 1. *An isomorphism is both a monomorphism and an epimorphism.*

Proof. Suppose $e:A \to B$ is an isomorphism and let

$$X \xrightarrow{f} A \xrightarrow{e} B = X \xrightarrow{g} A \xrightarrow{e} B.$$

Then

$$X \xrightarrow{f} A = X \xrightarrow{f} A \xrightarrow{e} B \xrightarrow{e^{-1}} A = X \xrightarrow{g} A \xrightarrow{e} B \xrightarrow{e^{-1}} A = X \xrightarrow{g} A.$$

So e is a monomorphism and dually it is an epimorphism.

Theorem 2. *If* $A \xrightarrow{f} B \to C$ *is a monomorphism, so is* $A \xrightarrow{f} B$. *If* $A \xrightarrow{f} B$ *and* $B \xrightarrow{g} C$ *are monomorphisms, so is* $A \xrightarrow{f} B \xrightarrow{g} C$.

Proof. Suppose $X \xrightarrow{a} A \xrightarrow{f} B = X \xrightarrow{b} A \xrightarrow{f} B$ and $A \xrightarrow{f} B \longrightarrow C$ is a monomorphism. Then

$$X \xrightarrow{a} A \xrightarrow{f} B \longrightarrow C = X \xrightarrow{b} A \xrightarrow{f} B \longrightarrow C,$$

and by cancellability, $a = b$, and f is a monomorphism.

Suppose $A \xrightarrow{f} B$ and $B \xrightarrow{g} C$ are monomorphisms and that

$$X \xrightarrow{a} A \xrightarrow{f} B \xrightarrow{g} C = X \xrightarrow{g} A \xrightarrow{f} B \xrightarrow{g} C.$$

Then we cancel f and g successively to get that $a = b$ and show that the composi-tion of monomorphisms is a monomorphism.

Theorem 2*. *If the composition gf of two morphisms is an epimorphism, then g is an epimorphism. The composition of epimorphisms is an epimorphism.*

Proof. Dually to Theorem 2.

The next problem which we consider is how to compare objects and morphisms. Two monomorphisms $f_1:A_1 \to B$ and $f_2:A_2 \to B$ of a category $\mathscr{C}$ are *equivalent* if there exist morphisms $g_1:A_1 \to A_2$ and $g_2:A_2 \to A_1$ in $\mathscr{C}$ such that

$$
\begin{array}{ccc}
A_1 \searrow^{f_1} & & A_1 \searrow^{f_1} \\
g_1 \downarrow \quad \searrow B & \text{and} & g_2 \uparrow \quad \searrow B \\
A_2 \nearrow_{f_2} & & A_2 \nearrow_{f_2}
\end{array}
$$

are commutative, that is, $f_2 g_1 = f_1$ and $f_1 g_2 = f_2$.

It is clear that this defines an equivalence relation on the monomorphisms with a fixed object of $\mathscr{C}$ as their range. A *subobject* of B is an equivalence class of monomorphisms into B. We observe that a subobject is not itself an object of the category. Frequently, but imprecisely, we refer to a representative of such a class as a "subobject," and even more inaccurately we may call its domain a "subobject" of the range. We assume that in any category which we consider there is a *set* of monomorphisms which contains a representative of each subobject and similarly for the quotient objects. We define a partial ordering on subobjects of an object B as follows: The subobject represented by $f_1 : A_1 \to B$ is *contained in* that represented by $f_2 : A_2 \to B$ if there exists a monomorphism $g : A_1 \to A_2$ such that

$$
\begin{array}{c}
A_1 \overset{f_1}{\searrow} \\
g \downarrow \quad \nearrow B \\
A_2 \diagup_{f_2}
\end{array}
$$

is commutative. The morphism g is necessarily unique since f_2 is a monomorphism.

Dually, two epimorphisms $f_1 : B \to C_1$ and $f_2 : B \to C_2$ of a category $\mathscr{C}$ are equivalent if there are morphisms $g_1 : C_1 \to C_2$ and $g_2 : C_2 \to C_1$ in $\mathscr{C}$ such that

$$
B \begin{array}{c} \overset{f_1}{\nearrow} C_1 \\ \downarrow g_1 \\ \underset{f_2}{\searrow} C_2 \end{array}
\quad \text{and} \quad
B \begin{array}{c} \overset{f_1}{\nearrow} C_1 \\ \uparrow g_2 \\ \underset{f_2}{\searrow} C_2 \end{array}
$$

commute.

A *quotient object* is an equivalence class of epimorphisms. A partial ordering dual to that for subobjects is defined for quotient objects of a given object. When we refer to the smallest or largest subobject or quotient object, we mean with respect to these orderings.

A commutative diagram in a category $\mathscr{C}$

$$(*)\qquad\begin{array}{ccc} P & \overset{b_2}{\longrightarrow} & A_2 \\ b_1 \downarrow & & \downarrow a_2 \\ A_1 & \underset{a_1}{\longrightarrow} & A \end{array}$$

is called a *pullback* for a_1 and a_2 if for every pair of morphisms b_1', b_2' in $\mathscr{C}$ such that

$$P' \overset{b_1'}{\longrightarrow} A_1 \overset{a_1}{\longrightarrow} A = P' \overset{b_2'}{\longrightarrow} A_2 \overset{a_2}{\longrightarrow} A,$$

there exists a unique morphism $m : P' \to P$ such that $b_1' = b_1 m$ and $b_2' = b_2 m$.

Theorem 3. *If $(*)$ is a pullback and a_1 is a monomorphism, then b_2 is also.*

Proof. Let $b_2 f = b_2 g$. Then $a_1 b_1 f = a_2 b_2 f = a_2 b_2 g = a_1 b_1 g$, so since a_1 is a monomorphism, $b_1 f = b_1 g$. But the factorization through the pullback diagram is unique, so $f = g$, and b_2 is a monomorphism.

The dual of a pullback, namely a *pushout*, is obtained by reversing the arrows in the diagram defining a pullback. The dual of Theorem 3 also holds.

An object T is *terminal* in a category $\mathscr{C}$ if for each object A in $\mathscr{C}$ there is exactly one morphism $A \to T$. Dually, an object J in $\mathscr{C}$ is *initial* if for each object A in $\mathscr{C}$ there is exactly one morphism $J \to A$. A *zero object* of $\mathscr{C}$ is an object with precisely one morphism of $\mathscr{C}$ to and from any other object, i.e., it is both terminal and initial in $\mathscr{C}$. If a category has a zero object, denoted by 0, we define the *zero morphism* $0 : A \to B$ to be the unique morphism $A \to 0 \to B$; thus each zero morphism is a distinguished element of the corresponding $\hom(A, B)$. This definition is independent of which zero object is used, for any two zero objects must, from the definition, be isomorphic.

Most categories of algebraic structures have a zero object, e.g., a (the) trivial group, with homomorphisms whose image is the identity alone as zero morphisms. However, the category of fields does not have a zero object. Also, if $\mathscr{A}_R$ is the category of algebras with identity over a commutative ring R with identity, R is itself an initial object; as terminal object, but not as initial, we have the algebra consisting of only one element; hence if R is nontrivial, there is no zero object.

Categories of objects without structure do not in general have a zero object; hence we often "impose" one. For example, the category of sets has no zero object but the category of sets with distinguished point and maps taking distinguished point to distinguished point has any distinguished point as a zero object and similarly for topological spaces with base points. In fact, if $\mathscr{C}$ is a category, not necessarily with zero object, such that each set $\hom(A, B)$ has a distinguished element and the composition of any two distinguished elements is again a distinguished element, then we can adjoin a zero object to $\mathscr{C}$ and the distinguished morphisms become zero morphisms in this new category with zero object.

4. KERNELS AND IMAGES

A *kernel* of a morphism $f : A \to B$ of a category $\mathscr{C}$ with zero object is a morphism $k : K \to A$ such that:

1) $K \xrightarrow{\ k\ } A \xrightarrow{\ f\ } B = K \xrightarrow{\ 0\ } B$,

2) for any $X \to A$ such that $X \to A \xrightarrow{\ f\ } B = X \xrightarrow{\ 0\ } B$, there is a unique $X \to K$ such that $X \to K \xrightarrow{\ k\ } A = X \to A$. Equivalently, the kernel of f is given by the pullback diagram

$$
\begin{array}{ccc}
K & \longrightarrow & 0 \\
{\scriptstyle k}\downarrow & & \downarrow \\
A & \xrightarrow[\ f\ ]{} & B
\end{array} .
$$

A kernel is necessarily a monomorphism and two kernels of the same morphism are equivalent. We call the subobject represented by a kernel *the* kernel or, loosely, the representing morphism itself *the* kernel. If a subobject is the kernel of some morphism, it is called a *normal* subobject, and if all subobjects of a category $\mathscr{C}$ are normal, $\mathscr{C}$ is called a *normal category*.

The *cokernel* of a morphism $f: A \to B$ is a morphism $u: B \to C$ such that

1) $A \xrightarrow{f} B \xrightarrow{u} C = A \xrightarrow{0} C,$

2) for any $B \to X$ such that $A \xrightarrow{f} B \to X = A \xrightarrow{0} X$, there is a unique $C \to X$ such that $B \xrightarrow{u} C \to X = B \to X.$

An equivalent definition is given by a pushout diagram. Conormality is defined dually to normality.

The *image* of a morphism $f: A \to B$ of a category $\mathscr{C}$ is the smallest subobject of B such that f factors through the representing monomorphisms, i.e., a monomorphism $I \to B$ represents the image of f if:

1) There is a morphism $A \to I$ in $\mathscr{C}$ such that $A \to I \to B = A \xrightarrow{f} B.$

2) If $I' \to B$ is a monomorphism of $\mathscr{C}$ such that there is a morphism of $\mathscr{C}$, $A \to I'$, such that $A \to I' \to B = A \xrightarrow{f} B$, then $I' \to B$ contains $I \to B.$

The *coimage* of a morphism $f: A \to B$ of $\mathscr{C}$ is the smallest quotient object of A in $\mathscr{C}$ through which f factors. As usual, we sometimes call a representing morphism the *image* or *coimage*. We note that a monomorphism is its own image and an epimorphism its own coimage.

Examples

1. Kernels in a category of algebraic objects are usually the embedding maps of the kernels (in the ordinary sense) into the object, e.g., if A and B are groups and $f: A \to B$ a group homomorphism, then $j: \text{kernel } f \to A$ is the kernel (in the category sense) of f. In some categories this map may not be in the category, e.g., the category of algebras with identity over a commutative ring with identity, where an ideal may fail to have an identity and hence to be in the category. Also, the category of rings with minimal condition fails to have kernels. The normal subobjects in the category of groups are those represented by the injective homomorphisms whose images are normal subgroups of the range. Indeed, if $f: A \to B$ is an injective homomorphism such that $f(A)$ is a normal subgroup of B, then f is the kernel of the projection $B \to B/f(A)$. However, if $f(A)$ is not a normal subgroup, the only candidate for f to be the kernel of would be $B \to B/(\text{normal closure of } f(A))$. But the injection $(\text{normal closure } f(A)) \to B$ is the kernel of this morphism and it is not equivalent to f. Thus the category of groups is not normal. The situation is similar in the case of rings.

2. We consider cokernels for the category of groups. If $f: A \to B$ is a group homomorphism, its cokernel is $B \to B/(\text{normal closure } f(A))$. Also, every epimorphism is the cokernel of its kernel, so that the category is conormal. In various categories, particularly those of certain types of topological spaces, e.g., normal, morphisms may fail to have cokernels because quotient spaces do not inherit the properties of the original space.

3. The category $\mathcal{T}'$ of compact Hausdorff spaces with base points and continuous maps (taking base points to base points) is normal. To see this we first observe that every morphism $f: A \to B$ has a cokernel, constructed as follows. Let

$$g: B \to (B - f(A)) \cup \{0\}$$

be the identity map on $(B - f(A)) \cup \{0\}$ and take $f(A)$ onto the base point $\{0\}$, where $(B - f(A)) \cup \{0\}$ has the quotient topology so that g is continuous. Since $f(A)$ is closed, $(B - f(A)) \cup \{0\}$ is Hausdorff. Clearly

$$A \xrightarrow{f} B \xrightarrow{g} (B - f(A)) \cup \{0\} = 0;$$

and if $A \xrightarrow{f} B \xrightarrow{k} X = 0$, we define $h: (B - f(A)) \cup \{0\} \to X$ by $h(x) = k(x)$ so that

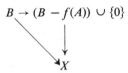

is commutative. Also, we claim that the monomorphisms in this category are the one-one maps. Clearly, one-one implies monomorphic. So suppose that $f: A \to B$ is a monomorphism and that $f(x) = f(y)$, $0 \neq x \neq y \neq 0$. The subspace of A consisting of $\{x, y, 0\}$, with the subspace topology, is compact Hausdorff, so we consider the inclusion map and the map taking x and y onto x and 0 onto 0. Their compositions with f are equal, but they are not, which is a contradiction.

Now if $f: A \to B$ is a monomorphism of the category, it is clearly the kernel of its cokernel as constructed above.

However, the category fails to be conormal; for consider the map which takes $\{x, y, 0\}$ onto $\{x, 0\}$, $0 \neq x \neq y \neq 0$, with x and y going onto x, 0 onto 0 as above. This is clearly an epimorphism and the map is continuous. However, the only map whose cokernel it could be is the zero morphism. But, $\{0\} \to \{x, y, 0\} \to \{x, y, 0\} = 0$ and there is no map $\{x, 0\} \to \{x, y, 0\}$ with the necessary commutativity property.

4. In the category of groups, the domain of the image morphism is the image in the usual sense and the image (in the categorical sense) is represented by the injection homomorphism. The coimage is the map of the domain of a homomorphism onto its image.

We note that these definitions—of kernel, image, etc.—avoid the use of elements and hence can be used in categories which have no objects with elements, as in the case of a group considered as a category.

The following theorems require no assumptions about the existence of kernels or cokernels for arbitrary morphisms of the category.

Theorem 4. *If $f: A \to B$ is an epimorphism of a category with zero object, then $B \to 0$ is the cokernel of f.*

Proof. Let $B \to X$ be such that $A \xrightarrow{f} B \to X = 0$. Then there exists uniquely $0 : 0 \to X$ such that

is commutative, since f is right cancellable. Hence $B \to 0$ is the cokernel of f.

Theorem 4*. *If $f : A \to B$ is a monomorphism of a category with a zero object, then $0 \to A$ is the kernel of f.*

Proof. The proof is dual to that of Theorem 4.

Theorem 5. *If kernel f and kernel gf are defined, then kernel f is contained in kernel gf. If g is a monomorphism, then kernel $f = $ kernel gf if either is defined.*

Proof. Let $k : K \to A$ be the kernel of $f : A \to B$ and $k' : K' \to A$ the kernel of $gf : A \to C$. Then $gfk = 0$ and so there is a morphism $k'' : K \to K'$ such that $k'k'' = k$ and k is contained in k'. The second part of the proposition is a straightforward application of the cancellation property of monomorphisms.

Theorem 5*. *If cokernel g and cokernel gf are defined, then cokernel g is contained in cokernel gf. If f is an epimorphism, then*

$$cokernel \ g = cokernel \ gf$$

if either is defined.

Theorem 6. *The diagram*

$$
\begin{array}{ccc}
A_1 & \xrightarrow{f} & A \\
 & & \downarrow h \\
B_1 & \xrightarrow{g} & B
\end{array}
$$

where g is the kernel of a morphism $m : B \to B_2$, can be extended to a pullback if and only if f is the kernel of mh.

Proof. If f is the kernel of mh, then since $mhf = 0$ and g is the kernel of m, there is a unique morphism $A_1 \to B_1$ which makes the diagram commutative. Now if $X \to A \xrightarrow{h} B = X \to B_1 \xrightarrow{g} B$, then $X \to A \xrightarrow{h} B \xrightarrow{m} B_2 = 0$, since g is the kernel of m. Thus there is a unique morphism $X \to A_1$ such that $X \to A_1 \xrightarrow{f} A = X \to A$. Moreover,

$$X \longrightarrow A_1 \longrightarrow B_1 \xrightarrow{g} B = X \longrightarrow A_1 \xrightarrow{f} A \xrightarrow{h} B = X \longrightarrow B_1 \xrightarrow{g} B.$$

But g is a monomorphism, so $X \to A_1 \to B_1 = X \to B_1$. Thus the filled-in diagram is a pullback.

On the other hand, if the diagram can be filled in to be a pullback, then by commutativity, $mhf = 0$. If $X \to A$ is such that $X \to A \to B \to B_2 = 0$, then $X \to A \to B$ must factor through g. Hence the pullback morphism $X \to A_1$ gives the desired morphism for the factorization of $X \to A$.

Theorem 7. *If $k:K \to A$ is the kernel of $f:A \to B$ and $g:A \to C$ the cokernel of k, then k is the kernel of g.*

Proof. We have

$$K \xrightarrow{k} A \xrightarrow{f} B$$

where u is any morphism such that $gu = 0$ and v is the morphism whose existence is guaranteed by the fact that $fk = 0$ and g is the cokernel of k. Then $fu = vgu = 0$ and since k is the kernel of f, we can fill in the left-hand triangle to make it commutative, say by $x:X \to K$. Also, $gk = 0$ so k is the kernel of g.

Theorem 7*. *If $g:B \to C$ is the cokernel of $f:A \to B$ and $k:K \to B$ the kernel of g, then g is the cokernel of k.*

These results lead directly to the following:

Theorem 8. *If a category $\mathscr{C}$ is normal and conormal and has kernels and cokernels (i.e., every morphism of $\mathscr{C}$ has a kernel and a cokernel in $\mathscr{C}$), then there is a bijective function from the (equivalence classes of) subobjects of an object A to the (equivalence classes of) quotient objects of A, which is given by the assignment of cokernels and whose inverse is given by the assignment of kernels.*

We also have:

Theorem 9. *A normal category is balanced.*

Proof. Let $f:A \to B$ be a monomorphism and an epimorphism in a normal category $\mathscr{C}$. Then f is the kernel of its cokernel. However, since f is an epimorphism, its cokernel is $B \to 0$. But 1_B is a kernel of $B \to 0$. Hence, being equivalent to the identity, f must be an isomorphism.

Theorem 9*. *A conormal category is balanced.*

5. EXACT CATEGORIES

It should now be apparent that we have available many of the necessary concepts for the formulation of homological algebra. We shall discuss some of the notions briefly.

Let $\mathscr{C}$ be a normal and conormal category with kernels and cokernels. $\mathscr{C}$ is an *exact category* if every morphism $f:A \to B$ of can be written as

$$A \to I \to B,$$

where $A \to I$ is an epimorphism and $I \to B$ a monomorphism. We note that the axioms for an exact category are self-dual, that is, $\mathscr{C}$ is exact if and only if $\mathscr{C}^*$ is exact.

Example. The category of R-modules and module homomorphisms over a ring R is exact.

> **Theorem 10.** *If* $k:K \to A$ *is the kernel of* $c:A \to I$ *and* $g:B \to C$ *the cokernel of* $i:I \to B$, *where* $A \xrightarrow{c} I \xrightarrow{i} B$ *is a factorization of a morphism* $f:A \to B$ *of an exact category* $\mathscr{C}$, *then* k *is the kernel of* f *and* g *is cokernel of* f. *Moreover,* c *is the coimage of* f *and* i *the image of* f. *Thus the factorization is unique (up to equivalence).*

Proof. The first part of the theorem follows directly from Theorems 5 and 5*. We shall show that i is the image; that c is the coimage can be shown dually. Suppose that $S \to B$ is a subobject through which f factors. We have

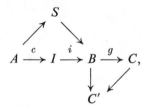

$$A \xrightarrow{c} I \xrightarrow{i} B \xrightarrow{g} C,$$

where $B \to C'$ is the cokernel of $S \to B$. The morphism $C \to C'$ is defined since $A \to B \to C'$ is zero. We have $I \to B \to C' = I \to B \to C \to C' = 0$, so that i can be factored through $S \to B$, the kernel of $B \to C'$. Hence i is the image of f.

A sequence of morphisms

$$\cdots \longrightarrow A_{i-1} \xrightarrow{f_{i-1}} A_i \xrightarrow{f_i} A_{i+1} \xrightarrow{f_{i+1}} A_{i+2} \longrightarrow \cdots$$

in an exact category is an *exact sequence* if kernel $f_i = $ image f_{i-1}. If $f_i f_{i-1} = 0$ for all i, that is, image $f_{i-1} \subset$ kernel f_i, the sequence is called a *complex*. An exact sequence

$$(*) \qquad\qquad\qquad 0 \to A \to B \to C \to 0$$

is called a *short exact sequence*. We frequently write $0 \to A \to B \to B/A \to 0$ for the exact sequence $(*)$, since $B \to C$ is a quotient object with kernel $A \to B$.
  If

$$A: \cdots \longrightarrow A_{i-1} \xrightarrow{f_{i-1}} A_i \xrightarrow{f_i} A_{i+1} \xrightarrow{f_{i+1}} A_{i+2} \longrightarrow \cdots$$

and

$$B: \cdots \longrightarrow B_{i-1} \xrightarrow{g_{i-1}} B_i \xrightarrow{g_i} B_{i+1} \xrightarrow{g_{i+1}} B_{i+2} \longrightarrow \cdots$$

are exact sequences in an exact category $\mathscr{C}$, then a *morphism of exact sequences* is a collection of morphisms of $\mathscr{C}$, $\{h_i:A_i \to B_i\}$, written $h:A \to B$, such that the diagram

$$\cdots \longrightarrow A_{i-1} \xrightarrow{f_{i-1}} A_i \xrightarrow{f_i} A_{i+1} \longrightarrow \cdots$$

$$\big\downarrow h_{i-1} \qquad \big\downarrow h_i \qquad \big\downarrow h_{i+1}$$

$$\cdots \longrightarrow B_{i-1} \xrightarrow[g_{i-1}]{} B_i \xrightarrow[g_i]{} B_{i+1} \longrightarrow \cdots$$

is commutative. It is easy to verify that the collection $\mathscr{E}$ of exact sequences of objects and morphisms of an exact category together with the morphisms between them is again a category.

Theorem 11. *Let $\mathscr{C}$ be an exact category. Then*

1) $0 \to A \xrightarrow{f} B$ *is exact if and only if f is a monomorphism in $\mathscr{C}$.*

2) $A \xrightarrow{f} B \to 0$ *is exact if and only if f is an epimorphism in $\mathscr{C}$.*

3) $0 \to A \xrightarrow{f} B \to 0$ *is exact if and only if f is an isomorphism in $\mathscr{C}$.*

4) $0 \to A \xrightarrow{f} B \xrightarrow{g} C \to 0$ *is a short exact sequence if and only if f is a monomorphism, g is an epimorphism, and f is the kernel of g (equivalently g is the cokernel of f).*

Proof.

1) If f is a monomorphism, its kernel is zero and the sequence is exact. If the sequence is exact, the kernel of f is zero. Let $A \xrightarrow{c} I \xrightarrow{i} B$ be the factorization of $A \to B$, c an epimorphism, i a monomorphism. Then by Theorem 10, zero is the kernel of c, and c is equivalent to the identity. Hence $f = ic$ is a monomorphism.

2) Dually to part (1).

3) Follows from (1) and (2) since an exact category is balanced.

4) Follows from (1) and (2).

Corollary. In an exact category:
1) $A \to B$ is a monomorphism if and only if its kernel is $0 \to A$.
2) $A \to B$ is an epimorphism if and only if its cokernel is $B \to 0$.

The Nine Lemma. Given a diagram in an exact category,

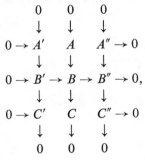

with exact columns and row, then either of the following implies the other:
1) There exist morphisms $A' \to A$ and $A \to A''$ making that row exact and the resulting diagram commutative.
2) There exist morphisms $C' \to C$ and $C \to C''$ making that row exact and the resulting diagram commutative.

Proof. We shall show that (1) implies (2).

If we can show that

$$0 \to A' \to B' \to C \to C'' \to 0$$

is exact; then $C \to C''$ is an epimorphism and the factorization of $B' \to C$ through its image is just $B' \to C' \to C$, that is, $C' \to C$ is the kernel of $C \to C''$ and

$$0 \to C' \to C \to C'' \to 0$$

is exact.

Thus suppose that $X \to B'$ is such that

$$X \to B' \to C = X \to B' \to B \to C = 0.$$

Then there is a morphism $X \to A$ such that

$$X \to A \to B = X \to B = X \to B' \to B.$$

Also

$$X \to A \to \dot{B} \to C =$$
$$X \to A \to A'' \to B'' = X \to A \to B \to B''$$
$$= X \to B' \to B \to B'' = 0.$$

So since $A'' \to B''$ is a monomorphism, $X \to A \to A'' = 0$. Hence there is a morphism $X \to A'$ such that $X \to A' \to A = X \to A$. Thus we have

$$X \to B' \to B = X \to A \to B = X \to A' \to A \to B = X \to A' \to B' \to B.$$

But $B' \to B$ is a monomorphism, so $X \to B' = X \to A' \to B'$ and $A' \to B'$ is the kernel of $B' \to C$.

Dually $C \to C''$ is the cokernel of $B' \to C$, and the sequence is exact.

One of the Noether isomorphism theorems, sometimes called the *freshman theorem*, which we have encountered before, is formulated for groups as follows: If G_1 and G_2 are normal subgroups of a group G, with $G_1 \subset G_2$, then

$$(G/G_1)/(G_2/G_1) \simeq G/G_2.$$

We have the same result for objects in an exact category; however, we observe that the result should hold in a more general type of category since the category of groups is not exact.

Theorem 12. *If A_1, A_2, and A are objects in an exact category and $A_1 \to A_2$ and $A_2 \to A$ are monomorphisms, then $A/A_1 \to A/A_2$ is the cokernel of $A_2/A_1 \to A/A_1$.*

Proof. We apply the Nine Lemma to

$$
\begin{array}{ccccccc}
& 0 & & 0 & & 0 & \\
& \downarrow & & \downarrow & & \downarrow & \\
0 \to & A_1 & \to & A_1 & \to & 0 & \to 0 \\
& \downarrow & & \downarrow & & \downarrow & \\
0 \to & A_2 & \to & A & \to & A/A_2 & \to 0. \\
& \downarrow & & \downarrow & & \downarrow & \\
0 \to & A_2/A_1 & & A/A_1 & & A/A_2 & \to 0 \\
& \downarrow & & \downarrow & & \downarrow & \\
& 0 & & 0 & & 0 &
\end{array}
$$

6. PRODUCTS AND LIMITS

An object P in a category $\mathscr{C}$ is a *product* of A_1 and A_2 in $\mathscr{C}$ if there exist morphisms $p_1 : P \to A_1$ and $p_2 : P \to A_2$ in $\mathscr{C}$ such that for every pair of morphisms $f : X \to A_1$ and $g : X \to A_2$ in $\mathscr{C}$ there exists a unique morphism of $\mathscr{C}$, $X \to P$, denoted by (f, g), such that

$$
X \xrightarrow{(f,g)} P \xrightarrow{p_1} A_1 = X \xrightarrow{f} A_1
$$

and

$$
X \xrightarrow{(f,g)} P \xrightarrow{p_2} A_2 = X \xrightarrow{g} A_2.
$$

It is clear that any two objects having these properties are isomorphic in $\mathscr{C}$; hence we denote any product of A_1 and A_2 by $A_1 \times A_2$.

Given a pair of objects A_1, A_2 in a category $\mathscr{C}$, the object C in $\mathscr{C}$ is a *coproduct* of A_1 and A_2 if there exist morphisms $u_1 : A_1 \to C$ and $u_2 : A_2 \to C$ in $\mathscr{C}$ such that for every pair of morphisms $f : A_1 \to X$ and $g : A_2 \to X$ in $\mathscr{C}$ there exists a unique morphism $C \to X$, denoted by

$$
\binom{f}{g},
$$

such that

$$
A_1 \xrightarrow{u_1} C \xrightarrow{\binom{f}{g}} X = A_1 \xrightarrow{f} X
$$

and

$$
A_2 \xrightarrow{u_2} C \xrightarrow{\binom{f}{g}} X = A_2 \xrightarrow{g} X.
$$

We denote a coproduct by $A_1 + A_2$ and note that any two coproducts of A_1 and A_2 are isomorphic. The coproduct is also sometimes called the *sum*.

Examples

1. In the category of sets, the Cartesian product of any two sets is their product. In fact, the Cartesian product of sets may be defined to be the set which has the mapping

properties ascribed to a product. Then the set of ordered pairs of elements of the sets is connected by a bijection to any set having these properties. Similarly, in topological categories in which the distinguishing properties of the spaces are preserved when taking Cartesian products, e.g., compact Hausdorff spaces with base points and continuous maps taking base points into base points, the Cartesian product is a product. The same is in general true in categories of algebraic structures. We consider the category of abelian groups. The direct sum (whose underlying set is the Cartesian product) of two groups is a product, with $(f, g) : X \to A_1 \oplus A_2$ given by $(f, g)(x) = (fx, gx)$, for $x \in X$, and the ordinary projection maps as the p_i, $i = 1, 2$. Also, in the category of all groups or in the category of rings, the direct sum is a product.

2. The direct sum of two abelian groups is also a coproduct in the category of abelian groups. The maps u_i are the embeddings of the components into the direct sum and

$$\binom{f}{g}$$

is given by

$$\binom{f}{g}(a, b) = fa + gb,$$

where $+$ denotes the group operation in X. We note that this does not necessarily define a group homomorphism if X is nonabelian and in fact the direct sum is not a coproduct in the category of all groups. The free product of groups is a coproduct in the category of all groups (see, for example, Scott, *Group Theory*, Prentice-Hall, 1964, for this construction.) In the category of commutative rings with identity, the tensor product of two rings as Z-modules is their coproduct.

3. We consider the category $\mathscr{T}'$ of compact Hausdorff spaces with base points and continuous maps. Let

$$A_1 \overset{disj}{\bigcup} A_2$$

be the disjoint union of A_1, $A_2 \in \mathscr{T}'$. Let $A_1 \vee A_2$ be the quotient space of

$$A_1 \overset{disj}{\bigcup} A_2$$

resulting from the identification of base points. $A_1 \vee A_2$ is the coproduct of A_1 and A_2. We define

$$\binom{f}{g} : A_1 \vee A_2 \to X$$

by

$$\binom{f}{g} x = fx \quad \text{if} \quad x \in A_1$$
$$= gx \quad \text{if} \quad x \in A_2, \quad \text{where} \quad f : A_1 \to X, \quad g : A_2 \to X$$

are morphisms of $\mathscr{T}'$.

It is clear that the definitions we have given can be extended to the product and coproduct of any finite number of objects in a category. However, it is possible to give a more general definition of the concepts, which can be applied to not necessarily finite families of objects of the category and which will coincide with those above in the finite case.

We let $\{A_i\}_{i\in I}$ be a family of objects of a category $\mathscr{C}$. We form a category $\mathscr{F}\{A_i\}$ whose objects are indexed families $\{f_i: B \to A_i \mid i \in I\}$ of morphisms of $\mathscr{C}$ with common domain B, while a morphism $\{f_i\} \to \{f_i'\}$ in $\mathscr{F}$ is a morphism $h: B \to B'$ of $\mathscr{C}$ for which each $f_i'h = f_i$. We note that for each family of objects of the original category, such a new category can be constructed. A terminal object in this category is a *product* of the A_i; thus a product consists of an object P of $\mathscr{C}$ together with morphisms $p_i: P \to A_i$ for $i \in I$ such that any family of morphisms $f_i: B \to A_i$ can be written as $f_i = p_ih$ for a unique morphism $h: B \to P$. Usually we refer to P itself as the product. In diagram terms, $(P, \{p_i\})$ is a product of the objects $\{A_i\}_{i\in I}$ if any diagram of the form

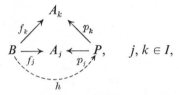

can be filled in by a unique h (at the dashed arrow) so as to be commutative. We use the notation $P = \prod_{i\in I} A_i$. A product, like any terminal object, is unique up to isomorphism (in the category $\mathscr{F}\{A_i\}$) and in particular the object of the product is unique up to isomorphism in the original category.

The dual notion of *coproduct* of a family $\{A_i\}_{i\in I}$ of objects of a category $\mathscr{C}$ is a diagram $\{u_i: A_i \to C\}$ which is initial in the category of such diagrams. If C is the coproduct of $\{A_i\}$, we write $C = \sum_{i\in I} A_i$.

We examine briefly the connections between products and coproducts and some of the previously defined concepts.

Lemma. If $f: A \to B$ and $g: B \to C$ are such that g and gf have images, then the image of gf is contained in the image of g.

Proof. Let $I \to C$ be the image of g. Then

$$A \to B \to I \to C = A \to B \to C,$$

so that $I \to C$ contains the image of gf.

Theorem 13. *In a category $\mathscr{C}$ with coproducts and images, the subobjects of a given object form a complete lattice.*

Proof. Let $\{s_i: A_i \to A \mid i \in I\}$ represent an arbitrary set of subobjects of $A \in \mathscr{C}$. Let $\{u_i: A_i \to \sum A_i \mid i \in I\}$ be the coproduct morphisms. Let u be the unique morphism $u: \sum A_i \to A$ whose composition with u_i is s_i for each i. Let $I \to A$ be the image of u. Then we have

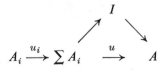

commutative, so that

$$A_i \xrightarrow{s_i} A$$

$$\downarrow \quad \nearrow$$

$$I$$

is commutative. $A_i \to I$ is a monomorphism since s_i is. Hence $I \to A$ is an upper bound.

Suppose $s': A' \to A$ is an upper bound for the s_i. Let s'_i be such that

$$A_i \xrightarrow{s_i} A$$

$$s'_i \downarrow \quad \nearrow s'$$

$$A'$$

is commutative. Let v be the unique morphism $\sum A_i \to A'$ whose composition with u_i is s'_i for each $i \in I$. Then we have $s'vu_i = uu_i$; therefore $s'v = u$, by the definition of coproduct. Hence the image of u, which is the image of $s'v$, is contained in s' by the lemma. Thus the image of u is the least upper bound.

Let $\{s'_k : A'_k \to A \mid k \in K\}$ be the set of monomorphisms $s' : A' \to A$ with s' contained in s_i for all $i \in I$. Then there exists s'', the lub of $\{s'_k \mid k \in K\}$, as constructed above, and s'' is the glb of $\{s_i \mid i \in I\}$.

Theorem 13*. *In a category with products and coimages, the quotient objects of a given object form a complete lattice.*

Theorem 14. *If every morphism of a category $\mathscr{C}$ with a zero object and coproducts can be factored into an epimorphism followed by a monomorphism, then every morphism of $\mathscr{C}$ has a kernel.*

Proof. Let $A \to B$ be a morphism of $\mathscr{C}$. Consider the coproduct $\sum A_i$ of all subobjects of A such that $A_i \to A \to B = 0$. Then $\sum A_i \to A \to B = 0$ by definition of coproduct, so let the factorization of $\sum A_i \to A$ be $\sum A_i \to I \to A$, $\sum A_i \to I$ an epimorphism, $I \to A$ a monomorphism. We have the commutative diagram

$$I$$

$$\nearrow \qquad \searrow$$

$$A_i \longrightarrow \sum A_i \quad \longrightarrow \quad A \longrightarrow B = 0.$$

Thus since $\sum A_i \to I \to A \to B = 0$ and $\sum A_i \to I$ is an epimorphism, $I \to A \to B = 0$. Moreover, $I \to A$ is an upper bound for the $A_i \to A$, for there is a map $A_i \to I = A_i \to \sum A_i \to I$ such that

$$I \to A$$

$$\uparrow \quad \nearrow$$

$$A_i$$

is commutative for each $i \in I$. Hence $I \to A$ is the desired kernel.

Theorem 14*. *If every morphism of a category $\mathscr{C}$ with a zero object and products can be factored into an epimorphism followed by a monomorphism, then every morphism of $\mathscr{C}$ has a cokernel.*

We conclude this section by introducing a notion somewhat related to products and coproducts.

If I is a partially ordered set of indices such that given $i, j \in I$, there is a $k \in I$ such that $i \leq k$ and $j \leq k$, then I is said to be *directed*. Let $\mathscr{C}$ be a category and $\{A_i\}$ a family of objects of $\mathscr{C}$ with the property that for each pair i, j with $i \leq j$ there is a morphism $f_j^i : A_i \rightarrow A_j$ such that whenever $i \leq j \leq k$ we have $f_k^j f_j^i = f_k^i$ and $f_i^i = 1_{A_i}$. Then $\{f_j^i, A_i\}$ is called a *directed system*. We define a *direct limit* for this system to be a terminal object in the category whose objects are pairs $(A, \{f^i\})$, A an object of $\mathscr{C}$, $\{f^i\}$ a family of morphisms of $\mathscr{C}$, $f^i : A_i \rightarrow A$, $i \in I$, such that for all $i \leq j$, $f^j f_j^i = f^i$. Of course, such an object may fail to exist.

The dual notion is that of *inverse limit*.

Examples

1. If the directed system consists of quotient objects of a given object, then the direct limit, if it exists, is the greatest lower bound of the quotient objects. Similarly, the inverse limit of subobjects is their greatest lower bound.

2. If $\mathfrak{A}$ is a family of objects of a category $\mathscr{C}$, indexed by I, and we define a partial ordering on finite subsets of I by set inclusion, then if $\mathscr{C}$ has finite coproducts we have a directed system whose objects are coproducts of finite subsets of objects in $\mathfrak{A}$ with the obvious inclusion morphism,

$$\sum_{i \in F} A_i \rightarrow \sum_{j \in G} A_j \qquad \text{whenever} \qquad F \subset G.$$

Then the direct limit of the directed system exists if and only if the coproduct $\sum_{i \in I} A_i$ exists (in which case they are equal).

3. Let G be a group and define the obvious ordering on its finitely generated subgroups. These subgroups, together with the injection maps, form a directed system whose direct limit is G.

4. In general, we can consider any set $\{s_i : A_i \rightarrow A\}$ of subobjects of an object A in a category $\mathscr{C}$. We define an ordering by $i \leq j$ if and only if s_i is contained in s_j to form a directed system. Then even if the direct limit does exist, it may fail to be a monomorphism.

5. For arbitrary directed systems $\{A_i\}$ of abelian groups it is possible to obtain the direct limit as a quotient group of the (weak) direct sum of the groups, with the requirements on the f_j^i of the definition determining what relations are factored out, and the inverse limit as a subgroup of the direct product (strong direct sum).

7. ABELIAN CATEGORIES

We have observed that an exact category provides a general setting in which many of the notions of homological algebra can be discussed. However, in order to reproduce all the properties which the category of R-modules over a ring R possesses, it is necessary to have some structure on the sets of morphisms, namely, we want $hom(A, B)$ to be an abelian group for each pair of objects A, B in the category. We shall first give a definition of abelian category due to Freyd and show how the group structure may be derived from the axioms listed, and then we shall give the more traditional formulization of the concept. In Section 8 we shall indicate that any abelian category is "essentially" a category of modules over a ring.

A category $\mathscr{A}$ is *abelian* if it satisfies the following axioms:

A0) $\mathscr{A}$ has a zero object.

A1) Every morphism of $\mathscr{A}$ has a kernel.

A1*) Every morphism of $\mathscr{A}$ has a cokernel.

A2) $\mathscr{A}$ is normal.

A2*) $\mathscr{A}$ is conormal.

A3) Every pair of objects of $\mathscr{A}$ has a product in $\mathscr{A}$.

A3*) Every pair of objects of $\mathscr{A}$ has a coproduct in $\mathscr{A}$.

We note that the dual of each axiom is also an axiom and hence a dual category of an abelian category must be abelian. The duality of the axiomatization of abelianess is very important in deriving the properties of such a category since whenever it is possible to prove a statement about an abelian category, the dual of the statement also holds.

Examples. It is clear, and fortunate, that abelian groups form an abelian category. This is a special case of the fact that the category of R-modules and R-module homomorphisms over any ring R is abelian. Moreover, the dual category of the category of abelian groups, that of compact abelian Hausdorff topological groups, is abelian.

We show first that an abelian category is exact.

Theorem 15. *Every morphism of an abelian category has an image and a coimage.*

Proof. Let $A \to I$ be the cokernel of the kernel of a morphism $f: A \to B$. Then from Theorem 8 it is clear that $A \to I$ is the largest quotient object of A through which f factors and hence is the coimage. Dually, the image of f is the kernel of the cokernel of f.

Lemma 1. If $I \to B$ is the image of $f: A \to B$, a morphism of an abelian category, then $A \to I$ is an epimorphism.

Proof. If $A \to I$ is not an epimorphism, then its coimage is not the identity. Thus $A \to I$ factors through a proper subobject of I. But then $A \to B$ factors through a smaller subobject of B than $I \to B$, contradicting the fact that $I \to B$ is its image.

Lemma 1*. If $A \to I$ is the coimage of $f: A \to B$, then $I \to B$ is a mono-morphism.

These give us immediately the following:

Theorem 16. *An abelian category is exact.*

Given a coproduct $A_1 + \cdots + A_n$ and a product $B_1 \times \cdots \times B_m$, every map from the coproduct to the product may be represented uniquely by a matrix (x_{ij}), where

$$A_i \xrightarrow{x_{ij}} B_j = A_i \xrightarrow{u_i} A_1 + \cdots + A_n \xrightarrow{(x_{ij})} B_1 \times \cdots \times B_m \xrightarrow{p_j} B_j.$$

In particular if both the product and the coproduct of A_1 and A_2 exist in a category $\mathscr{C}$, then we can form the morphism

$$A_1 + A_2 \xrightarrow{\left(\begin{smallmatrix} 1 & 0 \\ 0 & 1 \end{smallmatrix}\right)} A_1 \times A_2.$$

Nothing can be said in general about this morphism; for example, in the category of groups it is an epimorphism but not a monomorphism, and in the category of compact Hausdorff spaces it is a monomorphism but not an epimorphism. We have remarked, however, that the direct sum is both a product and a coproduct for the category of abelian groups, i.e., the morphism is an isomorphism. In fact we shall prove:

Theorem 17. *If A_1, A_2 are objects of an abelian category, then*

$$A_1 + A_2 \xrightarrow{\left(\begin{smallmatrix} 1 & 0 \\ 0 & 1 \end{smallmatrix}\right)} A_1 \times A_2$$

is an isomorphism.

We need some lemmas.

Lemma 1. In an abelian category, let $A_1 \to A$ and $A_2 \to A$ be subobjects of an object A, $A \to B_i$ the cokernel of $A_i \to A$, $i = 1, 2$. Let $A_{12} \to A_1$ be the kernel of $A_1 \to A \to B_2$. Then $A_{12} \to A$ is the greatest lower bound of $A_1 \to A$ and $A_2 \to A$ (equivalently, $A_{12} \to A$ may be obtained by letting $A_{12} \to A_2$ be the kernel of $A_2 \to A \to B_1$).

Proof. Clearly $A_{12} \to A$ is a lower bound. Suppose $C \to A$ is contained in $A_1 \to A$ and $A_2 \to A$. Then $C \to A \to B_2 = C \to A_1 \to A \to B_2 = 0$. But $A_{12} \to A_1$ is the kernel of $A_1 \to A \to B_2$ and hence contains $C \to A_1$; thus $C \to A$ is contained in $A_{12} \to A$.

Lemma 1*. In an abelian category, let $A \to A_1$ and $A \to A_2$ be quotient objects of an object A, $B_i \to A$ the kernel of $A \to A_i$, $i = 1, 2$. Let $A_1 \to A_{12}$ be the cokernel of $B_2 \to A \to A_1$. Then $A \to A_{12}$ is the greatest lower bound of $A \to A_1$ and $A \to A_2$.

Lemma 2. If A_1 and A_2 are objects of an abelian category, the following are exact sequences:

1) $0 \to A_1 \xrightarrow{u_1} A_1 + A_2 \xrightarrow{\binom{0}{1}} A_2 \to 0,$

2) $0 \to A_2 \xrightarrow{u_2} A_1 + A_2 \xrightarrow{\binom{1}{0}} A_1 \to 0,$

3) $0 \to A_1 \xrightarrow{(1,\,0)} A_1 \times A_2 \xrightarrow{p_2} A_2 \to 0,$

4) $0 \to A_2 \xrightarrow{(0,\,1)} A_1 \times A_2 \xrightarrow{p_1} A_1 \to 0.$

Proof. We prove that (1) is exact. The proof for (2) is analogous and those for (3) and (4) are dual.

First, u_1 is a monomorphism since

$$\binom{1}{0} u_1 = 1_{A_1}$$

is. Let

$$\binom{x_1}{x_2}$$

be such that

$$A_1 \xrightarrow{u_1} A_1 + A_2 \xrightarrow{\binom{x_1}{x_2}} X = 0.$$

Then, by the definition of coproduct, $x_1 = 0$, and so

$$A_1 + A_2 \xrightarrow{\binom{x_1}{x_2}} X = A_1 + A_2 \xrightarrow{\binom{0}{1}} A_2 \xrightarrow{x_2} X;$$

that is, $\binom{0}{1}$ is the cokernel of u_1.

Lemma 3. The greatest lower bound of

$$A_1 \xrightarrow{u_1} A_1 + A_2 \quad \text{and} \quad A_2 \xrightarrow{u_2} A_1 + A_2$$

is $0 \to A_1 + A_2$, for A_1, A_2 objects of an abelian category.

Proof. The greatest lower bound is the kernel of

$$A_2 \xrightarrow{u_2} A_1 + A_2 \xrightarrow{\binom{0}{1}} A_2,$$

a monomorphism. Hence the kernel is the zero morphism.

Lemma 3*. The greatest lower bound of

$$A_1 \times A_2 \xrightarrow{p_1} A_1 \quad \text{and} \quad A_1 \times A_2 \xrightarrow{p_2} A_2$$

is $A_1 \times A_2 \to 0$.

We are now ready to prove the theorem.

Proof of Theorem 17. Let $K \to A_1 + A_2$ be the kernel of

$$\begin{pmatrix} 1 & 0 \\ 0 & 1 \end{pmatrix}.$$

Then

$$K \longrightarrow A_1 + A_2 \xrightarrow{\begin{pmatrix} 1 & 0 \\ 0 & 1 \end{pmatrix}} A_1 \times A_2 \xrightarrow{p_2} A_2 = K \longrightarrow A_1 + A_2 \xrightarrow{\binom{0}{1}} A_2,$$

and thus $K \to A_1 + A_2$ is contained in u_1. Similarly it is contained in u_2 and hence in $0 \to A_1 + A_2$, their greatest lower bound, that is, $K = 0$ and $\begin{pmatrix} 1 & 0 \\ 0 & 1 \end{pmatrix}$ is a monomorphism. Dually it is an epimorphism. An abelian category is balanced so the morphism is an isomorphism.

In an abelian category we denote the isomorphic objects $A_1 \times A_2$ and $A_1 + A_2$ by $A_1 \oplus A_2$ and call this the *biproduct* of A_1 and A_2.

For the remainder of this section, all objects and morphisms are considered to be in an abelian category.

We shall now turn to developing the additive structure on the sets $\hom(A, B)$. Given two morphisms $f, g \in \hom(A, B)$, we define

$$A \xrightarrow[L]{f+g} B = A \xrightarrow{(1,\,1)} A \oplus A \xrightarrow{\binom{f}{g}} B$$

and

$$A \xrightarrow[R]{f+g} B = A \xrightarrow{(f,\,g)} B \oplus B \xrightarrow{\binom{1}{1}} B.$$

We want to show that these are the same operation.

Lemma 1. $\underset{L}{0 + f} = f = \underset{L}{f + 0}$ and $\underset{R}{0 + f} = f = \underset{R}{f + 0}.$

Proof. We show the first equality; the others can be verified similarly. We have

$$A \xrightarrow{(1,\,1)} A \oplus A \xrightarrow{\binom{f}{0}} B = A \longrightarrow A \oplus A \xrightarrow{p_1} A \xrightarrow{f} B = A \xrightarrow{f} B.$$

Lemma 2. For $x : B \to C$ and $y : C \to A$,

$$\underset{L}{xf + xg} = x(\underset{L}{f + g}) \quad \text{and} \quad \underset{L}{fy + gy} = (\underset{L}{f + g})y.$$

Proof.

$$A \oplus A \xrightarrow{\binom{f}{g}} B \xrightarrow{x} C = A \oplus A \xrightarrow{\binom{xf}{xg}} C,$$

and analogously for y.

Theorem 18. $\underset{L}{+}$ and $\underset{R}{+}$ are the same binary operation.

Proof. If

$$A \oplus A \xrightarrow{\begin{pmatrix} w & x \\ y & z \end{pmatrix}} B \oplus B,$$

then

$$\begin{pmatrix} w & x \\ y & z \end{pmatrix} = \left(\begin{pmatrix} w \\ y \end{pmatrix}, \begin{pmatrix} x \\ z \end{pmatrix} \right).$$

Thus since

$$A \oplus A \xrightarrow{\begin{pmatrix} w & x \\ y & z \end{pmatrix}} B \oplus B \xrightarrow{\begin{pmatrix} 1 \\ 1 \end{pmatrix}} B = \begin{pmatrix} w \\ y \end{pmatrix} \underset{R}{+} \begin{pmatrix} x \\ z \end{pmatrix},$$

then

$$A \xrightarrow{(1,\,1)} A \oplus A \xrightarrow{\begin{pmatrix} w & x \\ y & z \end{pmatrix}} B \oplus B \xrightarrow{\begin{pmatrix} 1 \\ 1 \end{pmatrix}} B = \left[\begin{pmatrix} w \\ y \end{pmatrix} (1,\,1) \right] \underset{R}{+} \left[\begin{pmatrix} x \\ z \end{pmatrix} (1,\,1) \right]$$

$$= (w + y) \underset{R}{+} (x + z).$$
$$ {\scriptstyle L} {\scriptstyle R} {\scriptstyle L}$$

But since

$$A \xrightarrow{(1,\,1)} A \oplus A \xrightarrow{\begin{pmatrix} w & x \\ y & z \end{pmatrix}} B \oplus B = (w, x) \underset{L}{+} (y, z),$$

we have

$$A \xrightarrow{(1,\,1)} A \oplus A \xrightarrow{\begin{pmatrix} w & x \\ y & z \end{pmatrix}} B \oplus B \xrightarrow{\begin{pmatrix} 1 \\ 1 \end{pmatrix}} B = (w + x) \underset{L}{+} (y + z).$$
$$ {\scriptstyle R} {\scriptstyle L} {\scriptstyle R}$$

Letting $x = y = 0$, we have $w \underset{L}{+} z = w \underset{R}{+} z$.

Henceforth we shall denote $\underset{L}{+}$ and $\underset{R}{+}$ by "+."

Theorem 19. *The set* hom(A, B), *together with* "+" *as defined above, is an abelian group.*

Proof. Associativity and commutativity. In

$$(w + y) + (x + z) = (w + x) + (y + z)$$

above, we let $y = 0$ to get

$$(w + x) + z = w + (x + z)$$

and let $w = z = 0$ to get $x + y = y + x$.

We have the zero morphism as the identity, so we need only the existence of inverses. Thus given $x : A \to B$, we consider the morphism

$$A \oplus B \xrightarrow{\begin{pmatrix} 1 & x \\ 0 & 1 \end{pmatrix}} A \oplus B,$$

whose kernel is given by $K \xrightarrow{(a,\,b)} A \oplus B$. Now

$$0 = K \xrightarrow{(a,\,b)} A \oplus B \xrightarrow{\begin{pmatrix} 1 & x \\ 0 & 1 \end{pmatrix}} A \oplus B = K \xrightarrow{(a,\,xa+b)} A \oplus B.$$

Hence $a = b = 0$. Thus

$$\begin{pmatrix} 1 & x \\ 0 & 1 \end{pmatrix}$$

is a monomorphism. Dually it is an epimorphism. But then it is an isomorphism and has an inverse which is of the form

$$\begin{pmatrix} 1 & y \\ 0 & 1 \end{pmatrix},$$

where $y + x = 0$.

We also note that from Lemma 2 to Theorem 18 we have that $\hom(A, A)$ is a ring.

We now shall give an equivalent definition of abelian category.

A category $\mathscr{C}$ is *additive* if:

1) $\text{Hom}(A, B)$ is an abelian group for each pair of objects $A, B \in \mathscr{C}$ and satisfies the distributive laws

$$x(f + g) = xf + xg \qquad \text{and} \qquad (f + g)x = fx + gx$$

whenever both sides are defined.

2) $\mathscr{C}$ has a zero object.

An additive category $\mathscr{A}$ is *abelian* if it is exact and has finite products.

We have shown that our earlier definition of an abelian category implies this one. That the present definition implies the other is left to the reader.

8. MORE ABOUT FUNCTORS

Having introduced various special types of categories we can now discuss the analogous properties of functors. For example, a (covariant) functor $F: \mathscr{C} \to \mathscr{C}'$, where $\mathscr{C}$ and $\mathscr{C}'$ are additive categories, is *additive* if for any f, g morphisms of $\mathscr{C}$ with $f + g$ defined, $F(f + g) = F(f) + F(g)$, that is, the induced functions

$$\hom_{\mathscr{C}}(A, B) \to \hom_{\mathscr{C}'}(F(A), F(B))$$

are group homomorphisms.

A (covariant) functor $F: \mathscr{C} \to \mathscr{C}'$, where $\mathscr{C}$ and $\mathscr{C}'$ are exact categories, is *left exact* if whenever

$$0 \to A \to B \to C \to 0$$

is exact in $\mathscr{C}$, then

$$0 \to F(A) \to F(B) \to F(C)$$

is exact in $\mathscr{C}'$. Equivalently, a left exact functor preserves kernels, i.e., if $K \to A$ is the kernel of $A \to B$, then $F(K) \to F(A)$ is the kernel of $F(A) \to F(B)$.

Dually a functor $F:\mathscr{C} \to \mathscr{C}'$ is *right exact* if whenever

$$0 \to A \to B \to C \to 0$$

is exact in $\mathscr{C}$, then

$$F(A) \to F(B) \to F(C) \to 0$$

is exact in $\mathscr{C}'$. A functor which is both left and right exact is said to be *exact*.

We have previously discussed the functor $H^A:\mathscr{C} \to \mathscr{S}$, where $\mathscr{C}$ is an arbitrary category and $\mathscr{S}$ the category of sets, defined by $H^A(B) = \hom(A, B)$. We have the following:

Theorem 20. *$f:B \to C$ is a monomorphism of a category $\mathscr{C}$ if and only if $H^A(B) \to H^A(C)$ is a monomorphism for all $A \in \mathscr{C}$.*

Proof. $f:B \to C$ is by definition a monomorphism if and only if $g, g':A \to B$ with $fg = fg'$ implies that $g = g'$. But this is true if and only if the induced function $\hom(A, B) \to \hom(A, C)$ is one-one; one-one functions are the monomorphisms in the category of sets.

If $A \in \mathscr{A}$, an abelian category, H^A is a left exact functor into the category of abelian groups.

For the remainder of this section $\mathscr{S}$ will denote the category of sets and $\mathscr{A}$ the category of abelian groups. Let $\mathscr{C}$ be an arbitrary category. If the functor $H^P:\mathscr{C} \to \mathscr{S}$ takes epimorphisms into epimorphisms, the object P is said to be *projective*; in more traditional (but equivalent) terms, P is projective if and only if for every diagram

$$P$$
$$\downarrow$$
$$A \to B,$$

with $A \to B$ an epimorphism, there is a morphism $P \to A$ making the diagram commutative. If $\mathscr{C}$ is an exact additive category, P is projective if and only if H^P is an exact functor.

Many of the properties of projective modules are, as would be expected, enjoyed by projective objects in arbitrary categories. For example, we have:

Theorem 21. *If $\mathscr{C}$ is a category with a zero object, then $P = \sum_{i \in I} P_i$ is projective if and only if each P_i is projective.*

Proof. Suppose P is projective, $A \to B$ an epimorphism, and $f_i:P_i \to B$ an arbitrary morphism. The morphisms $g_k:P_k \to P_i$ given by

$$g_k = \begin{cases} 1, & k = i, \\ 0, & k \neq i, \end{cases}$$

factor through the coproduct so that

$$\underbrace{P_i \xrightarrow{u_i} P \longrightarrow P_i}_{1_{P_i}} \longrightarrow B = P_i \longrightarrow B.$$

Then since P is projective, there is a morphism $v:P \to A$ such that

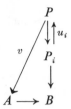

is commutative. Then vu_i is the desired morphism.

On the other hand, suppose that P_i is projective for each $i \in I$, $A \to B$ is an epimorphism, and $P \to B$ an arbitrary morphism. We let $f_i:P_i \to A$ be the morphisms whose existence is guaranteed by the projectiveness of the P_i. The f_i factor through P to give a morphism $P \to A$ such that $P \to A \to B = P \to B$.

The dual notion is that of an *injective* object.

Example. In the category of abelian groups, free abelian groups are the projective objects and divisible groups are the injective objects.

Suppose we were to consider the collection of all functors from a category $\mathscr{C}$ to a category $\mathscr{B}$, denoted by $\mathscr{B}^{\mathscr{C}}$. If we want to make this into a category, we need something to serve as morphisms. Consequently, we make the following definition:

Given two functors $F, G:\mathscr{C} \to \mathscr{B}$, a *natural transformation* $t:F \to G$ assigns to each object B of $\mathscr{C}$ a morphism $t(B):F(B) \to G(B)$ of $\mathscr{B}$ with the property that every morphism $f:B \to B'$ in $\mathscr{C}$ yields a commutative diagram

$$
\begin{array}{ccc}
F(B) & \xrightarrow{F(f)} & F(B') \\
{\scriptstyle t(B)}\Big\downarrow & & \Big\downarrow{\scriptstyle t(B').} \\
G(B) & \xrightarrow{G(f)} & G(B')
\end{array}
$$

If each $t(B)$ is an isomorphism, $t:F \to G$ is a *natural isomorphism*, and F and G are *naturally isomorphic*.

Example. Let $\mathscr{C}$ be the category of finite-dimensional vector spaces over a field. Then the identity functor and the functor which assigns to each vector space its double dual are naturally isomorphic.

We can define natural transformations of functors of several variables in the obvious way. If $S, T:\mathscr{B} \to \mathscr{C}$ are functors such that

$$\hom(S(B), A) \to \hom(B, T(A))$$

defines a natural isomorphism of bifunctors, then T is said to be an *adjoint* of S; S is a *coadjoint* of T.

Examples. If $\mathscr{B}$ is the category of R-modules and $\mathscr{C} = \mathscr{A}$, the category of abelian groups, then hom(A, –) is an adjoint of $A \otimes$ –, by the adjoint associativity relation

$$\text{hom}(A \otimes B, C) \simeq \text{hom}(B, \text{hom}(A, C)).$$

One difficulty remains; namely, the collection of natural transformations between two functors may fail to be a set. Hence we limit ourselves to the case when $\mathscr{C}$ is a small category. Then $\mathscr{B}^{\mathscr{C}}$ is a category with the functors $\mathscr{C} \to \mathscr{B}$ as objects and natural transformations as morphisms.

For the most part the category $\mathscr{B}^{\mathscr{C}}$ inherits the properties of the category $\mathscr{B}$—exactness, additivity, abelianess. Thus if $\mathscr{A}'$ is a small abelian category and $\mathscr{A}$ the category of abelian groups, then $\mathscr{A}^{\mathscr{A}'}$ is abelian. An important subcategory $\mathscr{C}$ of $\mathscr{A}^{\mathscr{A}'}$ is that consisting of all left exact functors $\mathscr{A}' \to \mathscr{A}$. In fact, one can show that the functor $H : \mathscr{A}' \to \mathscr{C}$ given by $H(A) = H^A$ is a full, exact embedding. This gives rise to the full embedding theorem, due to Mitchell, which states:

Theorem 22. *Every small abelian category admits a full exact (covariant) embedding into a category $\mathscr{G}^R$ of modules over an appropriate ring R.*

From this theorem is derived a metatheorem which says that any statement of the form "P implies Q," where P is a categorical statement about a finite diagram and Q a statement about the existence of finitely many additional morphisms which make some categorical statement true of the extended diagram, is true in an arbitrary abelian category $\mathscr{C}$ if it is true when $\mathscr{C} = \mathscr{G}^R$ for every ring R.

For a complete treatment of the subject of embedding theorems for abelian categories, see Mitchell, *Theory of Categories*, Academic Press, New York, N.Y., 1965.

PROBLEMS

1. Formulate the dual statement to Theorem 6.

2. Show that the category of finite groups fails to have finite coproducts, i.e., there is at least one pair of objects of the category which does not have a coproduct in the category.

3. Discuss the category of compact Hausdorff spaces with base points, noting which of the abelianess axioms hold and which other properties the category enjoys.

4. Show that in the category of rings all onto epimorphisms are cokernels.

5. Write out the proofs for Theorems 2*, 4*, 5*, 7*, 9*, 13*, and 14*.

6. Show that in an abelian category, every finite directed system has a direct and an inverse limit.

7. Show that the second definition of abelian category given in Section 7 implies the first.

8. Which of the functors discussed in Section 2 is faithful? An embedding? Full? Left exact? Right exact? Additive?

9. Construct a category of (some) abelian groups which is not small and which is not an abelian category.

10. Show that the two definitions of kernel given in Section 4 are equivalent.

11. Formulate and prove the dual of Theorem 3.

12. Show that in the category of Hausdorff spaces and continuous maps a morphism $f: A \to B$ is an epimorphism if and only if $f(A)$ is dense in B.

13. Show that an exact additive functor between exact additive categories is faithful.

14. Determine which objects in the category of sets are projective and which are injective. Do the same for the category of topological spaces.

15. Show that if $\mathscr{A}$ is a small category and $\mathscr{B}$ is an abelian category, then $\mathscr{B}^{\mathscr{A}}$ is an abelian category.

16. Formulate and prove Theorem 12 (freshman theorem) in a more general setting than an exact category.

CHAPTER 9

Radical Subcategories

In this chapter we use a categorical setting to generalize the concept of radical as defined in earlier chapters. To do this we define semi-abelian and co-semi-abelian categories. Such categories lack the convenient additive structure on the sets of morphisms which we established in the case of abelian categories, but, for example, the concept of semi-abelian category permits us to consider the categories of abelian groups, all groups, commutative rings with identity, all rings, rings with minimal condition, Lie algebras, and compact Hausdorff spaces with base points and continuous maps under the same categorical formulation.

We prove generalizations of the classical radical properties; for example, the fact that any object in a semi-abelian category is the extension of a radical object by a semisimple object and the dual statement. As special cases of our radical subcategory, we have Jacobson, Levitzki, and McCoy radicals; the Lie algebra radical; the Plotkin radical, and the torsion subgroup of an abelian group; an example of a coradical subcategory is found in topological groups.

1. SEMI-ABELIANESS

A category $\mathscr{C}$ with a zero object is *semi-abelian* if:

> *S1. Every morphism of $\mathscr{C}$ may be factored into (representatives of) its coimage followed by its image,*
>
> *S2. Every morphism has a cokernel,*

and

> *co-semi-abelian* if (*S1*) holds and
>
> *S2*. Every morphism has a kernel.*

We note that abelian categories are both semi-abelian and co-semi-abelian.

Examples

1. The category of all rings and ring homomorphisms is semi-abelian and co-semi-abelian.

2. The subcategory of Example 1 whose objects are commutative rings with identity and morphisms the ring homomorphisms between them is semi-abelian.

3. The subcategory of Example 1 whose objects are rings with a minimal condition and ring homomorphisms between them is semi-abelian.

4. The category of Lie algebras and Lie algebra homomorphisms is semi-abelian and co-semi-abelian. We also observe that the direct product is a product in this category.

5. The category of all groups and group homomorphisms is semi-abelian and co-semi-abelian.

6. The subcategory of Example 5 consisting of finite groups and group homomorphisms is semi-abelian and co-semi-abelian and has products. It does not, however, have coproducts (see Problem 2, Chapter 8).

7. The category of compact Hausdorff spaces with base points and continuous maps (taking base points into base points) is semi-abelian and co-semi-abelian.

As one would expect from the examples, semi-abelian categories have certain properties making the definition of radicals possible. Some of these are simply generalizations of properties of abelian categories. For example, Lemma 1 of Theorem 17, Chapter 8, can be generalized as follows:

> **Theorem 1.** *Let $\mathscr{C}$ be a semi-abelian or co-semi-abelian category. If two subobjects of $\mathscr{C}$, represented by $A_1 \to A$ and $A_2 \to A$, $A_1 \to A$ a kernel of $A \to F$, have a glb, its domain is the domain of the kernel of the morphism $A_2 \to A \to F$. Conversely, if $A_1 \to A$ and $A_2 \to A$ represent subobjects, $A_1 \to A$ a kernel of $A \to F$, then if the kernel of $A_2 \to A \to F$ exists, it is the glb of $A_1 \to A$ and $A_2 \to A$.*

Proof. Since the proof, modulo inserting "if it exists" at appropriate places, is the same as for abelian categories, we shall omit it.

> **Theorem 1*.** *Let $\mathscr{C}$ be a semi-abelian or co-semi-abelian category. If two quotient objects in $\mathscr{C}$, represented by $A \to A_1$ and $A \to A_2$, $A \to A_1$ a cokernel of $K \to A$, have a glb, its range is the range of the cokernel of the morphism $K \to A \to A_2$. Conversely, if $A \to A_1$ and $A \to A_2$ represent quotient objects and $A \to A_1$ is a cokernel of $K \to A$, then if the cokernel of $K \to A \to A_2$ exists, it is the glb of $A \to A_1$ and $A \to A_2$.*

Similarly we can extend Theorem 8, Chapter 8:

> **Theorem 2.** *If we consider the assignment of kernels and cokernels as functions on the set of quotient objects and on the set of subobjects of an object, respectively, then they are order-reversing where defined.*

If a category has (some) coproducts, but is not abelian, what can be said about the sequence

$$(*) \qquad 0 \longrightarrow A_1 \xrightarrow{u_1} A_1 + A_2 \xrightarrow{\binom{0}{1}} A_2 \longrightarrow 0 \ ?$$

For example, in the case of groups, a component group is not necessarily a normal subgroup of the free product, for example, Z in $Z + Z$; so u_1 may not be a kernel. However, we do have:

Theorem 3.   *In the sequence* $(*)$ u_1 *is a monomorphism and* $\begin{pmatrix}0\\1\end{pmatrix}$ *is the cokernel of* u_1.

Proof. u_1 is a monomorphism since

$$\begin{pmatrix}1\\0\end{pmatrix} u_1$$

is.   To prove that

$$\begin{pmatrix}0\\1\end{pmatrix}$$

is a cokernel of u_1, we let $A_1 + A_2 \xrightarrow{\ h\ } X$ be a morphism such that $hu_1 = 0$. Then we can write h as

$$\begin{pmatrix}hu_1\\hu_2\end{pmatrix}.$$

Then $hu_1 = 0$ and

$$\begin{pmatrix}hu_1\\hu_2\end{pmatrix} = hu_2 \begin{pmatrix}0\\1\end{pmatrix}$$

since

$$hu_2 \begin{pmatrix}0\\1\end{pmatrix} u_2 = \begin{pmatrix}hu_1\\hu_2\end{pmatrix} u_2,$$

and by definition of coproduct, the map from $A_1 + A_2$ must be unique.

Remark. If the category is normal, then by Theorem 2, u_1 is the kernel of

$$\begin{pmatrix}0\\1\end{pmatrix}.$$

Theorem 3*.   *In the sequence*

$$0 \longrightarrow A_1 \xrightarrow{\ (1,\,0)\ } A_1 \times A_2 \xrightarrow{\ p_2\ } A_2 \longrightarrow 0,$$

$(1, 0)$ *is the kernel of* p_2 *and* p_2 *is an epimorphism.*

In general p_2 may fail to be a cokernel. For consider the product of the unit interval with itself in the category of Example 7 above.

Suppose $p_1 : I_1 \times I_2 \to I_1$ is the cokernel of $f : X \to I_1 \times I_2$. Since

$$I_2 \to I_1 \times I_2$$

is the kernel of p_1, $f(X)$ is contained in I_2. Hence we retract the unit square into the triangle

$$\{(x, y) \mid y \le x\}$$

by a map r such that the complement of the triangle collapses onto the diagonal and the triangle remains fixed. Then there is no map from I_1 to the triangle which composed with p_1 gives the retraction r.

We have the following additional information

Theorem 4. *If $A_1 \times A_2 \xrightarrow{p_1} A_1$ or $A_1 \times A_2 \xrightarrow{2} A_2$ is a cokernel, their glb is the zero morphism.*

Proof. By Theorem 1*, the glb is the zero morphism, for the cokernel of $A_1 \to A_1 \times A_2 \to A_1$ is the cokernel of 1_A, which is the zero morphism.

Theorem 4*. *If $A_1 \xrightarrow{u_1} A_1 + A_2$ or $A_2 \xrightarrow{u_2} A_1 + A_2$ is a kernel, their glb is the zero morphism.*

2. RADICAL AND CORADICAL SUBCATEGORIES

Suppose $\mathscr{C}$ is a semi-abelian category and $\mathscr{R}$ a full subcategory of $\mathscr{C}$. We call $\mathscr{R}$ a *radical subcategory* of $\mathscr{C}$ if the following axioms are satisfied:

R1) If $A \in \mathscr{R}$, $f \in \hom(A, B)$ for some $B \in \mathscr{C}$, and $I \to B$ is the image of f, then $I \in \mathscr{R}$. If $S \to A$ is a kernel, $S \in \mathscr{R}$.

R2) For each $G \in \mathscr{C}$ there exists a unique (up to equivalence) morphism which is the lub in the set of all subobjects of G which are kernels and whose domains are objects of $\mathscr{R}$. We denote this morphism by x_G and call it the *radical* of G.

R3) If $G \to B$ is the cokernel of x_G, then x_B is the zero morphism.

If $\mathscr{C}$ is a co-semi-abelian category with a full subcategory $\mathscr{R}^*$ which satisfies the following axioms, $\mathscr{R}^*$ is called a *coradical subcategory*.

R1*) If $B \in \mathscr{R}^*$, $f \in \hom(A, B)$ for some $A \in \mathscr{C}$, and $A \to I$ is the coimage of f, then $I \in \mathscr{R}^*$. If $B \to C$ is a cokernel, $C \in \mathscr{R}^*$.

R2*) For each $G \in \mathscr{C}$, there exists a unique morphism which is the lub in the set of all quotient objects of G which are cokernels and whose ranges are objects of $\mathscr{R}^*$. We denote this morphism by x_G^* and call it the *coradical* of G.

R3*) If $A \to G$ is the kernel of x_G^*, then x_A is the zero morphism.

The objects of the radical subcategory are called *radical objects*. We call a subcategory $\mathscr{S}$ of a semi-abelian category $\mathscr{C}$ a *semisimple subcategory* with respect to a radical subcategory $\mathscr{R}$ if $S \in \mathscr{S}$ implies that the radical of S is the zero morphism. Dually, we define *coradical objects* and *co-semi-simple subcategory*.

Examples

1. The θ-radical groups described in Chapter 6 form a radical subcategory of the category of all groups for:

R1) Normal subgroups and homomorphic images of θ-radical groups are θ-radical. (Theorem 15, Corollary 3, Chapter 6.)

R2) We recall that the upper θ-radical of a group G always exists and is denoted by $\check{\theta}(G)$. Moreover, by Theorem 16, Chapter 6, $\check{\theta}(G)$ is θ-radical and contains all θ-radical normal subgroups of G.

R3) This follows from the construction of $\check{\theta}(G)$.

In particular, all groups which have no nontrivial homomorphic image with trivial Hirsch-Plotkin radical form a radical subcategory of the category of all groups.

2.   The classes of Jacobson, Levitzki, and McCoy semisimple rings are semisimple subcategories of the category of all rings and ring homomorphisms. We show, as an example, that Jacobson radical rings form a radical subcategory, using the quasi-regular characterization. The proofs in the other cases are similar:

R1) Any ideal or quotient ring of a quasi-regular ring is clearly quasi-regular.

R2) The Jacobson radical is defined in any ring to be the sum of the quasi-regular ideals, which is itself quasi-regular, and hence it is the lub in the subcategory of quasi-regular rings. The radical is the inclusion map of this ideal into the ring.

R3) If $\bar{z}$ is an element of the radical of R/J, where J is the Jacobson radical of R, and z is its preimage in R, zr is quasi-regular for all $r \in R$, so z is in the Jacobson radical of R, that is, $\bar{z} = 0$.

A necessary condition for a property of ideals to determine a radical subcategory is for the sum of radical objects to be a radical object. For example, the property of being quasi-regular or of being semi-nilpotent determines a radical subcategory of the category of rings, but that of being nilpotent does not, since the sum of nilpotent ideals is not in general nilpotent. However, in the semi-abelian category of rings with minimal condition, the property of nilpotency does determine a radical subcategory. Indeed, the radicals mentioned above coincide in this case with the classical radical, as discussed in Chapter 5.

3.   That the maximum solvable ideal of a Lie algebra determines a radical subcategory of the category of (finite-dimensional) Lie algebras and Lie algebra homomorphisms follows directly from the properties of this ideal described in Chapter 7. Moreover, by the correspondence between Lie algebras and (simply connected) Lie groups, we get that a radical subcategory of the category of Lie groups is determined by the maximum solvable subgroup of a Lie group. Similarly, the maximum nilpotent ideal of a Jordan or alternative algebra determines a radical subcategory.

4.   We consider the dual category to the category of abelian groups. By the Pontryagin duality theorems, there is a contravariant functor with a contravariant inverse from the category of abelian groups to the category of compact abelian (Hausdorff) topological groups which assigns to each group its character group. Hence, we consider a coradical which is dual to the torsion subgroup of an abelian group. In the category of abelian groups, the torsion groups constitute a radical subcategory, for:

R1) Clearly, any subgroup or factor group of a torsion group is a torsion group.

R2) By definition, the inclusion map of the torsion subgroup of an abelian group into the group itself is maximal with respect to the subcategory of torsion groups.

R3) If T is the torsion subgroup of an abelian group A, then A/T must be torsion-free.

It is the case that the character group of a torsion group is totally disconnected and that the character group of a torsion-free group is connected (see, e.g., Pontryagin, *Topological Groups*, Princeton University Press, 1939). Thus the totally disconnected groups form a coradical subcategory of the category of compact abelian topological groups. The coradical is defined for any group in this category by taking the projection map onto the factor group with the component of the identity.

3. PROPERTIES OF RADICALS AND CORADICALS

In this section we prove several results which are generalizations of the previously discussed properties of radicals of rings.

Theorem 5. *The zero object is the only object which is both radical and semisimple with respect to a radical subcategory $\mathscr{R}$ of a semi-abelian category.*

Proof. Suppose $R \in \mathscr{R}$ and $0 \to R = $ radical R. Then 0 is the largest subobject of R in $\mathscr{R}$. Hence $R = 0$.

Theorem 5*. *The zero object is the only object which is both coradical and co-semisimple with respect to a coradical subcategory of a co-semi-abelian category.*

An *extension* of an object A by an object B is a sequence

$$0 \to A \to C \to B \to 0$$

with $A \to C$ the kernel of $C \to B$ and $C \to B$ the cokernel of $A \to C$. We call C an *extension object*.

Theorem 6. *Every object of a semi-abelian category $\mathscr{C}$ is an extension object of a radical object by a semisimple object (with respect to any radical subcategory of $\mathscr{C}$.)*

Proof. For $G \in \mathscr{C}$, let $x_G : A \to G$ be the radical of G with respect to a radical subcategory of $\mathscr{C}$; $G \to B$ the cokernel of x_G. x_G is a kernel, so kernel$(G \to B) = x_G$, that is, $0 \to A \to G \to B \to 0$ is an extension with A radical and B semisimple.

Theorem 6*. *Every object of a co-semi-abelian category $\mathscr{C}^*$ is an extension object of a co-semisimple object by a coradical object.*

Once we have the radical of an object, the question of its relation with other subobjects of the object arises. We have the following result:

Theorem 7. *If $x: R \to A$ is the radical of A, $S \to A$ a kernel and $K \to S$ the radical of S, then if $K \to A$ is a kernel, it is equivalent to the glb of x and $S \to A$ (if it exists).*

Proof. Let $K_1 \to A$ be the glb of x and $S \to A$. Then $K_1 \to R$ is a kernel, so K_1 is radical. Hence $K_1 \to S$ is contained in $K \to S$. On the other hand,

$K \to A$ is a kernel, so it is contained in x by (R2), as well as in $S \to A$ and hence in their glb.

Theorem 7*. *If x is the coradical of A, $A \to B$ a cokernel, and $B \to C$ the coradical of B, then if $A \to C$ is a cokernel, it is equivalent to the glb of x and $A \to B$ (if it exists).*

What sort of structure does a radical subcategory itself have? For example, torsion abelian groups also form an abelian category. In general we have:

Theorem 8. *A radical subcategory $\mathcal{R}$ of a semi-abelian category $\mathcal{C}$ with finite products such that $A_1 \times A_2 \xrightarrow{p_i} A_i$, $i = 1, 2$, is a cokernel in $\mathcal{C}$ for each pair of objects A_1, $A_2 \in \mathcal{C}$, is semi-abelian with finite products.*

Proof. We note that under these hypotheses $A_1 \times A_2 \to A_1$ is the cokernel of

$$A_2 \xrightarrow{(0,\,1)} A_1 \times A_2,$$

or $A_1 \times A_2 \to A_2$ is the cokernel of

$$A_1 \xrightarrow{(1,\,0)} A_1 \times A_2,$$

since by Theorem 3*, $A_i \to A_1 \times A_2$ is the kernel of $A_1 \times A_2 \to A_j$, $i \neq j$, and by Theorem 7*, Chapter 8, a cokernel is the cokernel of its kernel.

Let A_1, $A_2 \in \mathcal{R}$, $A_1 \times A_2$ be their product in $\mathcal{C}$. Then the glb of

$$A_1 \times A_2 \to A_1 \qquad \text{and} \qquad A_1 \times A_2 \to A_2$$

is the zero morphism. According to Theorem 2, the lub of $A_1 \to A_1 \times A_2$ and $A_2 \to A_1 \times A_2$ is $A_1 \times A_2 \to A_1 \times A_2$. Hence by (R2), $A_1 \times A_2 \in \mathcal{R}$.

The semi-abelianess follows from (R1), with the existence of a zero object being clear.

Theorem 8*. *A coradical subcategory $\mathcal{R}$ of a co-semi-abelian category $\mathcal{C}$ with coproducts such that $A_i \xrightarrow{u_i} A_1 + A_2$ is a kernel, $i = 1, 2$, for each pair of objects A_1, $A_2 \in \mathcal{C}$, is co-semi-abelian with finite coproducts.*

We recall that a category with a zero object, factorization, and products of arbitrary sets of objects is semi-abelian, and dually that coproducts of arbitrary sets of objects give the existence of kernels (Theorems 14 and 14*, Chapter 8).

It is possible to compare the various radical subcategories of say, the category of rings.

Theorem 9. *If $\mathcal{R}_1$ and $\mathcal{R}_2$ are radical subcategories of a semi-abelian category $\mathcal{C}$ and x_G^i is the $\mathcal{R}_i$ radical of $G \in \mathcal{C}$, then $\mathcal{R}_1$ is a subcategory of $\mathcal{R}_2$ if and only if x_G^1 is contained in x_G^2 for each $G \in \mathcal{C}$.*

Proof. Suppose $\mathcal{R}_1$ is a subcategory of $\mathcal{R}_2$. Then the domain of x_G^1 is in $\mathcal{R}_2$ and hence x_G^1 is contained in x_G^2, by (R2).

Suppose x_G^1 is contained in x_G^2 for all $G \in \mathscr{C}$. Let $R \in \mathscr{R}_1$. Then 1_R is contained in x_R^2 and hence they are equivalent, that is, $R \in \mathscr{R}_2$.

Theorem 9*. *If $\mathscr{R}_1$ and $\mathscr{R}_2$ are coradical subcategories of a co-semi-abelian category $\mathscr{C}^*$ and x_G^i is the $\mathscr{R}_i$ coradical of $G \in \mathscr{C}^*$, then $\mathscr{R}_1$ is a subcategory of $\mathscr{R}_2$ if and only if x_G^1 is contained in x_G^2 for each $G \in \mathscr{C}^*$.*

Not much has been done as yet to discuss the structure of objects in semi-simple categories, although there are some results due to Dickson in the case of abelian categories. However, it is easy to see that if we define a *simple object* to be an object A such that $X \to A$ a kernel implies that $X = A$ or $X = 0$, then if none of the simple objects of a semi-abelian category is a radical object (except the zero object), the product of simple objects is semi-simple. For some structure theorems see, e.g., Sulinsky and Weigandt.

4. ABELIAN OBJECTS

We have noted that the direct sum is not a coproduct in the category of groups as it is in the category of abelian groups. What is lacking is a canonical map from the direct sum, i.e., the sum map of abelian groups; in particular, we need a map $A \times A \to A$ which when composed with $(1, 0)$ or $(0, 1)$ is the identity on A. For abelian groups this is the map$(1_A + 1_A)$, where

$$(f + g)(a, b) = fa + gb.$$

On the other hand, if such a map x exists for a group A, then for $a, b \in A$, since

$$(0, a) + (b, 0) = ((0 + b), (a + 0)),$$

and

$$x(1, 0) = x(0, 1) = 1_A,$$

we have

$$a + b = x((0, a) + (b, 0)) = ((0 + b), (a + 0)) = b + a,$$

that is, A is abelian.

This suggests that if we consider only objects where there is always a unique morphism from the product of the object with itself to either component which composes with either $(1, 0)$ or $(0, 1)$ to give the identity, we should get a generalization of abelian groups, provided the original category has certain properties which the category of groups has.

We let $\mathscr{C}$ be a category with a zero object, products, and coproducts and in which the map

$$A_1 + A_2 \xrightarrow{\begin{pmatrix} 1 & 0 \\ 0 & 1 \end{pmatrix}} A_1 \times A_2$$

is an epimorphism for each A_1, $A_2 \in \mathscr{C}$. Then we let $\mathscr{A}$ be the full subcategory of $\mathscr{C}$ determined by those $A \in \mathscr{C}$ which have a morphism j from $A \times A \to A$ such that $j(1, 0) = j(0, 1) = 1_A$. We call the objects of $\mathscr{A}$ *abelian objects*.

We ask the usual question: Under what operations is this property of abelianess preserved?

Theorem 10. *The product of abelian objects is abelian.*

Proof. Suppose $A_1 \times A_2$ is the product of abelian objects A_i, with projection maps p_i, $i = 1, 2$. We form the following products:

$$(A_1 \times A_2)_k \longrightarrow (A_1 \times A_2) \times (A_1 \times A_2) \xrightarrow{p_i'} (A_1 \times A_2)_i,$$

$$(A_i)_k \longrightarrow A_i \times A_i \xrightarrow{p_i^j} (A_i)^j,$$

$$A_k \times A_k \longrightarrow (A_1 \times A_1) \times (A_2 \times A_2) \xrightarrow{p_i''} A_i \times A_i,$$

$i = 1, 2$, $j = 1, 2$, $k = 1, 2$, and we use the symbol $A_k \to A_1 \times A_2$ to mean the map $(1_{A_1}, 0)$ for $k = 1$, $(0, 1_{A_2})$ for $k = 2$. Then we have

$$z_i = (p_i p_1', p_i p_2'):(A_1 \times A_2) \times (A_1 \times A_2) \to A_i \times A_i,$$

so that

$$(A_1 \times A_2)_k \longrightarrow (A_1 \times A_2) \times (A_1 \times A_2) \xrightarrow{z_i} A_i \times A_i \xrightarrow{p_i^j} (A_i)^j$$

$$= (A_1 \times A_2)_k \longrightarrow (A_1 \times A_2) \times (A_1 \times A_2) \xrightarrow{p_j'} (A_1 \times A_2)_j \xrightarrow{p_i} A_i$$

(by definition of z_i) and this is equal to

$$(A_1 \times A_2)_k \xrightarrow{p_i} (A_i)^k \longrightarrow A_i \times A_i \xrightarrow{p_i^j} (A_i)^j,$$

since both are projections or zero depending upon whether or not $j = k$. Moreover, the p_i^j are left cancellable since the results hold for both $j = 1$, $j = 2$, and $A_i \times A_i$ is a product. Since the A_i are abelian, there is a morphism $x_i : A_i \times A_i \to A_i$ such that

$$x_i(1_{A_i}, 0) = x_i(0, 1_{A_i}) = 1_{A_i}.$$

So we define $y = (x_1 p_1'', x_2 p_2'')$, $z = (z_1, z_2)$. Then we have where the triangles and squares are commutative from the definitions of z_i, y, and z. But by the above we obtain

$$(A_1 \times A_2)_k \longrightarrow (A_1 \times A_2) \times (A_1 \times A_2)$$

$$\xrightarrow{\;z\;} (A_1 \times A_1) \times (A_2 \times A_2) \xrightarrow{\;y\;} (A_1 \times A_2) \xrightarrow{\;p_i\;} A_i$$

$$= (A_1 \times A_2)_k \longrightarrow (A_1 \times A_2) \times (A_1 \times A_2) \xrightarrow{z_i} A_i \times A_i \xrightarrow{x_i} A$$

$$= (A_1 \times A_2)_k \longrightarrow (A_i)^k \longrightarrow A_i \times A_i \xrightarrow{x_i} A_i$$

$$= A_1 \times A_2 \xrightarrow{p_i} A_i$$

$$= A_1 \times A_2 \xrightarrow{\;1\;} A_1 \times A_2 \xrightarrow{p_i} A_i, \qquad i = 1, 2, \quad k = 1, 2.$$

Now the p_i are left cancellable since the equations hold for $i = 1, 2$. Hence $yz(1_{A_1 \times A_2}, 0) = 1_{A_1 \times A_2}$ and $yz(0, 1_{A_1 \times A_2}) = 1_{A_1 \times A_2}$, that is, yz is the desired morphism.

We have an equivalent condition for abelianess.

Theorem 11. *An object $X \in \mathcal{C}$ is abelian if and only if every morphism*

$$\binom{f}{g} : A_1 + A_2 \to X$$

can be factored through $A_1 \times A_2$ (A_1, A_2 arbitrary objects of $\mathcal{C}$).

Proof. If X is abelian,

$$\binom{f}{g} = x(f, g) \begin{pmatrix} 1 & 0 \\ 0 & 1 \end{pmatrix},$$

where $x : X \times X \to X$ is the abelianess morphism. If X has the given property, it is abelian by virtue of the factorization of

$$\binom{1}{1}.$$

Theorem 12. *The product of abelian objects in $\mathcal{C}$ is also their coproduct in the subcategory of abelian objects.*

Proof. If A_1 and A_2 are abelian, so is their product and since

$$\begin{pmatrix} 1 & 0 \\ 0 & 1 \end{pmatrix}$$

is an epimorphism, the factorization of Theorem 11 is unique.

We now define a type of category in which it will be shown that the abelian objects form an abelian subcategory.

Let $\mathscr{S}$ be a semi-abelian category with products and coproducts satisfying the following conditions:

1) If $K \to A$ is a kernel and $A \to B$ is an epimorphism, then image $(K \to B)$ is a kernel.

2) $\mathscr{S}$ is conormal.

Then $\mathscr{S}$ is a *nearly abelian* category. We note that condition (S2) in the definition of semi-abelian category can be derived from the other conditions in the definition of nearly abelian category.

Theorem 13. *Let $\mathscr{S}$ be a nearly abelian category. The subcategory $\mathscr{A}$ of abelian objects of $\mathscr{S}$ is an abelian category.*

Proof. A zero object is clearly abelian. Products and coproducts are abelian by Theorems 10 and 12 and the following lemma.

Lemma 1. In a semi-abelian category $\mathscr{C}$ with products and coproducts and satisfying condition (2) in the definition of nearly abelian

$$A_1 + A_2 \xrightarrow{\left(\begin{smallmatrix} 1 & 0 \\ 0 & 1 \end{smallmatrix}\right)} A_1 \times A_2$$

is an epimorphism for each $A_1, A_2 \in \mathscr{C}$.

Proof. We have

$$A_1 \xrightarrow{u_1} A_1 + A_2 \xrightarrow{\left(\begin{smallmatrix} 1 & 0 \\ 0 & 1 \end{smallmatrix}\right)} A_1 \times A_2 \xrightarrow{p_1} A_1$$

$$= A_1 \xrightarrow{(1,\,0)} A_1 \times A_2 \xrightarrow{p_1} A_1$$

and similarly for p_2. Then

$$\begin{pmatrix} 1 & 0 \\ 0 & 1 \end{pmatrix} u_1 = (1, 0),$$

since the equations hold for both projections. Similarly

$$\begin{pmatrix} 1 & 0 \\ 0 & 1 \end{pmatrix} u_2 = (0, 1).$$

By the construction of Theorem 13, Chapter 8, the lub of $(1, 0)$ and $(0, 1)$ is image$(A_1 + A_2 \to A_1 \times A_2)$. Hence by definition of product, domain image$(A_1 + A_2 \to A_1 \times A_2)$ is isomorphic to $A_1 \times A_2$. Thus

$$\begin{pmatrix} 1 & 0 \\ 0 & 1 \end{pmatrix} = 1_{A_1 \times A_2} \left(\text{coimage} \begin{pmatrix} 1 & 0 \\ 0 & 1 \end{pmatrix} \right) = 1_{A_1 \times A_2} \begin{pmatrix} 1 & 0 \\ 0 & 1 \end{pmatrix}$$

and since the identity is left cancellable,

$$\begin{pmatrix} 1 & 0 \\ 0 & 1 \end{pmatrix}$$

is its own coimage and hence it is an epimorphism.

It remains to show that every morphism of $\mathscr{A}$ has a kernel and cokernel in $\mathscr{A}$ and that $\mathscr{A}$ is normal and conormal. We need some additional lemmas.

We note that by Theorems 14 and 14* of Chapter 8, $\mathscr{S}$ has kernels and cokernels.

Lemma 2. In a conormal category with kernels and cokernels, if a morphism $A \to B$ factors through an epimorphism $A \to C$ and a monomorphism $C \to B$, the factorization is unique up to equivalence.

Proof. Suppose $A \to C' \to B$ and $A \to C \to B$ are two factorizations of $A \to B$ into an epimorphism followed by a monomorphism. We let $K \to A$ be the kernel of $A \to C$; then $A \to C$ is the cokernel of $K \to A$ and similarly for $K' \to A$ and $A \to C'$. Then $K \to A \to C' \to B = 0$ and $K \to A \to C' = 0$ since $C' \to B$ is left cancellable. Hence $K \to A$ is contained in $K' \to A$ and hence $A \to C$ contains $A \to C'$. Similarly $A \to C'$ contains $A \to C$. Now we have

$$
A \to C \to B,
$$
$$
\searrow \updownarrow \nearrow
$$
$$
C'
$$

where both triangles commute. Since $A \to C'$ is an epimorphism,

$$C' \to C \to B = C' \to B$$

and similarly $C \to C' \to B = C \to B$. Hence $C' \to B$ and $C \to B$ are also equivalent.

Lemma 3. In a category as in Lemma 1, if $f: A \to B$ is an epimorphism and $g: B \to C$, then the image of $gf =$ image of g.

Proof. Let $I \to C$ be the image of g. Then $A \to I$ is the composition of epimorphisms

$$
A \xrightarrow{f} B \xrightarrow{g} C
$$
$$
\searrow \; \downarrow \; \nearrow
$$
$$
I
$$

and hence is an epimorphism. Thus by Lemma 2 it is the coimage of $A \to C$, and $I \to C$ is the image of $A \to C$.

Lemma 4. In a category such as in Lemma 1, if $m_1: A_1 \to A$, $m_2: A_2 \to A$ are monomorphisms and $f: A \to C$, then

$$\text{image } f(\text{lub}\{m_1, m_2\}) = \text{image}(\text{lub}\{\text{image } fm_1, \text{image } fm_2\}).$$

Proof. Let $u_i: A_i \to A_1 + A_2$, $u'_i: A'_i \to A'_1 + A'_2$, where $A'_i \to C$ is the image of fm_i. Then we have

$$
A_i \xrightarrow{\;u_i\;} A_1 + A_2 \xrightarrow{\binom{u_1' \, \text{coimage}(fm_1)}{u_2' \, \text{coimage}(fm_2)}} A'_1 + A'_2 \xrightarrow{\binom{\text{image}(fm_1)}{\text{image}(fm_2)}} C
$$
$$
= A_i \xrightarrow{\text{coimage}(fm_i)} A'_i \to A'_1 + A'_2 \xrightarrow{\text{image}(fm_2)} C
$$
$$
= A_i \xrightarrow{\text{coimage}(fm_i)} A'_i \xrightarrow{\text{image}(fm_i)} C
$$
$$
= A_i \xrightarrow{\;u_i\;} A_1 + A_2 \xrightarrow{\binom{m_1}{m_2}} A \xrightarrow{\;f\;} C.
$$

Since these equations hold for u_1 and u_2,

$$\begin{pmatrix} \text{image}(fm_1) \\ \text{image}(fm_2) \end{pmatrix} \begin{pmatrix} u_1' \text{ coimage}(fm_1) \\ u_2' \text{ coimage}(fm_2) \end{pmatrix} = f\begin{pmatrix} m_1 \\ m_2 \end{pmatrix}.$$

Then

$$\text{image}(A_i \xrightarrow{u_i} A_1 + A_2 \to A_1' + A_2')$$

is contained in the image of $A_1 + A_2 \to A_1' + A_2'$. But by the factorization above and the fact that $A_1 + A_2$ is a coproduct, the image of

$$A_i \to A_1 + A_2 \to A_1' + A_2'$$

is u_i'. Thus since the lub of the u_i''s is $A_1' + A_2' \to A_1' + A_2'$, this identity is the image of $A_1 + A_2 \to A_1' + A_2'$ and $A_1 + A_2 \to A_1' + A_2'$ is its own coimage and hence an epimorphism. Then the image of

$$\begin{pmatrix} \text{image}(fm_1) \\ \text{image}(fm_2) \end{pmatrix} \begin{pmatrix} u_1' \text{ coimage}(fm_1) \\ u_2' \text{ coimage}(fm_2) \end{pmatrix}$$

is the image of $\begin{pmatrix} \text{image}(fm_1) \\ \text{image}(fm_2) \end{pmatrix}$, by Lemma 3.

Also we have

$$\text{image}\left[f\begin{pmatrix} m_1 \\ m_2 \end{pmatrix} \right] = \text{image}\left[f\left(\text{image}\begin{pmatrix} m_1 \\ m_2 \end{pmatrix} \right) \right]$$

since the coimage of $\begin{pmatrix} m_1 \\ m_2 \end{pmatrix}$ is an epimorphism. We have the commutative diagram

Then

$$\text{image}\left[f\left(\text{image}\begin{pmatrix} m_1 \\ m_2 \end{pmatrix} \right) \right] = \text{image}(f(\text{lub}\{m_1, m_2\}))$$

$$= \text{image}(\text{lub}\{\text{image}\,fm_1, \text{image}\,fm_2\}),$$

from Theorem 13, Chapter 7, and since we get from the above that

$$\text{image}\left[\begin{pmatrix} \text{image}(fm_1) \\ \text{image}(fm_2) \end{pmatrix} \begin{pmatrix} u_1' \text{ coimage}(fm_1) \\ u_2' \text{ coimage}(fm_2) \end{pmatrix} \right]$$

$$= \text{image}\left[\begin{pmatrix} \text{image}(fm_1) \\ \text{image}(fm_2) \end{pmatrix} \right]$$

$$= \text{image}\left[f\begin{pmatrix} m_1 \\ m_2 \end{pmatrix} \right] = \text{image}\left[f\left(\text{image}\begin{pmatrix} m_1 \\ m_2 \end{pmatrix} \right) \right].$$

This proves the lemma.

We now show that any subobject of an abelian object is an abelian object. If, in particular, the subobject is the kernel in $\mathscr{S}$ of a morphism of $\mathscr{A}$, then it is in $\mathscr{A}$ and clearly is the kernel in $\mathscr{A}$. Suppose $k:K \to A$ is a subobject of an abelian object A. Let $K \times K$ be the product of K with itself, p_i its projection morphisms, p'_i the projection morphisms for $A \times A$. Let x be the morphism $A \times A \to A$ such that

$$A_i \longrightarrow A \times A \overset{x}{\longrightarrow} A = 1_A, \qquad i = 1, 2.$$

Let $y = (kp_1, kp_2)$ so that

$$K_i \longrightarrow K \times K \overset{y}{\longrightarrow} A \times A \overset{x}{\longrightarrow} A = k, \qquad \text{where} \qquad K_i = K, \quad i = 1, 2,$$

as in Theorem 11. The identity on $K \times K$ is the lub of $K_1 \to K \times K$ and $K_2 \to K \times K$, so that

$$\text{image}(xy(\text{lub}\{K_1 \to K \times K, K_2 \to K \times K\})) = \text{image } xy.$$

Moreover,

$$\text{lub}\{\text{image}(K_1 \longrightarrow K \times K \overset{xy}{\longrightarrow} A), \text{image}(K_2 \longrightarrow K \times K \overset{xy}{\longrightarrow} A)\} = \text{image } k,$$

and by Lemma 4, image xy = image k. Since k is a monomorphism,

$$\text{image } k = k.$$

Now we let $x':K \times K \to K$ be the coimage of xy. Then

$$kx'(1_K, 0) = (\text{image}(xy))(\text{coimage}(xy))(1_K, 0) = xy(1_K, 0) = x(1_A, 0)k = k$$

(by definition of x) and similarly for $(0, 1_K)$. Then k is left cancellable, so $x'(1_K, 0) = 1_K$ and $x'(0, 1_K) = 1_K$. Hence x' is the desired morphism and $K \in \mathscr{A}$.

Dually to the above, any quotient object of an abelian object is abelian, and in particular the cokernel of a morphism of $\mathscr{A}$ is in $\mathscr{A}$.

We now show that $\mathscr{A}$ is normal. Suppose $f:A \to B$ is a monomorphism of $\mathscr{A}$. Let $B \times B \overset{p_i}{\longrightarrow} B_i$, $A \times B \overset{p'_1}{\longrightarrow} A$, $A \times B \overset{p'_2}{\longrightarrow} B$ be products. Then we have $(fp'_1, p'_2):A \times B \to B \times B$ and

$$A \overset{(1, 0)}{\longrightarrow} A \times B \longrightarrow B \times B = A \longrightarrow B \overset{(1, 0)}{\longrightarrow} B \times B,$$

since followed by either p_i they are equal. Moreover,

$$B \overset{(0, 1)}{\longrightarrow} A \times B \longrightarrow B \times B = B \overset{(0, 1)}{\longrightarrow} B \times B.$$

We let j be the morphism such that $j(1_B, 0) = 1_B = j(0, 1_B)$. Then

$$B \longrightarrow A \times B \longrightarrow B \times B \overset{j}{\longrightarrow} B = B \overset{(0, 1)}{\longrightarrow} B \times B \overset{j}{\longrightarrow} B = 1_B;$$

hence $j(fp_1', p_2')$ is an epimorphism since 1_B is. Then

$$A \longrightarrow A \times B \longrightarrow B \times B \xrightarrow{\;j\;} B = A \xrightarrow{\;f\;} B \xrightarrow{(1,\,0)} B \times B \xrightarrow{\;j\;} B$$

$$= A \longrightarrow B.$$

Now $A \to A \times B$ is a kernel of $A \times B \to B$ and since $A \times B \to B \times B \xrightarrow{\;j\;} B$ is an epimorphism,

$$A \longrightarrow A \times B \longrightarrow B \times B \xrightarrow{\;j\;} B = A \xrightarrow{\;f\;} B = \text{image}(A \xrightarrow{\;f\;} B)$$

(since $A \xrightarrow{\;f\;} B$ is a monomorphism) is a kernel by condition (1) of the definition of nearly abelian.

If $f: A \to B$ is an epimorphism in $\mathscr{S}$, we form its kernel as above and it is the cokernel of its kernel. It remains to show that if f is an epimorphism of $\mathscr{A}$, it is an epimorphism of $\mathscr{S}$.

Suppose $f: A \to B$ is an epimorphism of $\mathscr{A}$. Then suppose $B \to I$ is the cokernel of $A \to B$. Since I is abelian and $A \to B$ is right cancellable in $\mathscr{A}$, $B \to I = 0$, that is, the cokernel of f is zero. Then its kernel is the image of f, which is then equivalent to 1_B, that is, $A \to B$ is its own coimage and hence an epimorphism.

Thus $\mathscr{A}$ is abelian.

Since a nearly abelian category is semi-abelian, it is possible to define radical subcategories of it. Indeed, we have done so in Example 4 of Section 1 for the category of groups. The question arises of whether one can select a subcategory which is both abelian and radical. We can choose an abelian subobject of each object in the category so that the objects chosen form an abelian subcategory satisfying (R1). However, in general the lub of abelian subobjects of a given object may not be abelian, nor is it the case that the range of the cokernel of the lub is necessarily "semisimple." For example, in the category $\mathscr{G}$ of groups and group homomorphisms, we consider the quaternion group of order eight. (This is the multiplicative group of the basis $\{1, i, j, k\}$ for the quaternion division ring of Chapter 1.) It has three subgroups of order four which are abelian but whose lub is the entire (nonabelian) group. Hence the abelian groups do not form a radical subcategory of $\mathscr{G}$.

Moreover, any radical subcategory of $\mathscr{G}$ whose objects are all abelian must be the trivial subcategory (i.e., all of its objects are trivial groups), for suppose $(0) \neq G \in \mathscr{R}$, a radical subcategory of $\mathscr{G}$ all of whose objects are abelian. Then by (R1), $Z_p \in \mathscr{R}$ for some prime p. $\mathscr{R}$ does not contain all p-groups, for there exist nonabelian finite p-groups. Let X be a minimal finite p-group not contained in $\mathscr{R}$ and $R(X)$ the domain of its radical. Then $o(X/R(X)) = p$ by minimality of X. But $X/R(X) = Z_p \in \mathscr{R}$, that is, $X/R(X)$ is not semisimple.

5. CATEGORICAL CHARACTERIZATION OF GROUP ALGEBRAS

We recall that if G is a group (written multiplicatively), we define the group algebra of G over K, a commutative ring with identity, to be the free K-module with the elements of G as generators and product determined by the product in G. Moreover, this algebra is a Hopf algebra with coproduct $\psi(g) = g \otimes g$ for $g \in G$ and ψ extended linearly to the whole group algebra.

In this section we consider group algebras of finite groups and find a characterization for them as a subcategory of the category of Hopf algebras over a field of characteristic zero, using the notions of Section 2.

Let $A^* = \mathrm{Hom}_K(A, K)$, where A is the group algebra of a finite group G over a field K of characteristic 0. The elements of A^* may be considered simply as functions $G \to K$. The comultiplication $\psi : A \to A \otimes A$ induces a multiplication

$$\psi^* : A^* \otimes A^* \to A^*$$

given by pointwise multiplication in K:

$$
\begin{aligned}
\psi^*(a_1^* \otimes a_2^*)(x) &= (a_1^* \otimes a_2^*)(\psi x) \\
&= (a_1^* \otimes a_2^*)(x \otimes x) \\
&= a_1^*(x) a_2^*(x).
\end{aligned}
$$

Then we have $A^* \simeq K_1 \oplus \cdots \oplus K_n$, $K_i \simeq K$ and A^* is a commutative K-algebra. A^* is called the *dual algebra* of A.

The assignment of a group algebra to a group is functorial, and the assignment to an algebra of its dual algebra is a duality functor. Moreover, the composition of these functors is also a duality functor. Thus the dual of a group algebra has been called a "cogroup," but is more accurately described as a co-(group algebra); we note below that it is a co-algebra as well as an algebra. The questions remain of whether it is also a cogroup-algebra, and if so, what the nature of a cogroup might be.

There is an induced comultiplication, making A^* a co-algebra,

$$\pi^* : A^* \to A^* \otimes A^*,$$

given by

$$
\begin{aligned}
\pi^*(a^*)(x \otimes y) &= a^*(\pi(x \otimes y)) \\
&= a^*(xy).
\end{aligned}
$$

Since K is a simple K-algebra, and A^* is the direct sum of copies of K, A^* is semisimple, so we may decompose the identity of A^* as follows:

$$1 = e_1 + \cdots + e_n,$$

where the e_i are primitive idempotents. Then if $f : A^* \to K$ is an algebra homomorphism, there exists a unique i such that

$$
\begin{aligned}
f(e_i) &= 1, \\
f(e_j) &= 0 \qquad \text{for} \quad j \neq i.
\end{aligned}
$$

But $e_i \neq 0$, so there exists $x \in G$ such that $e_i(x) \neq 0$. Therefore $f(e_i) = e_i(x) = 1$. But the elements of G are units of A; thus we have shown that any algebra homomorphism $A^* \to K$ can be represented by a unit of A.

We have from Theorem 4, Chapter 6, that group algebras of finite groups are semisimple (with respect to the classical radical); the subcategory of the category of algebras consisting of group algebras is now seen to be co-semi-simple as well, since the dual algebras of group algebras form a semisimple subcategory.

We shall show that the subcategory $\mathscr{A}$ of Hopf algebras over a fixed field K, semisimple and co-semisimple in the above sense and with the property that $A \in \mathscr{A}$ implies that every homomorphism $f: A^* \to K$ can be represented by a unit x of A, that is,

$$f(a^*) = a^*(x),$$

is precisely the category of group algebras of finite groups.

The problem is to take an algebra in the selected subcategory and construct a group from it. We let $\mathscr{A}$ be the subcategory of the category of Hopf algebras over a field K of characteristic zero such that $A \in \mathscr{A}$ implies:

1) A is finitely generated.

2) A^* (dual of A) is a commutative algebra under the multiplication induced by the comultiplication of A and (as algebras)

$$A^* \simeq K_1 \oplus \cdots \oplus K_n, \qquad K_i \simeq K.$$

3) Every homomorphism $f: A^* \to K$ can be represented by a unit of A.

It is clear that if A is a group algebra of a finite group, then $A \in \mathscr{A}$. We show the converse.

Let $A \in \mathscr{A}$ be a Hopf algebra with multiplication π, comultiplication ψ. Let

$$G = \{x \in A \mid x \text{ is a unit with respect to } \pi \text{ and } \psi x = x \otimes x\}.$$

We show that G is a group and that A is its group algebra over K.

Lemma 1. G is finite.

Proof. Since $A^* \simeq K_1 \oplus \cdots \oplus K_n$, $K_i \simeq K$, there are exactly n distinct K-algebra homomorphisms $A^* \to K$ and each is represented by a distinct $x \in G$. Thus $o(G) = n$.

Lemma 2. G is a group, with operation $x \circ y$ given by $\pi(x \otimes y)$.

Proof. The identity 1_A of A is invertible and

$$\psi(1_A) = 1_A \otimes 1_A$$

by the definition of Hopf algebra. So $1_A \in G$. Moreover, $x \in G$ implies

$$\pi(x \otimes 1_A) = \pi(1_A \otimes x) = x.$$

Let ρ be the isomorphism defined by

$$\rho(a_1 \otimes a_2) = a_2 \otimes a_1, \qquad a_i \in A.$$

Then if $x, y \in G$

$$
\begin{aligned}
\psi(x \circ y) &= \psi(\pi(x \otimes y)) \\
&= (\pi \otimes \pi)(1 \otimes \rho \otimes 1)(\psi \otimes \psi)(x \otimes y) \\
&= (\pi \otimes \pi)(1 \otimes \rho \otimes 1)(\psi x \otimes \psi y) \\
&= (\pi \otimes \pi)(1 \otimes \rho \otimes 1)(x \otimes x \otimes y \otimes y) \\
&= (\pi \otimes \pi)(x \otimes y \otimes x \otimes y) \\
&= x \circ y \otimes x \circ y.
\end{aligned}
$$

Also, if x and y are units, xy is a unit, so G is closed.

Lemma 3. A is the group algebra over K of G, that is, A is freely generated as a K-algebra by the elements of G.

Proof. We have that

$$A^* \simeq K_1 \oplus \cdots \oplus K_n = Ke_1 + \cdots + Ke_n,$$

where the e_i are primitive idempotents, and if $f_i : A^* \to K$ is a homomorphism, it is represented by $x_i \in G$,

$$
\begin{aligned}
f_i(e_i) &= e_i(x_i) = 1, \\
f_i(e_j) &= e_j(x_i) = 0 \qquad \text{for} \quad j \neq i.
\end{aligned}
$$

Hence

$$A^{**} = \mathrm{Hom}(A^*, K) \simeq Kf_1 + \cdots + Kf_n,$$

and we can define an isomorphism $A^{**} \simeq A$ by sending $f_i \to x_i$ and requiring linearity.

We summarize the above results:

Theorem 14. *A finitely generated Hopf algebra A over K is the group algebra of a finite group if and only if its dual algebra is the direct sum of a finite number of copies of K and every algebra homomorphism $A^* \to K$ can be represented by a unit of A.*

We note that if G_1 and G_2 are groups and $K(G_1)$, $K(G_2)$ are their group algebras, then

$$K(G_1 \oplus G_2) \simeq K(G_1) \otimes K(G_2)$$

(see Problem 30, Chapter 3), so that in the category of group algebras the tensor product is a product. Moreover, we observe that since the tensor product is also a coproduct, the map

$$K(G_1) + K(G_2) \xrightarrow{\left(\begin{smallmatrix} 1 & 0 \\ 0 & 1 \end{smallmatrix}\right)} K(G_1) \times K(G_2)$$

is an isomorphism (and hence an epimorphism). Thus we can define abelian objects in the category of group algebras.

If μ is the group algebra multiplication

$$\mu : K(G) \otimes K(G) \to K(G),$$

then μ is an algebra homomorphism if and only if the multiplication in G, and hence in $K(G)$, is commutative. In this case μ satisfies the required properties for $K(G)$ to be an abelian object. Moreover, the existence of such an "abelianess" morphism, i.e., the fact that $K(G)$ is an abelian object in this category, gives a commutative multiplication.

Although if $K(G)$ is the group algebra of an abelian group, the multiplication in $K(G)$, as well as the comultiplication, is commutative, $K(G)$ is not necessarily the dual of a group algebra since it fails, in general, to be isomorphic as an algebra to the sum of copies of the field K.

PROBLEMS

1. Show directly that the coradical defined in Example 4 of Section 2 gives rise to a coradical subcategory of the category of compact abelian Hausdorff topological groups.

2. Use the definition of abelian object given in Section 4 to show that the fundamental group of an H-space is abelian.

3. Does each of the following define a radical subcategory of the category of groups? of the category of finite groups?
   (a) the Frattini subgroup   (b) the maximum solvable subgroup

CHAPTER 10

Applications of Sheaf Theory
to the Study of Rings

In this chapter we assume some acquaintance with topological notions.

When one computes the homology or homotopy groups of a space, one is looking at the space globally; on the other hand, a sheaf is essentially a system of local coefficients over a space. What one wishes to do is to assign some object, usually in topological and geometrical applications an abelian group, to each point of the space. However, if there is no relation between the objects assigned to various points, we have only a protosheaf, and while we may recover local properties of a space by looking at a protosheaf structure, we shall lose much of its global structure. This difficulty is overcome by the additional requirements we put on the assignment in order to obtain a sheaf, i.e., we want to make the local assignment in a meaningful way with respect to the whole space.

Sheaves of sets, groups, or rings have been used to study topological and geometrical problems, but not much has been done in using sheaf-theoretic techniques to study algebraic structures themselves, except for Grothendieck's work on commutative rings. To do so is somewhat the reverse of the usual procedure of introducing algebraic notions—homotopy, homology, cohomology—to simplify topological problems. However, topological methods have been used on rings; for example, Milnor proved that the only division algebras over the reals are the reals themselves, the complex numbers, the quaternions, and the Cayley numbers, using topological methods. The fundamental theorem of algebra has an elegant topological proof and many results in finite groups have recently been derived from the topology of Lie groups. Thus introducing sheaves to attack algebraic problems is a logical extension of the use of topology.

Essentially the problem which concerns us here is the same as in earlier chapters: to get some sort of structure theorems for various classes of rings—a convenient representation theory, as it were. Of course, there is the classical Wedderburn theorem of Chapter 2, and more recently the Jacobson density theorem of Chapter 4, but frequently we want more information than these give us. Our concern in this chapter will be primarily with results which have been obtained for the class of biregular rings, although other classes of rings are candidates for investigation by this technique.

Our first task, then, in seeking solutions by the use of sheaves is to associate a topological space in a meaningful way with the algebraic entity under discussion—in our case, rings. We shall do this, following the methods of Jacobson, before beginning the formal discussion of sheaves.

1. THE STRUCTURE SPACE OF A RING

We let R be any ring and let $P(R)$ denote the collection of primitive ideals of R. We introduce a topology by defining a closure operator Cl which satisfies the following conditions:

1) $Cl \, \phi = \phi$,

2) $Cl \, A \supset A$,

3) $Cl(Cl \, A) = Cl \, A$,

4) $Cl(A \cup B) = Cl(A) \cup Cl(B)$.

We then define closed sets to be sets invariant under this operator and open sets as the complements of the closed sets; this gives us a topology. Thus we make the following definition: Let $A \subset P(R)$, $D_A = \bigcap \{x \mid x \in A\}$; then

$$Cl \, A = \{x \mid x \in P(R), x \supset D_A\}.$$

$P(R)$ with this topology is called the *structure space* of the ring R. Note that we use lower case letters for ideals, since we are considering them as points of a topological space in this chapter.

Example. Suppose R is the ring of all real-valued continuous functions on $[0, 1]$. Then the maximal ideals are primitive, and conversely. Moreover, every maximal ideal is of the form

$$i(t) = \{f \mid f \in R, f(t) = 0\}$$

for some $t \in [0, 1]$. Thus the correspondence $t \to i(t)$ can be used to transfer the usual topology of $[0, 1]$ to the set of primitive ideals of R. We show that the topology described above coincides with the usual topology. We consider $A \subset P(R)$ as a subset of $[0, 1]$. If $f(x) = 0$ for all $x \in A$, then $f(x) = 0$ for all $x \in \bar{A}$ (the closure of A in the usual topology). On the other hand, if x is exterior to A, then there is a continuous function which vanishes on $\bar{A}$, but not at x. Hence

$$\bar{A} = \left\{ y \mid i(y) \supset \bigcap_{x \in A} i(x) \right\} = Cl \, A.$$

The structure space of any ring is T_0, but since one primitive ideal may properly contain another, it is not in general T_1. For example, if R is the ring of linear transformations of an infinite-dimensional vector space, (0) is a primitive ideal. But the set of all transformations of finite rank is a proper ideal, so (0) is not maximal. On the other hand, since R has an identity, maximal ideals exist; they are primitive and belong to $Cl\{(0)\}$.

The set $M(R)$ of primitive ideals which are maximal is a subspace of the structure space and is T_1; in particular if all primitive ideals are maximal as, for example, when R is commutative with identity, then $P(R) = M(R)$ is T_1. However, even for a commutative ring R, $P(R)$ need not be Hausdorff. For example, if $R = Z$ and if A is an infinite subset of $P(R)$, then $D_A = \{(0)\}$ and $Cl\ A = P(R)$, so the only open sets are the empty set and complements of finite subsets. Hence the topology is not Hausdorff.

Thus we have a convenient space associated with a ring. But its usefulness is subject to the following:

Theorem 1. *If x is an ideal in the ring R and*

$$Q = \{y \mid y \in P(R),\ y \supset x\},$$

then $y \to y/x$ is a homeomorphism of Q onto the structure space of R/x.

Proof. If $y \in Q$, $(R/x)/(y/x) \simeq R/y$, and so y/x is primitive in R/x. Conversely, any primitive ideal in R/x is of the form y/x, $y \in Q$. Also, $y \to y/x$ preserves arbitrary intersections.

Corollary. If r is the Jacobson radical of a ring R, then the mapping $y \to y/r$ is a homeomorphism onto the structure space of the semisimple ring R/r.

Proof. $Q = P(R)$ since the radical is contained in every primitive ideal.

Hence it is apparent that the structure space will prove an effective tool only in the study of semisimple rings. There are other ways of associating with a ring the necessary base space for the definition of a sheaf, but since this is useful for the type of ring we chiefly want to consider, we shall confine ourselves to it.

We now look more closely at the topology of the structure space.

Lemma. If F is the intersection of a family $\{F_\alpha\}$ of closed subsets of $P(R)$ for some ring R, then $F = \phi$ if and only if $R/\sum_\alpha D_{F_\alpha}$ is a radical ring.

Proof. A primitive ideal p of R is an element of F if and only if $p \supset \sum_\alpha D_{F_\alpha}$. Hence $F = \phi$ if and only if there does not exist a primitive ideal p containing $\sum_\alpha D_{F_\alpha}$. But this is the case if and only if $R/\sum D_{F_\alpha}$ is radical.

Theorem 2. *The structure space of a ring R with identity is compact.*

Proof. We show that if $\{F_\alpha\}$ is a family of closed sets such that $\bigcap F_\alpha = \phi$, then there exists a finite subfamily $\{F_{\alpha_i} \mid i = 1, \ldots, n\}$ such that $\bigcap F_{\alpha_i} = \phi$. If $\bigcap F_\alpha = \phi$, we have from the lemma that $R/\sum_\alpha D_{F_\alpha}$ is radical. But R has an identity so $R = \sum_\alpha D_{F_\alpha}$ and $1 \in \sum_\alpha D_{F_\alpha}$. But then by the definition of the sum of ideals,

$$1 \in \sum_{i=1}^{n} D_{F_{\alpha_i}}$$

for some finite subset $\{F_{\alpha_i}\}$ of $\{F_\alpha\}$. Thus

$$\frac{R}{\sum\limits_{i=1}^{n} D_{F_{\alpha_i}}} = (0)$$

is radical and $\bigcap F_{\alpha_i} = \phi$.

It also turns out that direct sum decompositions and (connected) components of the structure space are related.

Theorem 3. *Let R be a semisimple ring such that no nonzero homomorphic image of R is radical. If $R = R_1 \oplus R_2$, R_i an ideal of R, $i = 1, 2$ and $P_i = P(R_i) = \{x \mid x \in P(R), x \not\supset R_i\}$, then the P_i are closed and*

$$P_1 \cup P_2 = P(R), \ P_1 \cap P_2 = \phi.$$

Moreover, $R_i = D_{P_j}$, $i \neq j$.
Conversely, if $P(R) = P_1 \cup P_2, P_1 \cap P_2 = \phi$, with P_i closed and $R_i = D_{P_j}$, $i, j = 1, 2$, $i \neq j$, then $R = R_1 \oplus R_2$ and $P(R_i) = P_i$.

Proof. Suppose $R = R_1 \oplus R_2$ and $P_i = P(R_i)$. Since $R_1 R_2 = (0)$, if x is primitive, either $R_1 \subset x$ or $R_2 \subset x$. Hence $P_1 \cap P_2 = \phi$. Also, no primitive ideal can contain both R_1 and R_2, so $P_1 \cup P_2 = P(R)$. But then

$$P_j = \{x \mid x \supset R_i\}, \ \ i \neq j,$$

so P_j is closed, $j = 1, 2$. R/R_i is also semisimple, so $R_i = \bigcap \{x \mid x \in P(R), x \supset R_i\}$. Thus $R_i = D_{P_j}$, $i \neq j$.

Suppose $P(R) = P_1 \cup P_2$, $P_1 \cap P_2 = \phi$, P_i closed, $i = 1, 2$. Let $R_i = D_{P_j}$, $i \neq j$. Then $R_1 \cap R_2 = D_{P(R)} = (0)$, since R is semisimple. If $R_1 + R_2 \neq R$, then $R/(R_1 + R_2)$ is not radical, so there exists a primitive ideal containing D_{R_1} and D_{R_2} (by the lemma to Theorem 2). But this contradicts the fact that the P_i, $i = 1, 2$, are closed and disjoint. Hence $R = R_1 \oplus R_2$. It is clear that $P(R_i) = P_i$.

We note (see Problem 1) that $P(R_i)$ is homeomorphic to the structure space of R_i as a ring, so the notation is not ambiguous.

We say that an idempotent is *central* if it is in the center of a ring.

Lemma. *The set of central idempotents of a ring R is a lattice relative to the operations of multiplication and*

$$e \circ f = e + f - ef.$$

The proof is straightforward verification.

We relate this lattice to the lattice of compact open and closed subsets of the structure space.

Theorem 4. *Let R be a semisimple ring such that no homomorphic image of R is a radical ring. If e is a central idempotent, then $P(Re)$ is a compact* *open and closed subset of $P(R)$. The correspondence $e \to P(Re)$ is a lattice isomorphism of the lattice of central idempotents onto a lattice of subsets of $P(R)$. If A is any open and closed subset of $P(Re)$, then there exists a central idempotent f such that $P(Rf) = A$.*

Proof. We first show that $P(Re)$ is compact, open, and closed. We have

$$R = Re \oplus R(1 - e),$$

Re, $R(1 - e)$ ideals of R. Then by Theorem 3, $P(Re)$ is open and closed. Moreover, $P(Re)$ is homeomorphic to the structure space of Re. But e is an identity for Re, so $P(Re)$ is compact.

Next we show that if e and f are central idempotents, $e \neq f$, then $P(Re) \neq P(Rf)$. Since $R(1 - e) = D_{P(Re)}, P(Re) = P(Rf)$ would imply that $R(1 - e) = R(1 - f)$, from which it follows that $e = f$.

Suppose that e and f are central idempotents; then ef and $e + f - ef$ are central idempotents. If x is a primitive (and hence prime) ideal such that $x \in P(Re) \cap P(Rf)$, then since $x \not\supset Re$ and $x \not\supset Rf$ imply $x \not\supset Ref$, we have $x \in P(Ref)$. Conversely, if $x \in P(Ref)$, $x \in P(Re) \cap P(Rf)$. To see whether the other lattice operation is preserved, we observe that $R(1 - (e + f - ef)) = R(1 - e)(1 - f)$ so that $x \supset R(1 - (e + f - ef))$ if and only if $x \supset R(1 - e)$ or $x \supset R(1 - f)$. But this means that

$$P[R(e + f - ef)] = P(Re) \cup P(Rf)$$

as desired.

Finally, we let A be an open and closed subset of $P(Re)$. Since $P(Re)$ is homeomorphic to the structure space of Re, we get from Theorem 3 that $Re = R_1 \oplus R_2$, where

$$R_1 = \bigcap_{x \in P(Re) \setminus A} (Re \cap x).$$

But

$$Re = \bigcap_{x \in P(R) \setminus P(Re)} x, \qquad \text{so} \qquad R_1 = \bigcap_{x \in P(Re) \setminus A} x.$$

Since $R = R_1 \oplus R_2 \oplus R(1 - e)$, we have that $A = P(R_1)$. But e is an identity for Re, so R_1 must have an identity, say f. It is now apparent that f is a central idempotent of R and $R_1 = Rf$. Thus $A = P(Rf)$.

2. BIREGULAR RINGS

A ring R is *biregular* if every principal ideal (a), $a \in R$, is generated by a central idempotent.

Examples

1. A ring with identity, each of whose elements is idempotent, is called a *Boolean ring*. The usual example is the set of subsets of a given set with the operations of intersection and symmetric difference. Such a ring is necessarily commutative and also biregular. Moreover, it is a Z_2-algebra.

2. We recall that a ring R is regular if for every $r \in R$ there exists an $x \in R$ such that $axa = a$. A ring R is *π-regular* if for each $a \in R$ there exists an $x \in R$ and a positive integer $n(a)$ such that $a^{n(a)}xa^{n(a)} = a^{n(a)}$. We claim that every π-regular ring without nonzero nilpotent elements is biregular. To show this we note that for any ring R the elements of $eR(1 - e)$ and $(1 - e)Re$ are nilpotent. Hence if R has no nonzero nilpotent elements, its Peirce decomposition has the form

$$R = eRe \oplus (1 - e)R(1 - e).$$

But this implies that e is central. Thus we need only show that if $0 \neq a \in R$, there is an idempotent $e \in (a)$ such that $ea = a$. But if $a^n x a^n = a^n$, then $e = a^n x$ is idempotent and $ea^n = a^n$ for some positive integer n. Let n be minimal and suppose $n > 1$. Then

$$(ea^{n-1} - a^{n-1})^2 = ea^{2n-2} - 2ea^{2n-2} + a^{2n-2} = a^{2n-2} - ea^{2n-2} = 0$$

and $ea^{n-1} = a^{n-1}$. Thus we must have $ea = a$. Since regular rings are π-regular, if they have no nonzero nilpotent elements, they are biregular. However, in general, biregularity does not imply regularity nor conversely.

3. Any ideal or homomorphic image of a biregular ring is biregular.

From the definition of biregular ring we have:

Theorem 5. *A biregular ring is semisimple. It is primitive if and only if it is a simple ring with an identity element.*

The structure space of a biregular ring has some nice properties.

Theorem 6. *The structure space of a biregular ring is locally compact and totally disconnected.*

Proof. We must show that (1) every point of the space is contained in a compact set and (2) for any two points of the space there are disjoint closed sets, each of which contains one of the points and whose union is the whole space.

Every primitive ideal in R is maximal so that $P(R)$ is T_1. We let x_1 and x_2 be distinct primitive ideals and suppose $a \in x_2$, $a \notin x_1$. Let e be a central idempotent such that $(a) = (e) = Re$ and consider $P(Re)$. This set is compact, so (1) is satisfied. It is also open and closed and contains x_1 but not x_2, so it and its complement satisfy (2). Thus $P(R)$ is locally compact and totally disconnected.

Theorem 7. *If A is a compact and open subset of $P(R)$, R a biregular ring, then there exists a central idempotent $f \in R$ such that $P(Rf) = A$.*

Proof. As in the proof of the preceding theorem, if A is a compact and open subset of $P(R)$ then for each $x \in A$ we can find $P(Re)$, e a central idempotent, such that $x \in P(Re)$. A finite number of such open sets, say $P(Re_1), \ldots, P(Re_n)$, cover A and so do

$$U_i = P(Re_i) \cap A, \qquad i = 1, \ldots, n.$$

But by Theorem 4 there exists a central idempotent f_i such that $P(Rf_i) = U_i$. We now let

$$f = f_1 \circ f_2 \circ \cdots \circ f_n,$$

where the circle composition is that of Theorem 4. Then $P(Rf) = A$.

If R has an identity, $P(R)$ is compact, but in the biregular case we also have

Corollary. If R is biregular, $P(R)$ is compact if and only if R has an identity.

We note the following easily verified fact: If R is biregular, for every $x \in P(R)$, R/x is a simple ring with identity (whether or not R has an identity).

In the following discussion we let P be any topological space and R a ring with the discrete topology (i.e., every subset of R is open and closed). If $f:P \to R$ is continuous, then

$$f^{-1}(a) = \{p \mid p \in P, f(p) = a\}$$

is an open and closed subset of P and $\{f^{-1}(a) \mid a \in R\}$ partitions P into nonintersecting open and closed subsets. If $C \subset P$ is compact, then

$$f^{-1}(a) \cap C \neq \phi$$

for only a finite number of elements $a \in R$. A function f has *compact carrier* if $f = 0$ on the complement of a compact subset of P. If f is continuous with compact carrier, then only a finite number of the sets $f^{-1}(a)$ are nonempty. Conversely, if C is a compact open and closed subset of P and

$$C = C_1 \cup \cdots \cup C_n,$$

a partition of C into disjoint open and closed subsets, we let $r_i \in R, i = 1, \ldots, n$, and assign $f(a_i) = r_i$ for all $a_i \in C_i, f(a) = 0, a \notin C$. Then f is continuous on P and has compact carrier.

If A is the collection of continuous functions from P to R with compact carrier, then A is a ring closed under multiplication by any constant function, and is a left algebra over R in the following sense:

A ring A is a *left algebra* over a ring R if and only if

1) A is a left R-module

2) $r(ab) = (ra)b$ for all $r \in R, a, b \in A$.

If A is biregular, then $a \in A$ can be written as $a = ea$, e a central idempotent. Then if I is an ideal of A, for $a \in I$, $r \in R$, $ra = (re)a$ so that I is an R-ideal. Thus I and A/I are also left algebras. If A has an identity, the module multiplication is the same as left multiplication by the elements $r \cdot 1, r \in R$. We have

$$ra = r(1 \cdot a) = (r \cdot 1)a$$

and

$$(r_1 r_2)1 = r_1(r_2 \cdot 1) = (r_1 \cdot 1)(r_2 \cdot 1), \qquad r, r_1, r_2 \in R, \quad a \in A,$$

so that $r \to r \cdot 1$ is a homomorphism.

Of course the Jacobson density theorem applies to biregular rings, but we can now prove a theorem which gives us additional information about the structure of these rings.

Theorem 8. *If A is a ring and R a simple ring with identity, then the following are necessary and sufficient conditions that A be isomorphic to the ring of continuous functions with compact carriers on a locally compact totally disconnected space to R:*

1) *A is biregular.*

2) *A is a left R-algebra.*

3) *For each primitive ideal p of A the mapping $r \rightarrow r \cdot 1 + p$ of R into A/p is an isomorphism.*

Proof. Let A be the ring of continuous functions with compact carriers from a totally disconnected space X to R. We have observed that (2) is then necessary. Let $0 \neq a \in A$, $0 \neq r_1 \in$ image a and

$$U_1 = \{x \mid x \in X, a(x) = r_1\}.$$

We denote the characteristic function of U_1 by e_1 and observe that e_1 is a central idempotent in U_1 and $a_1 = ae_1 \in (a)$. Then

$$a_1(x) = r_1, \quad x \in U_1, \qquad e_1(x) = 1, \quad x \in U_1,$$
$$a_1(x) = 0, \quad x \notin U_1, \qquad e_1(x) = 0, \quad x \notin U_1.$$

Since R is simple, r_1 generates all of R. In particular,

$$1 = rr_1 + r'r_1, \qquad \text{some } r, r' \in R,$$

and

$$e_1 = ra_1 + r'a_1.$$

Thus $e_1 \in (a)$. Now we let $U = \{x \mid x \in X, a(x) \neq 0\}$. Since a has only a finite number of nonzero values, letting e be the characteristic function of U, we have that

$$e = e_1 + \cdots + e_n,$$

with each e_i the characteristic function of the set where a has a nonzero value r_i, $i = 1, \ldots, n$. By the argument above each $e_i \in (a)$, so $e \in (a)$. But each e_i, $i = 1, \ldots, n$, is a central idempotent, so e is also. Thus A is biregular.

To prove that (3) is necessary we let p be a primitive ideal of A. We shall show first that p consists of all functions vanishing at some point x_0 of X. Since by Theorem 5 p is maximal, to do this it suffices to show that

$$p \subset M(x_0) = \{f \mid f \in A, f(x_0) = 0\};$$

for then we must have $p = M(x_0)$. Thus we let $x \in X$ and assume that for some $f \in p, f(x) \neq 0$. For $a \in A$ we define

$$U = \{y \mid y \in X, a(y) \neq 0\}.$$

For $y \in U$ we choose $f \in p$ such that $f(y) \neq 0$. We may as well suppose that f is a characteristic function. Since U is compact, there are a finite number of such f, say $f_1, \ldots, f_m$, such that $e = f_1 \circ \cdots \circ f_m$, where the circle composition is as above, is a characteristic function for some set $S \supset U$. But then $ea = a$, and since $e \in p$, a is also in p. But this means that $p = A$, a contradiction. Hence there exists $x_0 \in X$ such that $f(x_0) = 0$ for each $f \in p$ and $p \subset M(x_0)$. Since we know that $r \to r \cdot 1 + p$ defines a homomorphism, it is now easy to see that $R \simeq A/p$.

For the converse we let A be a ring satisfying (1), (2), and (3), $P(A)$ its structure space. Then by Theorem 6 we have that $P(A)$ is locally compact and totally disconnected. For $a \in A$, $p \in P(A)$, we write $a + p = r(1 + p)$, where $r \in R$ and $1 + p$ is the identity of A/p. $p \to r$ defines a function a' from $P(A)$ to R. The correspondence $a \to a'$ is an isomorphism of A onto a subring of the ring of functions from $P(A)$ to R. Writing $(a) = (e)$, e a central idempotent, we have that $P(Ae)$ is compact and open. Moreover, if e' is defined from e as above, e' is the characteristic function of the set $P(Ae)$. Thus e', and consequently a', has compact carrier. To show that a' is continuous, we let

$$U = \{p \in P(Ae) \mid a'(p) = r_1\}.$$

Then $U = P(Ae) \cap Q$, where $Q = \{q \mid q \text{ a primitive ideal of } A, a - r_1 e \in q\}$. Q is open and closed, so U is also. Hence a' is continuous and it remains only to show that every continuous function with compact carrier can be represented as a' for some a. But it is clear from Theorem 7 that the characteristic function of every compact open subset of $P(A)$ can be so represented. On the other hand, any continuous function with compact carrier can be written as a linear combination (with coefficients from R) of such characteristic functions.

As this theorem shows, the conditions under which a biregular ring can be represented as a function ring are rather restrictive. Thus the purpose of the introduction of sheaves is to achieve a representation theory which applies to all biregular rings, but which gives more information than the structure theorems for general semisimple rings.

3. SHEAVES

We shall discuss some of the basic material of sheaf theory with, however, an algebraic rather than topological emphasis. Although, as we remarked above, a sheaf may take values in various categories, we shall concern ourselves only with sheaves of rings.

A triple $\langle S, \pi, X \rangle$ consisting of two given sets X and S and a surjective function $\pi : S \to X$ is a *protosheaf* of rings (simple rings) with identity if $\pi^{-1}(x)$ is a ring (simple ring) with identity.

It is called a *sheaf* of rings (simple rings) with identity if the following are satisfied:

1) S and X are topological spaces.

2) Each point in S has an open neighborhood which is mapped homeomorphically onto an open set in X under π.

3) The functions $(s, t) \to s + t$ and $(s, t) \to st$ from

$$\{(s, t) \mid s, t \in S, \pi(s) = \pi(t)\}$$

into S are continuous.

4) The function which assigns to every $x \in X$ the identity of $\pi^{-1}(x)$ is continuous.

If we want to consider sheaves of groups, modules, etc., we replace (3) by the requirement that the appropriate operations be continuous.

$S_x = \pi^{-1}(x)$ is called the *stalk* over x. Usually the space S itself is called the *sheaf* or *sheaf space*, X the *base space*, and π the *projection*.

Examples

1. We let R be a ring with the discrete topology, X a topological space, and let $S = X \times R$ and $\pi:S \to X$ be the projection

$$\pi(x, r) = x.$$

Then $\langle S, \pi, X \rangle$ is a sheaf, called the *constant sheaf*. The stalk over $x \in X$ is (x, R).

2. Let X be the 1-sphere S^1; let S be the union of another copy of S^1, denoted by A, and a double covering of S^1 by a circle; let π be the projection. Then $\langle S, \pi, X \rangle$ is a sheaf and each stalk is Z_3, which is totally disconnected, and each element of A is the zero in the stalk in which it lies.

A *map* $F:\langle S, \pi, X \rangle \to \langle S', \pi', X \rangle$ *of sheaves*, usually written $F:S \to S'$, is a continuous function $S \to S'$ such that:

1) $\pi = \pi' \circ F$.

2) $F \mid S_x = F_x:\pi^{-1}(x) \to (\pi')^{-1}(x)$ is a ring homomorphism.

We note that sheaves must have the same base space in order for a map between them to be defined.

We define composition of sheaf maps in the usual way and observe that sheaves (of rings with identity) and sheaf maps form a category. If S and S' are sheaves, the set of sheaf maps $S \to S'$ is denoted as usual by $\hom(S, S')$. We define addition for sheaf maps $F, G:S \to S'$ by

$$(F + G)_x = F_x \oplus G_x.$$

Given sheaves $\langle S, \pi, X \rangle$ and $\langle S', \pi', X \rangle$, we let

$$S + S' = \{(x, y) \in S \times S' \mid \pi(x) = \pi'(y)\}$$

and define $\pi'':S + S' \to X$ by

$$\pi''(x, y) = \pi(x) = \pi'(y).$$

Then $\langle S + S', \pi'', X \rangle$ is a sheaf, called the *sum* of S and S'.

These operations make the category of sheaves of rings with the same base space into an exact category (Problem 5) and hom is a left exact functor from the category of sheaves to the category of abelian groups. Thus one may define homology and cohomology for sheaves, but we shall not concern ourselves with that theory.

If $\langle S, \pi, X \rangle$ is a sheaf of rings with identity and $U \subset X$ is open, then any continuous function $\sigma : U \to S$ for which $\pi \circ \sigma$ is the identity map of U is called a *section* over U.

The set of all sections over U is a ring with identity (under the obvious pointwise operations), which is denoted by $\Gamma(U, S)$. We let $\Gamma(X, S) = \Gamma(S)$; elements of $\Gamma(S)$ are called *global sections* of S.

If $\sigma \in \Gamma(S)$, then the *carrier* of σ is the closed subset consisting of all $x \in X$ for which $\sigma(x) \neq 0(x)$, the zero of $\pi^{-1}(x)$.

The global sections of a sheaf $\langle S, \pi, X \rangle$ of rings with identity over a locally compact base space X which have compact carriers clearly form a subring of the ring $\Gamma(S)$, which we denote by $\Gamma_0(S)$. $\Gamma_0(S)$ has no identity if X is not compact.

4. REPRESENTATION OF BIREGULAR RINGS

The results of this section are due to Dauns and Hofmann.

For a biregular ring A we let $S(A)$ be the union of all quotient rings A/x, where $x \in P(A)$, the set of primitive ideals of A, which by the results of Section 2 is locally compact and totally disconnected. Moreover, it is Hausdorff and $A/x \cap A/y = \phi$ for $x \neq y$. We let $\pi : S(A) \to P(A)$ be given by assigning to $s \in S(A)$ the unique $x \in P(A)$ such that $s \in A/x$. $\langle S(A), \pi, P(A) \rangle$ is clearly a protosheaf of simple rings with identity.

Now in order to turn the protosheaf into a sheaf we need a topology on $S(A)$. First we associate with A an appropriate ring of functions. If A is a biregular ring, $a \in A$, we define $a' : P(A) \to S(A)$ by $a'(x) = a + x$, $x \in P(A)$. The totality of all such functions, with the obvious operations, is a ring, which we denote by A'.

Lemma. The map $A \to A'$ given by $a \to a'$ is a ring isomorphism.

Proof. Everything is obvious except for injectivity. But the kernel of the map is

$$\{a \in A \mid a \in \cap \{x \mid x \in P(A)\}\}.$$

However, A is semisimple, so the kernel is zero.

We now proceed with the construction of the topology for $S(A)$.

Lemma 1. If $a \in A$, then $\{x \mid x \in P(A), a'(x) \neq x\}$ is compact and open in $P(A)$.

Proof. We have $a'(x) \neq x$ if and only if $a \notin x$ if and only if $x \notin P(Ae)$, where e is the central idempotent which generates the ideal (a). But $P(Ae)$ is compact and open.

Lemma 2. If $U \subset P(A)$ is compact and open, then there exists a central idempotent $e \in A$ such that the carrier of e' is exactly U.

Proof. This follows directly from Theorem 7.

Lemma 3. If $s \in a'(U) \cap b'(V)$, where $a, b \in A$ and U, V are compact open sets in $P(A)$, then there is a compact open neighborhood W of $\pi(s)$ with $W \subset U \cap V$ such that $a' \mid W = b' \mid W$. In particular $a'(W) \subset a'(U) \cap b'(V)$.

Proof. We know that $a'(\pi(s)) = b'(\pi(s)) = s$. The subset of $P(A)$ on which a' and b' are equal is the set where $(a - b)' = a' - b'$ vanishes, and thus by Lemma 1 it is open. But the compact open neighborhoods of $\pi(s)$ form a basis for all neighborhoods, so that there is a compact open neighborhood W of $\pi(s)$ such that $a' \mid W = b' \mid W$ and $W \subset U \cap V$.

Lemma 4. The set

$$\mathscr{B} = \{a'(U) \mid a \in A, \ U \text{ compact open in } P(A)\}$$

is a basis for a topology on $S(A)$. For all $a \in A$, the function $a' : P(A) \to S(A)$ is continuous and open.

Proof. If $s \in S(A)$, there is an $a \in A$ such that $a'(\pi(s)) = s$. Hence $S(A) = \bigcup \mathscr{B}$. That $\mathscr{B}$ is a basis follows from Lemma 3. The last statement of Lemma 4 is obvious.

Henceforth $S(A)$ will denote the set $S(A)$ together with this topology.

Theorem 9. *If A is a biregular ring, then $\langle S(A), \pi, P(A) \rangle$ is a sheaf of simple rings with identity.*

Proof. That the ring operations are continuous (and open) is apparent. We check the local homeomorphism property.

Let $s \in S(A)$ and U be a compact open neighborhood of $\pi(s)$ in $P(A)$. From the way a' was defined, we can choose an $a \in A$ such that $a'(\pi(s)) = s$. If $\mathscr{B}(U)$ denotes the basis $\mathscr{B}(U) = \{W \mid W \text{ compact open in } U\}$ for the induced topology on U, then $\mathscr{B}(U, a) = \{a'(W) \mid W \in \mathscr{B}(U)\}$ is a basis for the topology induced on $a'(U)$ by the topology of $S(A)$.

Finally we must verify that the map $P(A) \to S(A)$ which takes $x \in P(A)$ into the identity of $\pi^{-1}(x)$ is continuous. Let U be a compact open subset of $P(A)$. Then there exists a central idempotent $e \in A$ such that U is the carrier of e'. But $e'(u)$, $u \in U$, is a nonzero idempotent in the simple ring $\pi^{-1}(u)$, so it must be the identity element. Hence $e' \mid U$ is the restriction of the map $x \to 1_{\pi^{-1}(x)}$ to U, and the latter is continuous and open since the former is.

We now connect the ring with the sheaf which we have derived from it by looking at the global sections. We shall use the following result from point set topology.

Lemma 1. If C is a compact totally disconnected Hausdorff space and $\mathscr{A}$ is any open cover of C, then there are a finite number of disjoint compact open subsets of C whose union is all of C such that each is completely contained in at least one open set of the cover $\mathscr{A}$.

We also need:

Lemma 2. If $\sigma \in \Gamma(S(A))$ is a section and U a compact open subset of $P(A)$, then there exists $a \in A$ such that $a' \mid U = \sigma \mid U$.

Proof. In any sheaf, if two sections coincide at a point, they must agree on a whole neighborhood of that point. Hence for each point $x \in P(A)$ there exists a compact open neighborhood $W(x)$ and an element $a_x \in A$ such that $a'_x \mid W(x) = \sigma \mid W(x)$. Due to Lemma 1 we may represent U as the disjoint union of a finite number of compact open subsets $U_1, \ldots, U_n$, every one of which is completely contained in some set $W(x)$; we may therefore assume that we have n elements $a_1, \ldots, a_n \in A$ such that $a'_i \mid U_i = \sigma \mid U_i$. We have central idempotents $e_1, \ldots, e_n$ whose carriers are exactly the U_i. So we replace the a_i by $a_i e_i$ and by renaming them we may assume that U_i is the exact carrier of a_i. Now we let $a = a_1 + \cdots + a_n$; then $a' \mid U = \sigma \mid U$.

Using this lemma we can prove the first half of our structure theorem.

Theorem 10. *For a biregular ring A, the ring A' is exactly the ring $\Gamma_0(S(A))$ of all global sections of $\langle S(A), \pi, P(A) \rangle$ with compact carriers.*

Proof. By Lemmas 1 and 3 to Theorem 9, $A' \subset \Gamma_0(S(A))$ and Lemma 2 to this theorem gives the other containment.

We now want to prove the converse, for which we need another series of lemmas.

Lemma 1. Let $\langle S, \pi, X \rangle$ be a sheaf of simple rings with identity over a locally compact totally disconnected Hausdorff space X. Let I be an ideal of $\Gamma_0(S)$ and suppose that for some $x \in X$ and $\sigma \in I$, $\sigma(x) \neq 0(x)$, the zero of $\pi^{-1}(x)$. Then I contains the characteristic function of some compact open neighborhood U of x.

Proof. Since $\pi^{-1}(x)$ is simple, there exist $2n$ elements

$$s_1, \ldots, s_n, t_1, \ldots, t_n \in \pi^{-1}(x)$$

such that $s_1 \sigma(x) t_1 + \cdots + s_n \sigma(x) t_n = 1(x)$. From the fact that π is a local homeomorphism and the fact that the topology of X has a basis of compact open sets, we conclude that there exist global sections $\alpha_i, \beta_i \in \Gamma_0(S)$ such that for all i

$$\alpha_i(x) = s_i, \quad \text{and} \quad \beta_i(x) = t_i.$$

The set

$$U = \{ y \mid y \in X, \ \sum \alpha_i(y) \sigma(y) \beta_i(y) = 1(y) \}$$

is compact and open since the set of points in the base space at which two
sections agree is open for any sheaf. After multiplying α_i and β_i by the characteristic function of U and renaming them, we may assume that each α_i and
β_i has the compact open set U as its carrier.

Hence I·contains $\alpha_1\sigma\beta_1 + \cdots + \alpha_n\sigma\beta_n$, the characteristic function of the
compact open neighborhood U of x.

Lemma 2. Let $\langle S, \pi, X \rangle$ be any sheaf of simple rings with identity over a
locally compact, totally disconnected Hausdorff space X and let $\sigma \in \Gamma(S)$.
Then

$$W = \{x \mid x \in X, \sigma(x) \neq 0(x)\}$$

is closed and open.

Proof. In any sheaf of rings, the map $X \to S$ given by $x \to 0(x)$ is continuous
and open. Since any section is an open map, $\sigma(X)$ is also open.

But $X \setminus W$ is the inverse image of the open set $\sigma(X) \cap \{0(x) \mid x \in X\}$ under
σ. Hence W is closed.

If $\sigma(x) \neq 0(x)$ for some $x \in X$, let the ideal I in the preceding lemma be
the principal ideal generated by $\sigma e \in \Gamma_0(S)$, where e is the characteristic function
of some compact open neighborhood of x. Then there exist $\alpha_i, \beta_i \in \Gamma_0(S)$ and
a compact open neighborhood U of x such that

$$\alpha_1\sigma e\beta_1 + \cdots + \alpha_n\sigma e\beta_n$$

is the characteristic function of U. In particular $\sigma(y) \neq 0(y)$ for all $y \in U$ and
W is open.

Now we can prove:

Theorem 11. *Let $\langle S, \pi, X \rangle$ be a sheaf of simple rings with identity over a
locally compact, totally disconnected Hausdorff space. Then $\Gamma_0(S)$ is a
biregular ring whose structure space is homeomorphic to X. The ring $\Gamma_0(S)$
has an identity if and only if X is compact. Furthermore, $\Gamma_0(S)$ determines
the topology of S; the sets*

$$\mathscr{B} = \{\sigma(U) \mid \sigma \in \Gamma_0(S), U \text{ compact, open in } X\}$$

form a basis for the topology of S.

Proof. Let U be the carrier of $\sigma \in \Gamma_0(S)$. Then by Lemma 2, U is compact and
open. Thus $e: X \to S$, the characteristic function of U, is a central idempotent
in $\Gamma_0(S)$. Since (e) is the ideal of all sections vanishing on $X \setminus U$, $(\sigma) \subset (e)$. On
the other hand, σ never vanishes on $U = \{x \mid x \in X, \sigma(x) \neq 0(x)\}$. Hence by
Lemma 1 to this theorem and by Lemma 1 to Theorem 10 we have that U is
the disjoint union of compact open subsets $C_1, \ldots, C_n$ of X such that the ideal
(σ) contains the characteristic function of each C_i and hence also e. Thus
$(\sigma) = (e)$ and $\Gamma_0(S)$ is biregular.

If I is an ideal of $\Gamma_0(S)$, we let

$$N(I) = \{x \mid x \in X, \sigma(x) = 0(x) \text{ for all } \sigma \in I\}.$$

Then by Lemma 1 if $x \notin N(I)$, I contains the characteristic function of some compact open neighborhood of x. Hence by Lemma 1 to Theorem 10, if $N(I) = \phi$, then I contains the characteristic function of every compact open subset of X and $I = \Gamma_0(S)$. Thus if I is proper, $N(I)$ is nonempty. But if I is maximal, $N(I)$ cannot contain more than one point. Conversely, if $N(I) = \{x\}$, then I is contained in the ideal J of all $\sigma \in \Gamma_0(S)$ which vanish at x. But again I contains the characteristic function of any compact open set not containing x and thus the characteristic function of the carrier of $\sigma \in J$. Hence $\sigma \in I$. Therefore, the kernel of the map $\sigma \to \sigma(x)$ is exactly I. But $\pi^{-1}(x)$ is simple, so I is maximal. The mapping $\varphi : P(\Gamma_0(S)) \to X$ which assigns to a maximal ideal I the element x with $N(I) = \{x\}$ is thus injective and surjective. To show that it is a homeomorphism, it suffices to show that φ induces a one–one correspondence between the compact open subsets of $P(\Gamma_0(S))$ and those of X. But we have that for any compact open subset C of $P(\Gamma_0(S))$ there exists a central idempotent $e \in \Gamma_0(S)$ such that C consists exactly of all maximal ideals not containing e. Every central idempotent $e \in \Gamma_0(S)$ is the characteristic function of some compact open subset U of X. Thus $\varphi(C) = U$ and since the characteristic function of a compact open subset of X is in $\Gamma_0(S)$ and thus determines a compact open set $C \subset P(\Gamma_0(S))$ with $\varphi(C) = U$, then $P(\Gamma_0(S))$ is homeomorphic to X. It is clear that $\Gamma_0(S)$ has an identity if and only if X is compact.

Finally we must show that if we start with the biregular ring $\Gamma_0(S)$ and identify its structure space with the base space X, then the original topology of the sheaf S is the same as the one obtained by applying the construction of Theorem 9 to $\Gamma_0(S)$. But since in any sheaf sections are open mappings, all the sets in

$$\mathscr{B} = \{\sigma(U) \mid \sigma \in \Gamma_0(S), \ U \text{ compact open in } X\}$$

are open. On the other hand, since π is a local homeomorphism and X has a basis of compact open sets, any open subset of S must be a union of members of $\mathscr{B}$.

To complete the structure theory for biregular rings, we look at the ring of all sections, of which the ring of sections with compact carriers is a subring, and ask whether we may also associate it with a biregular ring. For a biregular ring A we let $L(A)$ be the ring of all endomorphisms of A as a right module over itself, the operations of $L(A)$ being addition and composition. If A has an identity, $L(A)$ is the ring of left translations by elements of A and thus is isomorphic to A. In general, for $0 \neq b \in A$, left translation by b is a nonzero element of $L(A)$, so that A is isomorphic to a subring of $L(A)$. Moreover, $L(A)$ is a left algebra over A.

Lemma. Let A be a biregular ring, $L(A)$ the ring of endomorphisms of A as a right A-module. If A is identified with the ring $\Gamma_0(S(A))$ of global sections with compact carriers ($S(A)$ as above), then $L(A)$ is isomorphic to the ring of all sections $\Gamma(S(A))$, where $\Gamma(S(A))$ acts on $\Gamma_0(S(A))$ by left multiplication.

Proof. It is clear that left multiplication by $\sigma \in \Gamma(S(A))$ gives rise to an element of $L(A)$. On the other hand, we let $f \in L(A)$ and let $\mathcal{J}$ be the lattice of compact open subsets of the structure space $P(A)$ of A, with respect to union and intersection. Then $P(A) = \bigcup \mathcal{J}$.

For $C \in \mathcal{J}$ we let e_C be the characteristic function of C and let $\varphi_C = f(e_C)$. Then

$$f(e_C) = f(e_C^2) = (fe_C)e_C,$$

so that the carrier of φ_C is in C. Now for $C, D \in \mathcal{J}$,

$$\varphi_{C \cap D} = f(e_{C \cap D}) = f(e_C e_{C \cap D}) = (fe_C)e_{C \cap D}$$
$$= e_{C \cap D}(f(e_C)) = e_{C \cap D}\varphi_C,$$

and similarly

$$\varphi_{C \cap D} = e_{C \cap D}\varphi_D.$$

Thus $\varphi_C \,|\, C \cap D = \varphi_D \,|\, C \cap D$. Let $\bar{\varphi}_C : C \to S(A)$ be defined by

$$\bar{\varphi}_C(x) = \varphi_C(x) \qquad \text{for} \quad x \in C.$$

If $C \cap D \neq \phi$, we have that

$$\bar{\varphi}_C \,|\, C \cap D = \bar{\varphi}_D \,|\, C \cap D.$$

Hence

$$\varphi = \cup \{\bar{\varphi}_C \,|\, C \in \mathcal{J}\}$$

is a function from $P(A)$ to $S(A)$. Furthermore φ is continuous since $\varphi \,|\, C = \bar{\varphi}_C$ is continuous for each $C \in \mathcal{J}$. If $x \in P(A)$, we choose $C \in \mathcal{J}$ such that $x \in C$; then $\pi(\varphi(x)) = \pi(\varphi_C(x)) = x$ since $\varphi_C \in \Gamma_0(S(A))$ and thus $\pi \circ \varphi_C$ is the identity.

But then $\varphi \in \Gamma(S(A))$.

Finally for arbitrary $\sigma \in \Gamma_0(S(A))$, we let C be the carrier of σ. Then $C \in \mathcal{J}$ and

$$f\sigma = f(e_C\sigma) = (fe_C)\sigma = (fe_C)e_C\sigma = \varphi_C e_C\sigma = \varphi\sigma.$$

We restate the results of this section.

Theorem 12

1) *If A is a biregular ring, $L(A)$ the ring of generalized left translations of A, $i : A \to L(A)$ the ring injection which assigns to an element of A the left translation defined by it, then there is a sheaf $\langle S(A), \pi, P(A) \rangle$ of simple rings with identity over the locally compact, totally disconnected Hausdorff structure space $P(A)$. The ring $\Gamma_0(S(A))$ of global sections of $\langle S(A), \pi, P(A) \rangle$*

with compact carriers is an ideal in the ring $\Gamma(S(A))$ of all global sections. If $j: \Gamma_0(S(A)) \to \Gamma(S(A))$ is the inclusion map then there exist isomorphisms $\psi_0: A \to \Gamma_0(S(A))$ and $\psi: L(A) \to \Gamma(S(A))$ such that the following diagram commutes:

$$
\begin{array}{ccc}
A & \xrightarrow{\;\;i\;\;} & L(A) \\
\psi_0 \downarrow & & \downarrow \psi \\
\Gamma_0(S(A)) & \xrightarrow{\;\;j\;\;} & \Gamma(S(A)).
\end{array}
$$

Moreover, if $\theta \in L(A)$, $a \in A$, then $\psi_0(\theta a) = \psi(\theta)\psi_0(a)$.

2) *If $\langle S, \pi, X \rangle$ is a sheaf of simple rings with identity over a locally compact, totally disconnected Hausdorff space X, then the ring $\Gamma_0(S)$ of global sections of $\langle S, \pi, X \rangle$ with compact carriers is a biregular ring whose structure space is homeomorphic to X. The sheaf associated with $\Gamma_0(S)$ according to (1) is canonically isomorphic to $\langle S, \pi, X \rangle$.*

Example. If X is a totally disconnected, locally compact Hausdorff space and R a simple ring with identity, then we denote by $C(X, R)$ the ring of all continuous maps of X into the discrete ring R and by $C_0(X, R)$ the ideal of functions with compact carriers. Then $C_0(X, R)$ is a biregular ring whose associated sheaf is the constant sheaf $\langle X \times R, \pi, X \rangle$ of R over X, which is isomorphic to the sheaf of germs of continuous functions on open sets of X into R.

5. BOOLEAN RING MODULES

We conclude with a structure theorem which is not directly related to radicals, but which is an easy application of the sheaf techniques we have developed in this chapter. Pierce has used sheaves extensively to study modules over commutative regular rings; we look at a simple special case.

Let X be a topological space, $B(X)$ the set of all subsets of X which are both open and closed. Then $B(X)$ is a Boolean ring under the operations of intersection and symmetric difference—recall that the symmetric difference of A and B is defined to be $(A \cup B) \backslash (A \cap B)$. Moreover, Stone has proved:

Theorem 13. *If R is a Boolean ring, there exists a unique compact totally disconnected Hausdorff space $R(X)$ such that R is isomorphic to $B(R(X))$, the ring of open and closed subsets of $R(X)$.*

We shall describe the construction of the space $R(X)$, but shall omit the topological details of the proof. We let

$$S = \{f \mid f: R \to Z_2 \text{ is a ring homomorphism and } f(1) = 1\}.$$

Let Z_2 have the discrete topology. S is a subset of the product space

$$Z_2^R = \{f \mid f: R \to Z_2 \text{ is a function}\},$$

so we give S the relative product topology. S is compact, totally disconnected, and Hausdorff.

Now we let $C(S, Z_2)$ be the ring of continuous functions from S to Z_2. Then $B(S)$, the Boolean ring of open and closed subsets of S, is isomorphic to $C(S, Z_2)$ under the correspondence of $U \in B(S)$ to its characteristic function f_U. Finally $C(S, Z_2)$ is isomorphic to R under the isomorphism defined by

$$r \to e(r),$$

where $e(r)$ is the function on S whose value at $s \in S$ is $s(r)$.

A space related to a Boolean ring in the manner described in Theorem 13 is called a *Boolean space*.

If X is a Boolean space and $R = C(X, Z_2)$, then

$$J_x = \{r \in R \mid r(x) = 0\}$$

is a maximal ideal of R (see Chapter 1). Since J_x is the kernel of the homomorphism $r \to r(x)$, we have

$$R/J_x \simeq Z_2.$$

If A is a (left) R-module,

$$J_x A = \{ja \mid j \in J_x, a \in A\}$$

is a submodule of A, and $\bigcap_{x \in X} J_x A = (0)$ (see Problem 11). Letting

$$\mathscr{A}_x = A/J_x A,$$

we observe that $\mathscr{A}_x$ is an R/J_x-module under the operation

$$r(a + J_x A) = ra + J_x A = \begin{cases} 0 & \text{if } r \in J_x, \\ a + J_x A & \text{if } r \notin J_x. \end{cases}$$

We let $\mathscr{A} = \bigcup_{x \in X} \mathscr{A}_x$ and note that $x \neq y$ implies that $\mathscr{A}_x \cap \mathscr{A}_y = \phi$. Since $R/J_x \simeq Z_2$, $\mathscr{A}$ is a collection of Z_2-modules. We define

$$\pi : \mathscr{A} \to X$$

by $\pi(a) = x$ if and only if $a \in \mathscr{A}_x$. Now we assume that we have a topology on $\mathscr{A}$ such that:

1) For each $a \in \mathscr{A}$ there is a neighborhood U of a in $\mathscr{A}$ and a neighborhood N of $\pi(a)$ in X such that $\pi : U \to N$ is a homeomorphism.

2) The addition in $\mathscr{A}$ is continuous.

Then $\mathscr{A}$ is a sheaf of Z_2-modules over X.

As usual we let $\Gamma(X, \mathscr{A})$ be the set of all global sections of $\mathscr{A}$. The following is clear:

Theorem 14. $\Gamma(X, \mathscr{A})$ *is a* $C(X, Z_2)$-*module under pointwise operations*

$$(r \cdot \alpha)(x) = \begin{cases} 0 & \text{if } r \in J_x \\ \alpha(x) & \text{if } r \notin J_x \end{cases}$$

and

$$(\alpha + \beta)(x) = \alpha(x) + \beta(x) \qquad \text{for} \quad r \in C(X, Z_2), \quad \alpha, \beta \in \Gamma(X, \mathscr{A}).$$

From this and Stone's theorem we get:

Theorem 15. *Given a Boolean ring R and an R-module A, there exists a sheaf of Z_2-modules such that the set of global sections is isomorphic (as an R-module) to A.*

Proof. We form the space X from R as above; we construct the sheaf from A as above and we have

$$A \simeq \Gamma(X, \mathscr{A})$$

under the assignment

$$a \to \alpha,$$

where α is given by

$$\alpha(x) = a + J_x A.$$

Then the verification is straightforward.

Thus we see that if there is a convenient way of associating a fairly "nice" topological space with an algebraic entity, it is possible that we can use sheaves to study the algebraic structure. As yet no representation theory for general rings in terms of sheaves has been developed; however, certain classes of rings, e.g., regular, Jacobson, or Brown-McCoy semisimple, might be particularly suited to such techniques.

PROBLEMS

1. Let B be an ideal of a ring A. Show that $I \to I \cap B$ is a homeomorphism of $P(B)$ onto the structure space of the ring B, where $P(B) = \{x \mid x \in P(A), x \not\supset B\}$.

2. An algebra A is *algebraic* over a field K if and only if every subalgebra of A generated by a single element of A is finite-dimensional over K. Show that an algebraic algebra is biregular.

3. Given an example of a regular ring which is not biregular.

4. If A is a biregular algebra over a field F and for each primitive ideal p of A, A/p is isomorphic to a fixed finite-dimensional algebra K over F, show that A is isomorphic to the ring of continuous functions on a totally disconnected compact space to the algebra K.

5. Prove that the category of sheaves of rings with identity over a fixed base space is exact.

6. Prove Stone's theorem: Any Boolean ring is isomorphic to the ring of continuous functions with compact carriers from a suitable totally disconnected locally compact space to Z_2.

7. Is the assignment of a sheaf to a biregular ring as described in Section 4 of this chapter functorial?

8. Show that for an algebraic algebra or a ring with minimal condition, the following are equivalent:

   (a) strong regularity, i.e., for every $a \in R$ there exists $x \in R$ such that $a^2x = a$;
   (b) there are no nonzero nilpotent elements in R.

      Further show that if the algebraic algebra or ring with minimal condition is commutative the following are equivalent: (c) regularity, (d) no nonzero nilpotent elements, and (e) Jacobson semisimplicity.

9. What can be said about the structure of Boolean rings if one does not require the existence of an identity?

10. Is the assignment described in Section 5 of the module of global sections to a sheaf of modules functorial?

11. A module is *subdirectly irreducible* if the intersection of its nonzero submodules is nonzero. Show that if $\mathscr{J}$ is a collection of ideals of a ring R, then

$$\bigcap_{J \in \mathscr{J}} JM = 0 \quad \text{for all } R\text{-modules } M$$

if and only if for every subdirectly irreducible R-module N there exists $J \in \mathscr{J}$ such that $J \subset A(N)$.

Selected Bibliography

Albert, A. A., "The radical of a non-associative algebra," *Bulletin American Mathematical Society*, 48(1942), 891–897.

Albert, A. A. (editor), *Studies in Modern Algebra*, Mathematical Association of America Studies in Mathematics, Vol. 2, 1963.

Ambrose, W., "Structure theorems for a special class of Banach algebras," *Transactions American Mathematical Society*, 57(1945), 364–386.

Amitsur, S., "A general theory of radicals," I. *American Journal of Mathematics*, 74(1952), 774–786; II. *American Journal of Mathematics*, 76(1954), 100–125; III. *American Journal of Mathematics*, 76(1954), 126–136.

Arens, R. F., and Kaplansky, I., "Topological representation of algebras," *Transactions American Mathematical Society*, 63(1948), 457–481.

Armendariz, E. P., and Leavitt, W. G., "The hereditary property in the lower radical construction," *Canadian Journal of Mathematics*, 20(1968), 474–476.

Artin, Emil, *Galois Theory*, Notre Dame Mathematical Lectures, No. 2, 1946.

Artin, Emil, Nesbitt, C., and Thrall, R., *Rings with Minimum Condition*, University of Michigan Press, 1944.

Baer, R., "Radical ideals," *American Journal of Mathematics*, 65(1943), 537–568.

Baer, R., "Rings with duals," *American Journal of Mathematics*, 65(1943), 569–584.

Birkhoff, G., "The radical of a group with operators," *Bulletin American Mathematical Society*, 49(1943), 751–753.

Blackett, D. W., "Simple and semi-simple near-rings," *Proceedings American Mathematical Society*, 4(1953), 772–785.

Bourbaki, N., *Élément de Mathématique, Algèbre*, Chapter 7, *Algèbre commutative*, Chapter 1, Hermann, Paris, 1958, 1961.

Brauer, R., "On the nilpotency of the radical of a ring," *Bulletin American Mathematical Society*, 48(1942), 752–758.

Braun, H., and Koecher, M., *Jordan-Algebren*, Springer, Berlin, 1966.

Bredon, G., *Sheaf Theory*, McGraw-Hill, New York, 1967.

Brown, B., "An extension of the Jacobson radical," *Proceedings American Mathematical Society*, 2(1951), 114–117.

Brown, B., and McCoy, N. H., "Radicals and subdirect sums," *American Journal of Mathematics*, 69(1947), 46–58.

Brown, B., and McCoy, N. H., "The radical of a ring," *Duke Mathematical Journal*, 15(1948), 495–499.

Brown, B., and McCoy, N. H., "The maximal regular ideal of a ring," *Proceedings American Mathematical Society*, 1(1950), 165–171.

Brown, R. B., and Gray, A., "Vector cross products," *Comm. Math. Helv.*, 42(1967), 222–236.

Chevalley, C., *Theory of Lie Groups*, Princeton University Press, Princeton, N.J., 1946.

Dauns, J., and Hofmann, K. H., "The representation of biregular rings by sheaves," *Mathematische Zeitschrift*, 91(1966), 103–123.

Deskins, W. E., "A radical for near-rings," *Proceedings American Mathematical Society*, 5(1954), 825–827.

Deskins, W. E., "On the radical of a group algebra," *Pacific Journal of Mathematics*, 8(1958), 693–697.

Dickson, S. E., "A torsion theory for Abelian categories," *Transactions American Mathematical Society*, 121 (1966), 223–235.

Dickson, S. E., "A note on hypernilpotent radical properties for associative rings," *Canadian Journal of Mathematics*, 19(1967), 447–448.

Divinsky, N., "General radicals that coincide with the classical radical on rings with d.c.c.," *Canadian Journal of Mathematics*, 13(1961), 639–644.

Divinsky, N., *Rings and Radicals*, University of Toronto Press, Toronto, 1965.

Fitting, H., "Primärkomponentenzerlegung in nichtkommutativen Ringen," *Mathematische Annalen*, 111(1935), 19–41.

Freyd, Peter, *Abelian Categories*, Harper and Row, New York, 1964.

Gilmer, R. W., "The pseudo-radical of a commutative ring," *Pacific Journal of Mathematics*, 19(1966), 275–284.

Godement, R., *Topologie algébrique et théorie des faisceaux*, Hermann, Paris, 1958.

Goldman, O., "A characterization of semi-simple rings with the descending chain condition," *Bulletin American Mathematical Society*, 52(1946), 1021–1027.

Gray, M. W., "Abelian objects," *Pacific Journal of Mathematics*, 23(1967), 69–78.

Gray, M. W., "Radical subcategories," *Pacific Journal of Mathematics*, 23(1967), 79–89.

Grothendieck, A., *Elements de geometrie algebrique*, III. *Etude cohomologique des faisceaux coherents*, Inst. Hautes Etudes Sci. Publ. Math., No. 11, Paris, 1961.

Halmos, P. R., *Finite-Dimensional Vector Spaces*, 2nd ed., Van Nostrand, Princeton, N.J., 1958.

Helgason, S., *Differential Geometry and Symmetric Spaces*, Academic Press, New York, 1962.

Helwig, K. H., "Halbeinfache reelle Jordan-Algebren," *Mathematische Zeitschrift*, 109(1969), 1–28.

Herstein, I. N., "A generalization of a theorem of Jacobson," I. *American Journal of Mathematics*, 73(1951), 756–762; III. *American Journal of Mathematics*, 75(1953), 105–111.

Herstein, I. N., *Noncommutative Rings*, Carus Mathematical Monographs, No. 15, 1968.

Herstein, I. N., *Topics in Algebra*, Blaisdell, New York, 1964.

Hochschild, G. P., *The Structure of Lie Groups*, Holden-Day, San Francisco, 1965.

Hofmann, K. H., "Über das Nilradikal lokal kompakter Gruppen," *Mathematische Zeitschrift*, 91(1966), 206–215.

Hopkins, C., "Rings with minimal conditions for left ideals," *Annals of Mathematics*, 40(1939), 712–730.

Jacobson, N., *Lie Algebras*, Interscience, John Wiley & Sons, New York, 1962.

Jacobson, N., "The radical and semi-simplicity for arbitrary rings," *American Journal of Mathematics*, 67(1945), 300–320.

Jacobson, N., "Structure theory of simple rings without finiteness assumptions," *Transactions American Mathematical Society*, 57(1945), 228–245.

Jacobson, N., "A topology for the set of primitive ideals in an arbitrary ring," *Proceedings National Academy of Science*, 31(1945), 333–338.

Jacobson, N., "On the theory of primitive rings," *Annals of Mathematics*, 48(1947), 8–21.

Jacobson, N., *Theory of Rings*, American Mathematical Society Surveys, No. 2, 1943.

Jacobson, N., *Structure of Rings*, American Mathematical Society Colloquium Publications, Vol. 37, 1956.

Jans, J. P., *Rings and Homology*, Holt, Rinehart and Winston, New York, 1964.

Jenkins, T. L., "A maximal ideal radical class," *Journal of Natural Sciences and Mathematics*, 7(1967), 191–195.

Johnson, B. E., "The Wedderburn decomposition of Banach algebras with finite-dimensional radical," *American Journal of Mathematics*, 90(1968), 866–876.

Kelley, J. L., *General Topology*, Van Nostrand, Princeton, N.J., 1955.

Kelley, J. L., "Duality for compact groups," *Proceedings of the National Academy of Science*, 49(1963), 457–458.

Kelly, G. M., "On the radical of a category," *Journal Australian Mathematical Society*, 4(1964), 299–307.

Koethe, G., "Die Strucktur der Ringe, deren Restklassenring nach dem Radikal vollständig reduzibel ist," *Mathematische Zeitschrift*, 32(1935), 13–26.

Koh, Kwangil, and Newborn, A. C., "The weak radical of a ring," *Proceedings American Mathematical Society*, 18(1967), 554–560.

Koifman, L. A., "The radical of a module," *Sibirskii Matematicheskii Zhurnal*, 7(1966), 1204–1207.

Kurosh, A., "Radicals of rings and algebras," *Matematicheskii Sbornik*, 33(1953), 13–26.

Kuzmin, E. N., "A locally nilpotent radical of Mal'cev algebras satisfying the nth Engel condition," *Doklady Akademii Nauk, SSSR*, 177(1967), 508–510.

Lambek, J., *Lectures on Rings and Modules*, Blaisdell, Waltham, Mass., 1966.

Lang, S., *Algebra*, Addison-Wesley, Reading, Mass., 1965.

Leavitt, W. G., and Armendariz, E. P., "Nonhereditary semi-simple classes," *Proceedings American Mathematical Society*, 18(1967), 114–117.

Leavitt, W. G., and Jenkins, T. L., "Non-hereditariness of the maximal ideal radical class," *Journal of Natural Sciences and Mathematics*, 7(1967), 203–205.

Leavitt, W. G., and Lee, Y.-L., "A radical coinciding with the lower radical in associative and alternative rings," *Pacific Journal of Mathematics*, 30(1969), 459–462.

Levitzki, J., "On the radical of a general ring," *Bulletin American Mathematical Society*, 49(1943), 462–466.

Levitzki, J., "Semi-nilpotent ideals," *Duke Mathematical Journal*, 10(1943), 553–556.

Levitzki, J., "Prime ideals and the lower radical," *American Journal of Mathematics*, 73(1951), 25–29.

Levitzki, J., "On the structure of algebraic algebras and related rings," *Transactions American Mathematical Society*, 74(1953), 384–409.

Livsic, A. H., "Category-theoretic foundations of the duality of radicality and semi-simplicity," *Sibirskii Matematicheskii Zhurnal*, 5(1966), 319–336.

MacLane, S., *Homology*, Springer, Berlin, 1963.

Marubayashi, H. and Murata, K., "A note on radicals of ideals in nonassociative rings," *Proc. Japan Acad.*, 45(1969), 131–134.

McCarthy, P. J., *Algebraic Extensions of Fields*, Blaisdell, Waltham, Mass., 1966.

McCoy, N. H., "Subdirect sums of rings," *Bulletin American Mathematical Society*, 53(1947), 856–877.

McCoy, N. H., "Note on subdirect sums of rings," *Proceedings American Mathematical Society*, 6(1953), 554–557.

McCoy, N. H., "Subdirect sum representations of prime rings," *Duke Mathematical Journal*, 22(1955), 357–364.

McCoy, N. H., "Prime ideals in general rings," *American Journal of Mathematics* 71(1949), 823–833.

McCoy, N. H., "Prime radical in a polynomial ring," *Publ. Math. Debrecen*, 4(1956), 161–162.

McCoy, N. H., *Rings and Ideals*, Carus Mathematical Monographs, No. 8, 1948.

McCoy, N. H., *The Theory of Rings*, Macmillan, New York, 1964.

McCrimmon, K., "The radical of a Jordan algebra," *Proceedings of the National Academy of Science*, 55(1969), 671–678.

Mitchell, Barry, *Theory of Categories*, Academic Press, New York, 1965.

Motzkin, T., "The Euclidean algorithm," *Bulletin American Mathematical Society*, 55(1949), 1142–1146.

Nagata, M., "On the theory of radicals in a ring," *Journal of the Mathematical Society of Japan*, 3(1951), 330–344.

Nagata, M., *Local Rings*, Interscience, John Wiley & Sons, New York, 1962.

Ornstein, A. J., "Rings with restricted minimum condition," *Proceedings American Mathematical Society*, 19(1968), 1145–1150.

Perlis, S., "A characterization of the radical of an algebra," *Bulletin American Mathematical Society*, 48(1942), 128–132.

Pierce, R. S., *Modules over Commutative Regular Rings*, American Mathematical Society Memoirs, No. 70, 1967.

Plotkin, B. I., "On a radical of automorphism groups of a group with maximal condition," *Doklady Akademii Nauk SSSR*, 130(1960), 977–981.

Plotkin, B. I., "Radicals in group pairs," *Doklady Akademii Nauk SSSR*, 140(1961), 1019–1022.

Plotkin, B. I., "Radical groups," *Matematicheskii Sbornik, N.S.*, (79) 37(1955), 507–526.

Pontryagin, L., *Topological Groups*, Princeton University Press, Princeton, N.J., 1939.

Rickart, C. E., *Banach Algebras*, Van Nostrand, Princeton, N.J., 1960.

Rieffel, M. A., "A general Wedderbarn theorem," *Proceedings National Academy of Science*, 54(1965), 1513.

Sah, C., *Abstract Algebra*, Academic Press, New York, 1967.

Sands, A. D., "On radicals of infinite matrix rings," *Proceedings Edinburgh Mathematical Society*, 16(1969), 195–204.

Schafer, R. D., *An Introduction to Nonassociative Algebras*, Academic Press, New York, 1966.

Schneider, H., and Weissglass, J., "Group rings, semigroup rings and their radicals," *Journal of Algebra*, 5(1967), 1–15.

Scott, W. R., *Group Theory*, Prentice-Hall, Englewood Cliffs, N.J., 1964.

Segal, I. E., "The group algebra of a locally compact group," *Transactions American Mathematical Society*, 61(1947), 69–105.

Smiley, M. F., "Application of a radical of Brown and McCoy to non-associative rings," *American Journal of Mathematics*, 72(1950), 93–100.

Spicer, D. Z., "Semi-simplicity of group algebras of vector-valued functions," *Proceedings American Mathematical Society*, 19(1968), 573–578.

Stone, M. H., "Application of the theory of Boolean rings to general topology," *Transactions American Mathematical Society*, 41(1937), 375–381.

Sulinski, A., "The Brown-McCoy radical in categories," *Fund. Math.*, 59(1966), 23–41.

Swan, R. G., *The Theory of Sheaves*, University of Chicago Press, Chicago, 1964.

Taft, E. J., "On the Whitehead first lemma for Jordan algebras," *Mathematische Zeitschrift*, 107(1968), 83–86.

Takahashi, S., "A characterization of group rings as a special class of Hopf algebras," *Canadian Mathematical Bulletin*, 8 (1965), 465–475.

Tominaga, H., "Some remarks on radical ideals," *Mathematics Journal Okayama University*, 3(1954), 139–142.

Tsai, C., "The prime radical in a Jordan ring," *Proceedings American Mathematical Society*, 113(1968), 1171–1175.

Tsushima, Yukio, "Radicals of group algebras," *Osaka Journal of Mathematics*, 4(1967), 179–182.

van der Waerden, B. L., *Moderne Algebra*, Springer, Berlin, 1931.

Villamayor, O. E., "On the semisimplicity of group algebras," I. *Proceedings American Mathematical Society*, 9(1958), 621–627; II. *Proceedings American Mathematical Society*, 10(1959), 27–31.

Wallace, D. A. R., "Lower bounds for the radical of the group algebra of a finite p-soluble group," *Proceedings Edinburgh Mathematical Society*, 16(1968), 127–135.

Wedderburn, J. H. M., "On hypercomplex numbers," *Proceedings London Mathematical Society*, Section 2, 6(1908), 77–117.

Weissglass, J., "Radicals of semi-group rings," *Glasgow Mathematical Journal*, 10 (1969), 85–93.

Wiegandt, R., "Radical and semi-simplicity in categories," *Acta Math. Acad. Sc. Hungaricae*, 19(1968), 345–364.

List of Symbols

Symbol	Page
$R[x]$	2
$R\langle x \rangle$	2
$\mathscr{M}_n$	3
R_n	3
$\mathrm{Hom}_K(V, V)$	4
$A_r(S)$	5
$\{a\}_r$	5
$I:J$	6
$A + B$	6, 167
$\sum$	6, 47, 169
R/I	8
$A \oplus B$	9
$A_1 \times A_2$	9, 167
$R \setminus S$	11
$\sqrt{A}$	14
$R(x)$	23
$\prod$	47
$\mathrm{Hom}_R(A, B)$	56
$A \otimes B$	63
$\mathrm{hom}(A, B)$	152
(f, g)	167
$\begin{pmatrix} f \\ g \end{pmatrix}$	167
$A_1 \vee A_2$	168

226

Index